A PIS
OF CAK

A PIS OF CAK

OF CAK

CHILDREN AT THEIR
MOST SERIOUSLY FUNNY

PETER A. JEFFCOCK

SUMMERSDALE

Summersdale Publishers Ltd
46 West Street
Chichester
West Sussex
PO19 1RP
United Kingdom

www.summersdale.com

Printed and bound in Great Britain.

ISBN 1 84024 132 2

Cartoons and cover illustration by Kate Taylor

CONTENTS

Introduction	7
Skool Daze	10
History	20
English and the Arts	39
Maths	47
Geography	53
Free Period	65
Religious Studies	78
Science	83
Creative Writing	94
Natural History	111
Sick Bay	128
Friends and Family	133
Bedtime	157

Introduction

Children are never more amusing than when they try to be serious. The unintentional humour of spelling mistakes and malapropisms makes their writing a delight to read.

Due to their unique command of the misuse of the English language they manage to create a level of humour not yet achieved by any adult comedy writer. The humour is born out of the contrast between the child's innocence and the adult's worldly wise experience of double entendre and subtle hidden meaning.

And they can get away with it because they are children.

So how do they do it?

Well, shortly after learning to form their letters, young children develop the skill of switching b's and d's in strategic places. This immediately permits them to *take the bog for a walk* and, at the end of the day, to go *upstairs to the land of nob*.

As they progress to joined writing, they learn that it can be easy to confuse a's and o's, and if they are very skilful, to mix up r's and n's. Thus, they enter a new-found utopia in which *'two halves make a whale'*, money is obtained from *'a bonk'* and one day, they will have to *'wank for a living'*.

As the fluency of a child's writing increases, there comes the little matter of remembering to cross the t's, to stop them from becoming l's and vice versa. Great joy! Suddenly it becomes possible for footballers to *'score a goat'* and landlords can collect money from their *todgers*!

Advanced abuse of the English language comes with the development of the high level skills. These include the omission of key letters, the inclusion of additional unwanted letters and the switching of letters to change the spelling of a word. Revel, if you will, in the mental imagery of *'wild breasts in the jungle'* and Uncle Percy *'going over the widows with a damp cloth'*! There was even a law demanding *sexy quality* for women. Bet you didn't know that!

INTRODUCTION

Older children enter the scientific and technical world and here, a whole new series of opportunities for errors open up and true havoc can be played with the language. Envision *haemorrhoids flying through space* and everyday items weighed in *killer grams.*

So enjoy these genuine examples of children's writing, and marvel at their capacity to entertain us with their unintentional, unrepeatable, unadulterated filth.

You have been warmed!

I already know a bit about
the school and I am looking
forward to it. My brother
is there and he is a
perfect. I would like to be
a perfect too.

In the headteacher's
office he has a black chair
that snivels around.

If you are really naughty
at the big school you will
get exploded from school
and you can't go back then.

The hell is being painted so
we had to have assembliy
in our classroom.

Mrs. Pearson said I could
stay in at playtime and help
her sick up some pictures
on the wall.

I found a spare seal so I
quickly sat on it.

Wen the pepol cam into our school and askt us cwestons I did not lick it. Mrs Maw said our school was being infected.

To play the game you need to be in gropes. It is best if you let sumbody like a teacher grope you because then you get a fair team. If you grope yourselfs you pick all the best players.

The teacher looked across
the room and shouted
"Slop that at once!" That
was a real surprise.

We was playing futbol and
we fell out and we started
to have a fit. It was not a
bad fit but the teacher
tolled us of.

When PC Handley visited us he wore a helmet and a smart white shit.

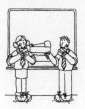

And now it was up to me and Tich. I passed the ball to him and he got past the defenders but he was being marked. He passed to me and with one kick I sent the ball flying past the keeper. I had scored the winning goat.

I like sewing. I would like
to be a sewer when I grow
up. I am helping my mum to
make a pachwork kilt.

When I grow up I want to
learn how to tipe quickly
and I want to be a tipissed.

It is bark when we go home
from school in the winter.
I don't like the bark.

The teacher looked at
Mark and growled, "I
expose you think that's
clever!

My favourite subject is history. I like looking into the post to see what I can find out.

If you had no money in the 1930s you could get some by going to the porn shop. The man at the porn shop had 3 balls hanging over his entrance.

We buy poopies and ware them all week. On poopy day we all go quiet and thinck about dead people.

In the olden days cars were not aloud to go fast. The first cars had to follow a man with a fag in his hand.

For the frist time in history people could have mashines to help them with their work at home. You could have a frig in your kichen.

If you did something brave in the war you might get a meddle.

In wartime children who lived in big cities had to be evaporated because it was safer in the country.

...and in the 1970s there was a law that said there must be sexy quality for women.

There was no transpot in Roman times. The soldiers had to walk everywhere and some other people came from Rome on their carrots.

Florence Nitingale was known as the lady with the lump. I think this is because she was the worlds first nurse.

In the oldern days the streets were very bumpy because they were full of cobblers

You had to keep your food
in a panty before you had a
frig.

Sometimes in the war they
take prisners and keep
them as ostriges until the
war is over. It must be
scarry to be an ostrige in
the war.

When they danced to pope
music in the 1950s they
had a famos dance callled
The Twits

Victorian girls had to work
as mades. They had to
clean the house and polish
the sliver.

Captin Cok was a famos
exploder.

There are two houses of
parliament in our country.
The main one is the house
of comons. The other is
the house of lards.

The sufrajets complaned
for voles for women.

The people who run our country are the prim minster and the leader of the expedishon.

They used to go down the mine on a lift and ride on a little train with a helmet on until they got to where the coat was growing in the rock. People used to put this coat on their fire.

In the field near our house
they think they have found
the remains of a Roman
fart.

They used to go down the mine on a lift and ride on a little train with a helmet on until they got to where the coat was growing in the rock. People used to put this coat on their fire.

They used to go down the mine on a lift and ride on a little train with a helmet on until they got to where the coat was growing in the rock. People used to put this coat on their fire.

I had traveled back in time to the war. I tried to buy a drink but I only had new money on me and it was going to cost me a shitting. What could I do?

I deamed I was a soiler in the middle ages. I was soiling the seas in my soiling ship.

Our country has a govement but at the top of everything is queer elizabeth.

After the war they had to build houses quickly to replace the ones that had been bombed. These houses were called perverts. There are still some old perverts around today.

Robert Louis Stephenson
tried to build a rocket but
he ended up with a train.

The Easter game of egg
rolling started in
debenhams and cornwall.

The lady who stoped peple
from being nasty to black
peple was Rachel Ickwality.

Rember Rember!
On 5th November we have
bonfires and firewanks.
This is because a man tired
to blow up the house of
parliament. The man was
called Giy Fuks.

Dansing
Dico dansing started when my mum was young. Before that there was lots of other danse fashons. In the 1920s there were girls called floppers....

Greek Gods
The three gods in my project are the king of gods - Zeus, the messenger of the gods – Hermes, and the god of war – Arse.

ENGLISH AND THE ARTS

My faverit sujbect is speling.

My faverit book is Charlie and the Chocolate Factory. I would love to meet Willy Wanka like Charlie does.

When you write a story you should do a daft copy first. Then you can change it round and make it sound better.

A glossary is shiny.

A man who writes books is called Arthur.

My favourite book is The Animals Of Farting Wood.

If you don't want to use a full stop you can use an exsitement mark instead.

2 words can be joind together by a syphen. A syphen is sometimes called a bash.

In last year's Christmas concert, Linzi played the main prat. I played one of the smaller prats and I woud like to have a bigger prat this year.

When my big sister palyed Glodilocks I was aloud in the concert too. I just had to be a little bare.

...and at the end of the show we all sing away in a manager.....

Music is written on a slave.

All string instruments have stings on them. Some string instuments are gitar, violin, banjo and triangle.

I love drawing and painting so my favourite subject is rat.

I need to work hard on my
maths so I will be god at it.

We drew a giraf to show
how many trafics went
passed the school.

Fractions are like harvs
qarters and tirds.

I would like to be an
accountant but you have to
know a lot about moths.

Two halves make a whale.

The total is when you add
up all the numbers and a
remainder is an animal that
pulls santas sleaigh.

If it is less than 90
degrees it is a cute angel.

The most popular crisps
were salt and vinegar and
the least popular were
ready slated.

If you gess but you don't
gess hiy enuf you undres to
mate.

My conclusion from the
survey is that people who
don't have cars don't drive
to work.

In the middle of London, towering over the River Thames is an enormous cock called Big Ben. It is the biggest in the world and it is very famos.

The Sarah Dessert is the biggist dessert in the world. If you are crossing the sarah you haf to leave your name and tell them when you will be back. A lot of people have died in the sarah.

They are triying to close the pubic footpath behind our house.

I have found out about Venus for my project. Venus is in Italy and it is special because its streets are water. People travel round Venus on boats called Gonderlas. I found some photos because my mum and dad went to Venus for their honeymoon.

The closet town to France is Dover. You can get to France on a train in the Tunnel or you can go on a fairy.

People can live in all kinbs of bildings. Most people live in hoses, fats or dungalows.

In London you can go around on a speshal train called the tub. There is a famos shop calld Harolds where rich people go.

York is Roman town built on the river Ooze.

They used to think the
earth was fat but it is
really round. Its shape is
called a spear.

You can get across the
canal on a ferry or a
hoovercraft. Or you can go
under it in a tunnel.

I have been finding out about whales. This is what I have found out. Whales can be found on the west coast of mainland Britain. The central part of Whales is very hilly but around the coast there are many good beaches. Whales used to be famous for its mines but not so much now...

The Empire Stale Building is one of the world's tallest buildings and my Aunty Julie has been up it.

We spend two weeks in
grease every year.

A flat mop of the world is
an atless. A round mop is a
glob. Globs are more
interesting.

...a ship's window is called a
pothole...

The bigest city in Holland
is Hamsterdam and the
bigest port is Rottendam.

I feel sorry for children in Africa. They are starving to death. They only get a little groin to eat. I would not like to eat the groin.

We stayed in Wales in summer. We stayed on a kind of campsight but instead of tents or caravans there were wooden todges. Ours was lovely.

Wen we were in Scotland
we used to go into the
woobs for a walk. Dad liked
to see how many beers he
could see.

Sugar Plum Mountain is a
famous landmark in Brazil

The Irish speak Garlic...

At brownies this week we
lernt to do sin language.

We had a game of it's a
konkout at janes party. We
had to ware silly cloths and
go over a hospital corse. It
was like the reel it's a
konkout on telly.

...and we all said happy new ear.

We got our tea from the chinees last night. I love ornimental food.

...and then Mr. Browning showed us how climbers use tampons to grip on to their roc.

I hepled my dad in the garage. He let me hit some nails in with his hamster.

For my praty we went to the blowing alley. When we had been blowing we went for a drinck and a buger.

...and tow times a week we have a nashonal tottery. There are six balls and a boneless ball.

It is a hard job to be the ref but there has to be a ref if you want fore play.

My best persent was my music sisterm. It has a tap ricoder and a seedey player.

I have got a new dress. I am waring it to go to a weeding on Saturday.

I go to St. Johns to lern frist aid. I have lernt how to do a bondage and I got to practice on Mr. Terry. He is the leader.

At 9.00 all our class got on a couch and went to the museum in town. James was sick on the couch because he gets travell sick exspecshally on couches....

This holiday we got some slobs to make a patio in the back garden.

I think Boyzone is the best pap group in the wold.

I take the dog for a walk in the pork every morning.

Dear Mum, today we went fishing on Cromer pier and I caught crabs.

My uncle Steve took my
cusins to Blackpool to see
the aluminashons. We went
to Blackpool as well but we
went to see the lights.

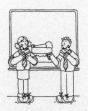

I am leaning to play the
flut and Rebecca who is my
big sister is leaning to play
the babboon.

They couldn't fit us in for
a meal because we hadn't
reversed a table.

Fensing is when you fite
with a sod.

Our pirate has died. We
are not going to have
another so we have to sell
his cage.

I got a goldfish on
Saterday. It cost 2 ponds.

The kitten jumped on the table and nocked a cup of tea all over a farm that my mum was filing in.

Dear God,
My wish is that there wood
be pis all over the world.
Make the wars end and let
pipol live in pis all their
lives...

A mosque is a sort of
church. The main
difference is that its roof
is doomed.

In jewish churches they do
not have vickers. In sted
they have rabbits.

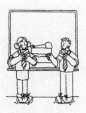

Jesuses dad was josef. He
was a crapinter.

One of my frends dusent
blive in gob. I blive in gob.
I think gob is very pawrful.

Jesus was born in a table.

Monks are men who give
their life to God and marry
nuns. They live in a
monster.

All over the wold there are different religons. The people dress different and do different things but one thing is the same. They all worship a dog.

Mary and Joseph had to go to Bethlehem on a donkey because everyone els had taken all the taxis.

Farces.
One of the most important farces is the farce that pulls things down to the ground. This farce is called gravy.

I think there would be less polution if people stoped using there cars and went on pubic transport a lot more.

I wayed the sandwich box and it wayed more than a killergram. Then I wayed the pencil cas and it wayed less than a killergram.

...it is a tube and when you look in it there are pattens. It is called a collide o scope.

Never play near pythons.
You will get an electric
shock and be killed.

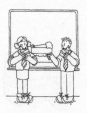

When the hot steam from
a kettle touches a cold
window it makes the steam
turn into water droplets.
This is how you get
compensation.

Things that are made from milk are called diary products. They are things like chese, butter and magazine.

...and suspenshon briges hang up by big ropes. I think they hang them from a cloud.

Snog is a kind of dirty fog. It is made by plution from cars and factrees. In some countrys they have snog every day and pepol even have to wer masks to stop it from herting them.

It is very important to have clean water. You can die by drinking dirty water. You can get diseeses like collera and tyfoon.

A volcano is mountin that explodes rock. Hot molting rock and larva comes out of a crate at the top of the mountin and it mit look like a firewerk. But bigger.

Helicopters are cleverer than planes. Not only can they fly through the air they can also hoover.

Our Solar System is made of a sun, nine planets, lots of moons and balls of fire which fly around between the planets. These are called hemaroids.

If there are alans out in space I would like for them to come to earth and say hello. Or what ever you say if you are an alan.

I think you haf to do the experiment more than once because you mit get a snog on one of your go's.

You breathe through your lugs they are like big bags of air. Each one has thousands of tiny bumps on it and they are called ravioli.

I would like to be sientist
and I would like to work in
a lavoratory.

You can make toste by
putting the bread in a
toster or by putting it
under a girl until it is done.

To lift the books off the
table you need a balloon
and a big puff.

We can all see things
because we have a septic
nerve that joins our eyes
to our brians.

CREATIVE
WRITING

"You are under a rest and you will be remembered in custard for the night," said the policeman. He wasn't expecting that!.....and the judge condomned the prisoner to death.

O.K. said the robber as he
waved his gun in the air,
you'd better close your
eyes and start prying.

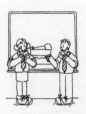

Know know, said Mrs
Green, you no what they
say, theres no use crying
over split milk.

"I'm sorry madam, but your husband has died a horrible death. He has been killed by a steak through the heart." Said Inspector Beel.

The pilot was bound to crash to plane. The moment he saw his wig come loose and fall to the ground he knew there was no chance of survival.

"And now" declared Mr
Scarlett-Jones "I shall
read your uncles last will
and testacle".

Dr. Brown praked his car
outside the Grand Hotel.
It had big white pillows
and a revolting door.

I was traped in the house.
It was getting darker and
a thick fag was about to
cover the countryside.

Thonks! She yelled. Now
you've reely let the cot out
of the bog!

The two cars sped down the road. The crooks had stolen the Jag but the police were catching up fast with their top of the range Grandad.

She knew that the therapist was her only hope. She felt scared as she looked at the name plate on the door to his office – Mike Brown – The rapist.

Robert was in a very bad crash and he has not wocken up from it. I think he is in cromer.

The girl who collects our rent has stopped coming. Now we have a rent boy instead.

He tried not to make a sound but he could not stop his feet crunching as he walked up the drivel path.

Time seemed to be standing still. Nothing was happening and I was getting scarred. I looked again at my cock. It hadn't moved since I last looked at it.

There was an axident on our road last night and a man was badly enjoyed.

The driver flashed at me so I decided to cross the road.

Lowry's pictures were mostly about the different prats of Manchester.

The whistle sounded and smoke pawed out from the ship's flannel.

The magician said
'abracadabra' and then
suddenly varnished.

"Look at your hands!" said
Mrs Grumble. "I don't know
where you've been but
they're as black as the
arce of spades!"

As he stepped outside he gave a quick nob of his head and everybody knew what he meant.

Some of the houses were so big that the owners turned them into flats so they could make lots of money from their todgers.

When it gets neer crismas
I get choclat penis. I get
one every morning.

There was a very thick
frog on the roads last
night and it maid a car
crash into a bus.

We put our cristmas tree up last night. It looks reely good. We have lights and tinsle round it. There are all kinds of different borbles and on top there is a beatiful ferry.

Mr. Brown walked into the
room and sat on his
favourite choir.

When I grow up I would
like to work for a
newspapper. The job is
called a jurney list.

Santa carries all the toys
in a big sock on his back.

NATURAL HISTORY

A PIS OF CAK

There are wild breasts roaming around in the jungle. I think it would scar me if a wild breast came at me at night.

Every living thing is an orgasm. From the smallest cell to a whole mammal, we are all orgasms.

112

In Australia they have
small kangaroos as well.
They are called wallies.

Baby cows are claves and
baby bulls are bollocks.

We nearly ran over a peasant in the weekend. It ran out from a framyard.

Conversation is very important because if we don't look after the rain forests many creatures will die.

Mice are scarred of big brids of pray like orks and blizzards.

My hobby is insest. I lern about all kinds of insest from a book I bort at the bring and bye sale. I speshly like ants and spiders.

Ostralia is famos for its speshal animals like kangeroos, cola bears and cookerbuggas. You carnt get these anywer els.

The best place to put pants is somewhere warm and damp.

....and then all the lemons
jumped off a cliff.

I picked up a smell on the beach. I still have it in my bedroom.

When we had collected the leaves we brought them into the classroom. We spread out a shit of paper and emptied the leaves on to it.

Planets can grow in pots or in soil. Planets come from a blub or sid.

It was a hot sunny day and there were no clods in the skiy.

That is the end of my project on porkypines. My next one will be about aunt eaters.

We have to look after the sky. Polution can spoil it and so can spraying too many arsols.

Crabs can be painfull because they have sharp little princes and they can nip you.

Lucy and me are going to make a potishon to stop them killing seals. I am going to get people to sing the potishon. I will get as meny people to sing it as I can.

Crabs and creatures like them all belong to a family of crushed asians.

There are many kinds of
fish. They can be huge
monsters like a great big
shark or a little tiny thing
like a godfish.

Godfish £2 each

Crap rotation is what farmers do when they have groan the same crap in a field for a long time. They move the crap to another field so that the soil gets better. Then they might put the crap back again.

Some of the biggest fish my dad had caught are from our holidays. He has caught pikes and craps.

Fax hunting is cruel. Faxes can be a bit of a newsance at times, specially if they come at night but it is still wrong to get crowds of people and dogs to rip the poor little fax to shreds. I think fax hunting should be made iligitimate.

The jungles of Africa are very dangerous for the people who explore them. There must be hundreds of people who have been mauled to death by a tiger or lino.

....and there are monkeys
with red bottoms called
buffoons.

You use the 24 hour clock
in summer because it stays
light longer.

....and in the forest you can see dears and slags...

Badies have mushtup food bicos they carnt eat with a nife, or fuc.

Publicity is when you start to grow in to an adult. Some things are very easy to spot. Boys get deeper voces and girls grow beasts.

SICK
BAY

I went to see the docter because I keep getting orful crap. I woak up with the crap all down my leg yesterday and I cuddent put my foot down.

I feel sory for the tripelets because the little one has got terrible polsy.

I keep getting whacks in my ear and it makes me a bit def. I think the docter will try to suck it out.

I was scarred of going to the bentist but I just felt a little prick. The prick was in my mouth and I just went to sleep.

Sometimes if you are reely
reely poorly you go to a
speshal ward in hospital
and the ward is called
insensitive care.

I brock my tooth and I had to go for a feeling at the dentist.

A friend is someone you can thrust. Thrusting them means they wont tell lies or give away your secrits. I think I can thrust my friends and they they can thrust me.

My grandad has got a huge organ. He says one day he will give it to me but I have to lern how to play it.

We gave our mum a
neckless for her berthday.

Last week it was Jack's
berthday. He brort a cak
to school and we all had a
pis. I had a pink pis.

This wikend we went shoping. I got some new shoes and mummy got a new pair of tits.

Mum and dad were panting in my bedroom this weekend. They panted it blue and stuck a cute boarder round the middle.

All our family love sweets. I like sticky buns with icing on top but my mum is the worsed. She loves bras of chocolate. She had three chocolate bras on Friday eveing last week.

Mummy had been in the bath and when she dryed her hair she saw her bush was missing. We all lookd for it but daddy let her have his coam.

I have lots of fiends at school and I have even more fiends at home.

...and I took a bunch of violents home for my mum...

We have found out that anty Mary is stagnant and she will be having a baby in March.

I have a big bother. He went comping with some fiends on Dratmore.

The funny thing about my family is that they are all divers. My uncle Tim is a taxi diver, my uncle Steve is a bus diver and my dad is a van diver.

Me and Simon are best friends. We love to play with each other and we do it all the time.

My mum goes to jim every fireday. She always comes home too tired to do anything.

We went to visit my dad's boss this holiday. He lives in a big hose.

Every time we go shopping
we have the same fuss.
Dad wants to read the
Mirror and mum wants her
Daily Male.

Sarah is not my frend. I used to lick her but she dident lick me. She lickd Abigal instead so now I don't lick any of them.

We took my baby sister to the panto for the frist time this year. We went to see Seeping Beauty.

When we go out for tea I always want a desert but my mum says no.

On Sunday my dad filmed me falling into our pond by axident. We are going to send it to You've Been Farmed.

We are taking my little sister to see Satan this weekend.

My uncle is impotent. He is the boss of a big factory.

When my Uncle Dave was in the Forest he visited China and Japan.
(NB. Forest = Far East)

My mum writes the chek out and my dad looks at it and sins.

We have bort a new set of soot cases for our holidays.

Every morning dad has a slice of dread before he goes to work.

I am sory for wat I did. I went up behind Tom and gave him a shave. I shaved him over and I shuddentav.

It was a distaster at the weekend. Gradad's pet bog, sooki, ran of and we losted her. We askd evry boddy have you seen a brun and wit bog but they didn't have. We was going to ring the bogs home but she cam back. Don't bo it agen you norty bog we siad.

My dad looks funny. He has groan a bread. He had a must dash befor but I thinck his bread looks silly.

My dad says we will have a swimming pool if we ever win the national tottery.

My grandad yoused to be a cool miner wen he was young.

I am verry verry sorry. It is wrong to keep giving massages to my friends when I should be listening to the teacher. I will not do it again.

My uncle had to wipe the widows with a wet cloth yestday because the rain made them derty.

My dad was doing some secret panting in the bedroom. He has done it in purple.

Dad was working in the garden and he ascked mum if she could come and give him a hard. She was bisy so aunty jo went instead.

My mum was a bit shook up
yesterday because she had
a dump in the car.

When we were in Blackpool
my dad ran out of money so
he had to go to find a bonk.
He asked three people
before he found the one
he wanted.

My dad has got a new car.
It is a Raver.

I have been to wank with
my dad. He wanks in a bonk
on Hih Sheet.

Mummy givs chang for the
slat mashins and baddy is a
dingo caller.

My grandma has no central heating. She still has a coat fire in the living room.

When Lucy's cat ran away I felt a little sod for her.

My gran has a huge chest. We keep our toys in it.

My uncle Jake died last week and he still isent better.

When we did the coin game
I was the looker and Mark
was the tosser.

Grandad wont let me have
his old programmes
because he wants to keep
them for posterior.

Since her axident my mum
has to go to a fizzy
therapist every week.

Sam's mum looked at her little boy. "Come on, it's up to the land of nob for you" she said.

It is verry noisy at night for me because we live above a pud.

I dident get to sleep
mutch because next doors
dog was baking all night.

....and suddenly the door
opened and banged against
the wall. I felt a lamp in my
throte.

My little sister still has to
sleep with the light on
because she is afraid of
the dork.

My dad works nights so he
spends all day in deb.

My baby bother sleeps in a
cat in my bedroom.

Ne...

Heathe...
novels. Sh...
America's Lu...
Writers' Silver L...
Award from ITS. S...
Thriller Writers and...
the founder of The S...
and theatrical group. ...
dancer and mother of f...
Florida home, but also loves to travel.

For more information, check out her website, theoriginalheathergraham.com, or find Heather on Facebook.

Elle James, a *New York Times* bestselling author, started writing when her sister challenged her to write a romance novel. She has managed a full-time job and raised three wonderful children, and she and her husband even tried ranching exotic birds (ostriches, emus and rheas). Ask her, and she'll tell you what it's like to go toe-to-toe with an angry three-hundred-and-fifty-pound bird! Elle loves to hear from fans at ellejames@earthlink.net or ellejames.com.

Also by Heather Graham

Law and Disorder
Shadows in the Night
Out of the Darkness
Echoes of Evil
Pale as Death
Fade to Black
A Dangerous Game
Wicked Deeds
Dark Rites
Dying Breath

Also by Elle James

One Intrepid SEAL
Two Dauntless Hearts
Three Courageous Words
Four Relentless Days
Hot Combat
Hot Target
Hot Zone
Hot Velocity
Navy SEAL Survival
Navy SEAL Casptive

Discover more at millsandboon.co.uk

UNDERCOVER CONNECTION

HEATHER GRAHAM

FIVE WAYS TO SURRENDER

ELLE JAMES

MILLS & BOON

First Published in Great Britain 2018
by Mills & Boon, an imprint of HarperCollins*Publishers*
1 London Bridge Street, London, SE1 9GF

Undercover Connection © 2018 Heather Graham Pozzessere
Five Ways To Surrender © 2018 Mary Jernigan

ISBN: 978-0-263-26606-1

1218

MIX
Paper from
responsible sources
FSC™ C007454

This book is produced from independently certified FSC™
paper to ensure responsible forest management.

For more information visit: www.harpercollins.co.uk/green

Printed and bound in Spain
by CPI, Barcelona

UNDERCOVER CONNECTION

HEATHER GRAHAM

For Lorna Broussard—with love and thanks for all
the help and support for…well, many years!

Chapter One

The woman on the runway was truly one of the most stunning creatures Jacob Wolff had ever seen. Her skin was pure bronze, as sleek and as dazzling as the deepest sun ray.

When she turned, he could see—even from his distance at the club's bar—that her eyes were light. Green, he thought, and a sharp contrast to her skin. She had amazing hair, long and so shimmering that it was as close to pure black as it was possible to be; so dark it almost had a gleam of violet. She was long-legged, lean and yet exquisitely shaped as she moved in the creation she modeled—a mix of pastel colors that was perfectly enhanced by her skin—the dress was bare at the shoulder and throat with a plunging neckline, and back, and then swept to the floor.

She moved like a woman accustomed to such a haughty strut: proud, confident, arrogant and perhaps even amused by the awe of the onlookers.

"That one—she will rule the place one day."

Jacob turned.

Ivan Petrov leaned on one elbow across the bar

from Jacob. Ivan bartended and—so Jacob believed thus far—ran all things that had to do with the on-the-ground-management of the Gold Sun Club. The burning-hot new establishment was having its grand opening tonight.

"I'd imagine," Jacob said. He leaned closer over the bar and smiled. "And I imagine that she might perhaps be…available?"

Ivan smiled, clearly glad that Jacob had asked him; Ivan was a proud man, appreciative that Jacob had noted his position of power within the club.

"Not…immediately," Ivan said. "She is fairly new. But all things come in good time, my friend, eh? Now you," he said, pouring a shot of vodka for Jacob, "you are fairly new, too. New to Miami Beach—new to our ways. We have our…social…rules, you know."

Jacob knew all too well.

And he knew what happened to those who didn't follow the rules—or who dared to make their own. He'd been south of I-75 that morning, off part of the highway still known as Alligator Alley, and for good reason. He'd been deep in the Everglades where a Seminole ranger had recently discovered a bizarre cache of oil drums, inside of which had been several bodies in various stages of decomposition.

"I have my reputation," Jacob said softly.

Ivan caught Jacob's meaning. Yes, Jacob would follow the rules. But he was his own man—very much a *made* man from the underbelly of New York City. Now, he'd bought a gallery on South Beach; but he'd been doing his other business for years.

At least, that was the information that had been fed to what had become known as the Deco Gang—so called because of the beautifully preserved architecture on South Beach.

Jacob was for all intents and purposes a new major player in the area. And it was important, of course, that he appear to be a team player—but a very powerful team player who respected another man's turf while also keeping a strict hold on his own.

"A man's reputation must be upheld," Ivan said, nodding approvingly.

"While, of course, he gives heed to all that belongs to another man, as well," Jacob assured him.

A loud clash of drums drew Jacob's attention for a moment. The Dissidents were playing that night; they were supposedly one of the hottest up-and-coming bands, not just in the state, but worldwide.

The grand opening to the Gold Sun Club had been invitation only; tomorrow night, others would flow in, awed by the publicity generated by this celebrity-studded evening. The rich and the beautiful—and the not-so-rich but very beautiful—were all on the ground floor, listening to the popular new band and watching the fashion show.

Jacob took in the place as a whole, noting a balcony level that ran the perimeter, with a bar above the stage. But that night all the guests were downstairs, and Ivan Petrov was manning the main bar himself.

The elegant model on the runway swirled with perfect timing, walking toward the crowd again, pausing to seductively steal a delicious-looking apple from the hands of a pretty boy—a young male model, dressed as Adonis—standing like a statue at the bottom of the steps to the runway.

"I believe," Jacob told Ivan, turning to look at him gravely again, "that my business will be an asset to your business, and that we will work in perfect harmony together."

"Yes," Ivan said. "Mr. Smirnoff invited you, right?"

Jacob nodded. "Josef brought me in."

Ivan said, "He is an important man."

"Yes, I know," Jacob assured him.

If Ivan only knew how.

JASMINE ADAIR—JASMINE ALAMEIN, as far as this group was concerned—was glad that she had managed to learn the art of walking a runway, without tripping, and observing at the same time. It wasn't as if she'd had training or gone to cotillion classes—did they still have cotillion classes?—but she'd been graced with the most wonderful parents in the world.

Her mother had been with the Peace Corps—maybe a natural course for her, having somewhat global roots. Her mom's parents had come from Jordan and Kenya, met and married in Morocco and moved to the United States. Jasmine's mom, Liliana, had been born and grown up in Miami, but had traveled the world to help people before she'd finally settled down. Liliana had been a great mom, always all about kindness to others and passionate that everyone must be careful with others. She had believed that words could make or break a person's day, and truly *seeing* people was one of the most important talents anyone could have in life.

Declan Adair, Jasmine's dad, was mostly Irish-American. He'd been a cop and had taught Jasmine what that meant to him—serving his community.

They had both taught her about absolute equality for every color, race, creed, sex and sexual orientation, and they had both taught her that good people were good people and, all in all, most of the people in the world were good, longing for the same things, especially in America—life, liberty and the pursuit of happiness.

They sounded like a sweet pair of hippies; they had been anything but. Her father had also taught her that those who appeared to be the nicest people in the world often were not—and that lip service didn't mean a hell of a lot and could hide an ocean of lies and misdeeds.

"Judging people—hardest call you'll ever make," he'd told her once. "Especially when you have to do so quickly."

He'd shaken his head in disgust over the result of a trial often enough, and her mother had always reminded him, "There are things that just aren't allowed before a jury, Declan. Things that the jury just doesn't see and doesn't know."

"Not to worry—we'll get them next time," he would assure her.

Jasmine scanned the crowd. Members of this group, the so-called Deco Gang, hadn't been gotten yet. And they needed to be—no one really knew the full extent of their crimes because they were good. Damned good at knowing how to game the justice system.

Fanatics came in all kinds—and fanatics were dangerous. Just as criminals came in all kinds, and they ruined the lives of those who wanted to live in peace, raising their children, working…enjoying their liberty and pursuing their happiness.

That's why cops were so important—something she had learned when sometimes her dad, the detective, hadn't made it to a birthday party.

Because of him, she'd always wanted to be a cop. And she was a damned good one, if she did say so herself.

At the moment, it was her mother's training that was paying off. As a child, Jasmine had accompanied her mom to all kinds of fund-raisers—and once she was a teenager, she'd started modeling at fashion shows in order to attract large donations for her mom's various charities. She had worked with a few top designers who were equally passionate about feeding children or raising awareness when natural disasters devastated various regions in the States and around the world.

So as Jasmine strutted and played it up for the audience, she also watched.

The event had attracted the who's who of the city. She could see two television stars who were acting in current hit series. Alphonse Mangiulli—renowned Italian artist—was there, along with Cam Li, the Chinese businessman who had just built two of the largest hotels in the world, one in Dubai and one on Miami Beach. Mathilda Glen—old, old Miami society and money—had made it, along with the famed English film director, Eric Summer.

And amid this gathering of the rich and famous was also a meeting of the loosely organized group of South Beach criminals that the Miami-Dade police called the Deco Gang.

They had come together under the control of a Russian-born kingpin, Josef Smirnoff, and they were an equal-opportunity group of very dangerous criminals. They weren't connected to the Italian Mafia or Cosa Nostra, and they weren't the Asian mob or a cartel from any South American or island country. And they were hard to pin down, using legitimate business for money laundering and for their forays into drug smuggling and dealing and prostitution.

Crimes had been committed; the bodies of victims had been found, but for the most part, those who got in the way of the gang were eliminated. Because of their connections with one another, alibis were abundant, evidence disappeared, and pinning anything on any one individual had been an elusive goal for the police.

Jasmine had used every favor she had saved up to get assigned to this case. It helped that her looks gave her a good cover for infiltration.

Her captain—Mac Lorenzo—probably suspected that she had her own motives. But he didn't ask, and she didn't tell. She hadn't let Lorenzo know that her personal determination to bring down the Deco Gang had begun when Mary Ahearn had disappeared. Her old friend had vanished without a trace after working with a nightclub that was most probably a front for a very high-scale prostitution ring.

She could see Josef Smirnoff in the front of the

crowd; he was smiling and looking right at her. He seemed to like what he saw. Good. He was the man in charge, and she needed access to him. She needed to be able to count his bodyguards and his henchmen and get close to him.

She wasn't working alone; Jasmine was blessed with an incredible partner, Jorge Fuentes.

Along with being a dedicated cop, Jorge was also extremely good-looking, and thanks to that, he'd been given leeway when he'd shown up at the Gold Sun Club, supposedly looking for work. Jasmine had told Natasha Volkov—manager of the models who worked these events or sat about various places looking pretty—that she'd worked with Jorge before and that he was wonderfully easygoing. Turned out the show was short a man; Jorge had been hired on for the day easily. They'd cast him as Adonis and given him a very small costume to wear.

Jorge had been trying to get a moment alone with her as preparations for the fashion show had gone on. Jasmine had been undercover for several weeks prior to the club's opening night, and briefings had been few and far between. The opportunity hadn't arisen as yet, but they'd be able to connect—as soon as the runway show part of the party was over. She was curious what updates Jorge had, but they were both savvy enough to bide their time. Neither of them dared to blow their covers with this group—such a mistake could result in instant death, with neither of them even aware or able to help the other in any way.

Her cover story was complete. She had a rented room

on Miami Beach, which she took for a week before answering the ad for models. She'd been given an effective fake résumé—one that showed she'd worked but never been on the top. And might well be hungry to get there.

After a lightning-quick change of clothes backstage, she made another sweep down the runway. She noted the celebrities in attendance. South Beach clubs were like rolls of toilet paper—people used them up and discarded them without a thought. What was popular today might be deserted within a month.

But she didn't think that this enterprise would care—the showy opening was just another front for the illegal activities that kept them going.

She noted the men and women surrounding Josef Smirnoff. He was about six feet tall, big and solidly muscled. His head was immaculately bald, which made his sharp jaw even more prominent and his dark eyes stand out.

On his arm was an up-and-coming young starlet. She was in from California, a lovely blue-eyed blonde, clearly hoping that Smirnoff's connections here would allow her to rub elbows with the right people.

Jasmine hoped that worked out for her—and that she didn't become involved with the wrong people.

Natasha was with him, as well. She had modeled in her own youth, in Europe. About five-eleven and in her midfifties, Natasha had come up through the ranks. One of the girls had whispered to Jasmine that Natasha had always been smart—she had managed to sleep her way up with the right people. She was an attractive woman, keeping her shoulder-length hair a silvery-white color that enhanced her slim features. She kept tight control of the fashion show and other events, and sharp eyes on everyone and everything.

Rumor had it she was sleeping with Josef. It wasn't something she proclaimed or denied. But there were signs. Jasmine wondered if she cared for Josef—or if it was a power play.

Jasmine had to wonder how Natasha felt about the beautiful women who were always around. But she understood, for Natasha, life hadn't been easy. Power probably overrode emotion.

The men by Smirnoff were his immediate body-guards. Jasmine thought of them as Curly, Moe and Larry. In truth, they were Alejandro Suarez, Antonio Garibaldi and Sasha Antonovich. All three were big men, broad-shouldered and spent their off-hours in the gym. One of the three was always with Smirnoff. On a day like today, they were all close to him.

Victor Kozak was there, as well. Victor was apparently the rising heir to receive control of the action. He was taller and slimmer than Josef, and he had bright blue eyes and perfectly clipped, salt-and-pepper facial hair. He was extremely pleasant to Jasmine—so pleasant that it made her feel uneasy.

She knew about them all somewhat because she had talked to Mary about what she was doing. She had warned Mary that there was suspicion about the group on South Beach that ran so many of the events that called for runway models or beautiful people just to be in a crowd. Beautiful people who, it was rumored, you could engage to spend time with privately. Mary had described many of these players before Jasmine had met them.

Before Mary had disappeared.

The club manager was behind the bar; he didn't often work that kind of labor himself. He usually oversaw what was going on there. He was like the bodyguards—solid, watching, earning his way up the ranks.

Still watching, Jasmine made another of her teasing plays with Jorge—pointing out the next model who was coming down the runway. Kari Anderson was walking along in a black caftan that accented the fairness of her skin and the platinum shimmer of her hair. Jorge stood perfectly still; only his eyes moved, drawing laughter from the crowd.

As Jasmine did her turn around, she noted a man at the bar. She did not know him, or anything about him. He was a newcomer, Kari had told her. A big man in New York City. He was taller and leaner than any of the other men, and yet Jasmine had the feeling that he was steel-muscled beneath the designer suit he was wearing. He hadn't close-cropped his hair either; it was long, shaggy around his ears, a soft brown.

He was definitely the best looking of the bunch. His face was crafted with sharp clean contours, high defined cheekbones, a nicely squared chin and wide-set, light eyes. He could have been up on the runway, playing "pretty boy" with Jorge.

But of course, newcomer though he might be, he'd be one of "them." He'd recently come to South Beach, pretending to be some kind of an artist and owning and operating a gallery.

The hair. Maybe he believed that would disguise him as an artist—rather than a murdering criminal.

When she had made another turn, after pausing to do a synchronized turn with Kari, she saw that the new guy had left the bar area, along with the bartender. They were near Josef Smirnoff now.

Allowed into the inner circle.

Just as she noticed them, a loud crack rang out. The sound was almost masked by the music.

People didn't react.

Instinct and experience told Jasmine that it was indeed a gunshot. She instantly grabbed hold of Kari and dragged her down to the platform, all but lying over her. Another shot sounded; a light exploded in a hail of sparks. Then the rat-tat-tat of bullets exploded throughout the room.

The crowd began to scream and move.

There was nothing orderly about what happened—people panicked. It was hard not to blame them. It was a fearsome world they lived in.

"Stay down!" Jasmine told Kari, rising carefully.

Jorge was already on the floor, trying to help up a woman who had fallen, in danger of being trampled.

Bodyguards and police hired for the night were trying to bring order. Jasmine jumped into the crowd, trying to fathom where the shots had been fired. It was a light at the end of the runway that had exploded; where the other shot had come from was hard to discern.

The band had panicked, as well. A guitar crashed down on the floor.

Josef Smirnoff was on the ground, too. His bodyguards were near, trying to hold off the people who were set to run over him.

It was an absolute melee.

Jasmine helped up a young man, a white-faced rising star in a new television series. He tried to thank her.

"Get out, go—walk quickly," she said.

There were no more shots. But would they begin again?

She made her way to Smirnoff, ducking beneath the distracted bodyguards. She knelt by him as people raced around her.

"Josef?" she said, reaching for his shoulder, turning him over.

Blood covered his chest. There was no hope for the man; he was already dead, his eyes open in shock. There was blood on her now, blood on the designer gown she'd been wearing, everywhere.

She looked up; Jorge had to be somewhere nearby. Instead she saw a man coming after her, reaching for her as if to attack.

She rolled quickly, avoiding him once. But as she prepared to fight back, she felt as if she had been taken down by a linebacker. She stared up into the eyes of the long-haired newcomer; bright blue eyes, startling against his face and dark hair. She felt his hands on her, felt the strength in his hold.

No. She was going to take him down.

She jackknifed her body, letting him use his own weight against himself, causing him to crash into the floor.

He was obviously surprised. It took him a second—

but only a second—to spin himself. He was back on his feet in a hunched position, ready to spring at her.

Where the hell is Jorge?

She feinted as if she would dive down to the left and dived to the right instead. She caught the man with a hard chop to the abdomen that should have stolen his breath.

He didn't give. She was suddenly tackled again, down on the ground, feeling the full power of the man's strength atop her. She stared up into his blue eyes, glistening like ice at the moment.

She realized the crowd was gone; she could hear the bustle at the doorway, hear the police as they poured in at the entrance.

But right there, at that moment, Josef Smirnoff lay dead in an ungodly pool of blood—blood she wore—just feet away.

And there was this man.

And herself.

"Hey!" Thank God, Jorge had found her. He dived down beside them, as if joining the fight. But he didn't help Jasmine; he made no move against the man. He lay next to her, as if he'd just also been taken down himself.

"Stop! FBI, meet MDPD. Jasmine, he's undercover. Jacob… Jasmine is a cop. My partner," Jorge whispered urgently.

The man couldn't have looked more surprised. Then, he made a play of socking Jorge, and Jorge lay still. The man stood and dragged Jasmine to her feet. For a long moment he looked into her eyes, and then he wrenched her elbow behind her back.

"Play it out," he said, "nothing else to do."

"Sure," Jasmine told him.

And as he led her out—toward Victor Kozak, who now stood in the front, ready to take charge, Jasmine managed to twist and deliver a hard right to his jaw.

He stared at her, rubbing his jaw with his free hand.

"Play it out," she said softly.

The Feds always thought they knew more than the locals, whether they were team people or not. He'd probably be furious. He'd want to call the shots.

But at least his presence meant that the Feds had been aware of this place. They had listened to the police, and they had sent someone in. It was probably what Jorge had been trying to tell her.

Jacob was still staring at her. Well, she did have a damned good right hook.

To her surprise, he almost seemed to smile. "Play it out," he said. And to her continued surprise, he added, "You are one hell of a player!"

Chapter Two

"Someone knew," Jorge said. "Someone knew that Smirnoff came in—that he was selling them all out."

"Maybe," Jacob Wolff said. He was sitting on the sofa in Jasmine's South Beach apartment.

She didn't know why, but it bothered her that he was there. So comfortable. So thoughtful. But it hadn't been until now, with him in her apartment, that she really understood what was going on.

Two weeks ago, Josef Smirnoff had made contact with Dean Jenkins, a special agent assigned to the Miami office. Jenkins had gone to his superiors, and from there, Jacob Wolff had been called in. Among his other talents, he was a linguist, speaking Russian, Ukrainian, Spanish, Portuguese and French, including Cajun and Haitian Creole. He also knew a smattering of Czech and Polish. And German, enough to get by.

Maybe that's why she was resenting him. No one should be that accomplished.

No, it was simply because he had taken her by surprise.

"Maybe someone knew," Wolff said. He added, "And maybe not."

"If not, why—?" Jorge asked.

Wolff leaned forward. "Because," he said softly, "I believe that Kozak set up that hit. Not because he knew about anything that Smirnoff had done, but because he's been planning on taking over. Perhaps for some time.

"Smirnoff came in to us because he was afraid—he'd been the boss forever, but he knew how that could end if a power play went down. He was afraid. He wanted out. Kozak was the one who wanted Smirnoff out. And he figured out how to do it—and make it look as if he was as pure as the driven snow in the whole thing himself. He was visible to dozens of people when Smirnoff was killed. He played his cards right. There were plenty of cops there today, in uniform. What better time to plan an execution, when he wouldn't look the least guilty? In *this* crime ring, he was definitely the next man up— vice president, if you will."

"The thing is, if Kozak figures out something is up, we're all in grave danger," Jorge pointed out. "Undercover may not work."

"Jorge, undercover work is the only thing that might bring them down," Jasmine protested.

She was leaning against the archway between the living-dining area of the apartment and the kitchen. It was late; she was tired. But it had been the first chance for the three of them to talk.

After the chaos, everyone had been interviewed by the police. Stars—the glittering rich and famous and especially the almost-famous—had done endless interviews with the press, as well. Thankfully, there had been plenty of celebrities to garner attention. Jasmine,

Jorge and Jacob Wolff had all managed to avoid being seen on television, but still, maintaining their cover had meant they were there for hours.

She'd been desperate to shower, and her blood-soaked gown had gone to the evidence locker.

In the end, they'd been seen leaving together, but that had been all right. Everyone knew that Jorge was Jasmine's friend—she'd brought him into the show, after all.

And as for Jacob Wolff...

"You shouldn't have made that show of going off with us in front of Victor Kozak," she said, glaring at Wolff. She realized her tone was harsh. Too harsh. But this was her apartment—or, at least, her cover persona's apartment—and she felt like a cat on a hot tin roof while he relaxed comfortably on her rented couch.

She needed to take a deep breath; start over with the agent.

He didn't look her way, just shrugged. "I told Ivan, the bartender, I wanted to get to know you. They believe I'm an important player out of New York. Right now, they're observing me. And they believe if they respect me, I'll respect them, play by their rules. I'm supposed to be a money launderer—I'm not into many of their criminal activities, including prostitution or any form of modern slavery. My cover is that of an art dealer with dozens of foreign ties.

"Before all this went down tonight, I was trying to befriend Ivan, who apparently manages the girls. I'm trying to figure out how the women are entangled in their web. Apparently, they move slowly. Most probably, with drugs. Before all this went down tonight, I'd asked about you, Jasmine, as if taking advantage of the 'friendship' they'll offer me. He said you weren't available yet, but that all good things come in time, or something to that effect. He'll think I took advantage of the situation instead—and that I'm offering you all the comfort a man in my position can offer."

"Really?" Jasmine asked. "But I was with Jorge."

Wolff finally looked at her, waving a hand in the air. "Yes, and they all know you two are friends, and that it's normal you would have left with Jorge. But Jorge is gay."

"That's what you told them?" Jasmine asked.

"I am gay," Jorge said, shrugging.

Jasmine turned to him. "You are? You never told me."

"You never asked. Hey, we're great partners. I never asked who you were dating. Oh, wait, you never do seem to date."

Jasmine could have kicked him. "Hey!" she protested. Great. She felt like an idiot. She and Jorge were close, but…it was true. They'd been working together for a while, they were friends. Just friends. And because of that, she hadn't thought to ask—

It didn't matter. They'd both tacitly known from the beginning as partners they'd never date each other, and neither had ever thought to ask the other about their love life.

She had to draw some dignity out of this situation.

"At least we did the expected," she said. "I guarantee we were watched. Oh, and by the way, Ivan Petrov controls the venue. But Natasha really runs the models. She gives the assignments, and she's the one who hands out the paychecks."

Wolff looked at her. "You're going to have to be very careful. From all that I've been told, she's been with this enterprise from the beginning. She may be almost as powerful as Kozak himself. When Natasha got into it, she wasn't manipulated into sex work. She used sex as an investment. She came into it as a model, slept with whomever they wanted—and worked her way up to Kozak."

"I am careful," Jasmine told him. "I'm a good cop—determined, but not suicidal."

"I'm glad to hear it. So, this is all as good as it can be," Wolff said, shaking his head. "What matters most here tonight is that we've lost Smirnoff, our informant. And we've still got to somehow get into this and take them all down. We have to take Kozak down, with all the budding lieutenants, too. My position with this group is pretty solid—the Bureau does an amazing job when it comes to inventing a history. But the fashion show is over. The opening is over. The club will be closed down for a few days."

"I'll have an in, don't worry. The last words from Natasha this evening had to do with us all reporting in tomorrow—for one, to return the clothing. For another, to find out where we go from here." Jasmine hesitated.

"They haven't asked you to entertain anyone yet?" Wolff asked.

"New girls get a chance to believe they're just models. After that, they're asked to escort at certain times, and, of course, from there…"

"We'll have this wrapped up before then," Jorge assured her.

"And if not, you'll just get the hell out of it," Wolff said.

"You don't have to be protective. I've been with the Special Investigations Division for three years now, and I've dealt with some pretty heinous people," Jasmine told him.

"I've dealt with them, too," Wolff said quietly. "And I spent this afternoon up in the Everglades, a plot of godforsaken swamp with a bunch of oil drums filled with bodies. And I've been FBI for almost a decade. That didn't make today any better."

"I'm not saying anything makes it better. I'm just saying I can take care of myself," Jasmine said.

She really hadn't meant to be argumentative. But she did know what she was doing, and throughout her career, she'd learned it was usually the people who felt the need to emphasize their competency who were the ones who weren't so sure of their competency after all. She was confident in her abilities—or, at least she had thought she was.

With this Fed, she was becoming defensive. She hated the feeling.

"Guys, guys! Time-out," Jorge said.

Wolff stood, apparently all but dismissing her. "I'm heading back to my place. Most days, I'll be hanging around a real art shop that's supposedly mine. Dolphin Galleries."

He handed Jorge a card, then turned to look at Jasmine. "Feel free to watch out for me. In my mind, no one cop can beat everything out there. We all need people watching our backs. I'm more than happy to know I have MDPD in deep with me."

His words didn't help in the least; Jasmine still felt like a chastised toddler. What made it worse was the fact he was right. They did need to look out for one another.

She wanted to apologize. They had met awkwardly. She wasn't brash, she wasn't an idiot—she was a team player. But despite his words, she had the sense that he was already doubting her.

"I'll be hanging as close as I can," he said. "The woman managing the shop, Katrina Partridge, is with us. If you need me and I'm not there, just ask her. I trust her with my life."

He didn't look back. If he had done so, Jasmine was certain, it would have been to look at Jorge with pity for having been paired with her.

When Jacob was gone, she strode to the door and slid the bolts. She had three.

"Jerk!" she said. She turned back into the room and flounced down on the sofa.

"Not really. Just bad circumstances," Jorge said, taking a seat beside her. "I, uh, actually like the guy."

She looked at him. "I don't dislike him. I don't really know him."

"Could have fooled me."

She ignored that. "Jorge, how did it happen? We were all there. The place was spilling over with cops.

And someone shot and killed Smirnoff—with all of us there—and we don't know who or how."

"They were counting on the place being filled with cops, Jasmine. Detectives will be on the case and our crime scene techs will find a trajectory for the bullet that killed him. We do our part, they do theirs. Thing is, whoever killed him, they were just the working part of the bigger machine. We have to get to the major players—Kozak, whoever else. Not that the man or woman who was pulling the trigger shouldn't serve life, but… it won't matter."

"No, it won't matter," she agreed. What they needed to do was find Mary. She nodded.

He took her hand and squeezed it. "You're just thrown. We weren't expecting to take them all down tonight."

"We weren't expecting Smirnoff to get killed tonight. I—I didn't even know he'd gone to the FBI!"

"I knew but couldn't tell you. And I didn't know that Smirnoff would be killed before I had a chance to loop you in. I'm sorry—I put you and Wolff both in a bad position. At least you didn't shoot each other. You know you're resenting him because he had you down."

"He did not have me down."

"Almost had you down."

"I almost had him down."

"Ouch. Take a breath," Jorge warned.

She did, and she shook her head. "I worked with a Fed once."

"And he was okay, right? Come on, we're all going in the same direction."

"He was great. Old dude—kept telling me he had a granddaughter my age. Made me feel like I should have been in bed by ten," Jasmine said and smiled.

Jorge arched his brow at her.

"Okay, okay," she said. "I resent the fact he almost had me down. But really, I almost had him, too." She squeezed his hand in return. "How come we never have discussed our love lives and this stranger knew more about you than I did?"

"'Cause neither of us cares what our preferences are, and we work well together—and we enjoy what we're doing. And Wolff for sure had all of us checked out before agreeing to work with us. He'd need to know our backgrounds and that we're clean cops. Also, you're a workaholic and even when we're grabbing quick food or popping into a bookstore, we're still working."

"Not really," she told him. "Honestly, not until this operation."

He nodded. "Mary," he said softly.

"Jorge, I'm so afraid she's dead." She paused. "Even more now. Do you have any details about the oil drums they found today? All I've seen is what has been on the news. Captain Lorenzo was even with the cops doing the interviews at the show, but I didn't get to ask him anything. Obviously, I did my best to be a near hysterical model."

"You were terrific."

She laughed. "So were you." Jasmine tried to smile, but she was searching out his eyes.

"Mary wasn't in one of the oil drums," he said.

"You're sure?"

"Positive. The bodies discovered were all men."

"Oh, thank God. I mean… I'm not glad that anyone was dead, but—"

"It's all right," Jorge assured her. "I understand. So, tomorrow will be tense. I'm going to get out of here. Let you get some sleep." He started to rise, and then he didn't. "Never mind."

"Never mind?"

"I'm going to stay here."

"I don't need to be protected," she said. "Bolts on the door, gun next to the bed."

"You don't need to be protected?" Jorge said. "I do! Safety in numbers. Bolt the door and let's get some sleep."

She rose. "Okay, I lied, and you're right—anyone can be taken by surprise. And I have been a jerk and I don't know why."

"I do," Jorge said softly. "You really shouldn't be working this case. You have a personal involvement. And in a way, so do I. I've met Mary."

Jasmine nodded. "I don't feel that I'm really up to speed yet, despite what we learned from Wolff. I'll get you some pillows and bedding," she told him.

"What time are we supposed to be where?" he asked her as she laid out sheets on the sofa.

"Ten o'clock, back at the club."

"I'm willing to bet half of it will still be shut down."

"We won't be going to the floor. We'll be picking up our pay in the offices, using the VIP entrance on the side to the green room and staging areas."

"You know that we can get in?"

She nodded. "I wound up with Natasha and the other girls in a little group when the police were herding people for interviews. Natasha asked the lead detective— Detective Greenberg is in charge for the City of Miami Beach—and he told her that they'd cordon off the club area until they finished with the investigation. Owners and operators were free to use the building where the police weren't investigating."

"Then go to bed. We'll begin again in the morning."

Jorge was clearly thinking something but not saying it.

"What?" she pressed.

"I didn't know until today that the FBI was in on this case—the briefing was why I arrived late. MDPD found the group operating the Gold Sun Club to be shady, as did the cops with the City of Miami Beach. But there's been no hard evidence against them and nothing that anyone could do. I know you've been talking to Captain Lorenzo about them for a while, but…we just found out today that Smirnoff was about to give evidence against the whole shebang. I'm just—"

"Just what?"

He grimaced. "I like the Feds. They have more resources than we do. They have more reach across state lines. Across international lines. And I don't know how long I'll get to be one of the models—if the big show ended in disaster, I could be out fast. And then I won't be around to help you."

"I'm willing to bet the Deco Gang will keep planning. Kozak will say that all the people who had been hired for jobs at the club will still need work. He'll go forward in Smirnoff's name—Smirnoff would not want to have been frightened off Miami Beach. We'll be in."

"You will be. I may not. So, I'm just glad that… well, that there's another law enforcement agent undercover on this case. Speaking of undercover…" Jorge grabbed his blanket and turned around, smiling as he feigned sleep.

Jasmine opened her mouth to speak. She shook her head and went to the bedroom. Ready for bed and curled up, she admitted to herself that she just might be glad for Jacob Wolff's involvement, too.

She had assumed the group was trading in prostitution, turning models into drug addicts and then trafficking them.

She hadn't known about the bodies in the barrels. And she hadn't suspected that Smirnoff was going to die.

So she was glad she would have backup if she had to continue getting close to these dangerous players. Otherwise she probably should back right out of the case.

Except she just couldn't. They had Mary. They had her somewhere.

And Jasmine had to pray her friend was still alive.

Chapter Three

Jacob could remember coming to South Beach with his parents as a child. Back then, the gentrification of the area was already underway.

His mom liked to tell him about the way it had been when she had been young, when the world had yet to realize the beauty and architectural value of the art deco hotels—and when the young and beautiful had headed north on South Beach to the fabulous Fontainebleau and other such hotels where the likes of Sinatra and others had performed. In her day, there had been tons of bagel shops, and high school kids had all come to hang out by the water with their surfboards—despite a lack of anything that resembled real surf.

It was where his parents had met. His father had once told him, not without some humor, that he'd fallen in love over a twenty-five-cent bagel.

The beach was beautiful. Jacob had opted for a little boutique hotel right on the water. Fisher House had been built in the early 1920s when a great deal around it had been nothing but scrub, brush and palms. It had been completely renovated and revamped about a decade ago and was charming, intimate and historic, filled with framed pictures of long ago. The back door opened to a vast porch—half filled with dining tables—and then a tiled path led to the pool and beyond down to the ocean.

Jacob started the morning early, out on the sand, watching the sun come up, feeling the ocean breeze and listening to the seagulls cry. The rising sun was shining down on the water, creating a sparkling scene with diamond-like bits of brilliance all around him.

It was a piece of heaven. Sand between his toes, and then a quick dip in the water—cool and yet temperate in the early-morning hour. He loved it. Home for him in the last few years had been Washington, D.C., or New York City. There were beaches to be found, yes, but nothing like this. So, for the first hour of the day, he let himself just love the feel of salt air around him, hear the lulling rush of waves and look out over the endless water.

There was nothing like seeing it like a native. By 9:00 a.m., he was heading along Ocean Drive. The city was coming alive by then; roller skaters whizzed by him and traffic was heavy. Art galleries and shops were beginning to open, and tourists were flocking out in all manner of beach apparel, some wearing scanty clothing and some not. While most American men were fond of surf shorts for dipping in the water, Europeans tended to Speedos and as little on their bodies as possible. It was a generalization; he didn't like generalizations, but in this case, he was pretty sure he was right.

A fellow with a belly that surely hid his toes from his own sight—and his Speedo—walked on by and greeted

Jacob with a cheerful "good morning" that was spoken with a heavy foreign accent.

Jacob smiled. The man was happy with himself and within the legal bounds of propriety for this section of the beach. And that was what mattered.

He stopped into the News Café. It was a great place to see…and be seen. Before he'd been murdered, the famous designer Gianni Versace had lived in one of South Beach's grand old mansions. He had also dined many a morning at the News Café. Tourists flocked there. So did locals.

Jacob picked up a newspaper, ordered an egg dish and sat back and watched—and listened.

The conversation was all about the shooting of Josef Smirnoff at what should have been one of the brightest moments in the pseudo-plastic environment of the beach.

"You can bring in all the stars you want—but with *those* people—"

"I heard it was a mob hit!"

"Did you know that earlier, like in the morning, three bodies were found in oil drums out in the Everglades?"

"Yeah. I don't think anyone had even reported them missing. No ID's as of yet, but hey…like we don't have enough problems down here."

People were talking. Naturally.

"Told you we shouldn't have come to Miami."

"Hey, mobsters kill mobsters. No one else was injured. Bunch of shots, from what I read, but only the mobster was killed."

Someone who was apparently a local spoke up.

"Actually, honestly, we're not that bad a city. I mean, my dad says that most of our bad crimes are committed by out-of-towners and not our population."

Bad crimes… Sure, like most people in the world, locals here wanted to fall in love, buy houses, raise children and seek the best lives possible.

But it was true, too, that South Florida was one massive melting pot—perhaps like New York City in the last decade. People came from all the Caribbean islands, Central and South America, the countries that had once comprised the Soviet Union, and from all over the world.

Most came in pursuit of a new life and freedom. Some came because a melting pot was simply a good place for criminal activity.

While he people-watched, Jacob replayed everything he had seen the day before in his mind. He remembered what he had heard.

Witnesses hadn't been lying or overly rattled when they had reported that it seemed the shots had come from all over. From the bar, he'd had a good place to observe the whole room. And then, as Ivan had muttered that they could go closer and see, they had done so.

The shooter hadn't been close to Josef Smirnoff—Jacob had been near him and if someone had shot him from up close, he'd have known.

He was pretty sure that the shooters had been stationed in the alcoves on the balcony that surrounded the ground floor, just outside the offices and private rooms on the second floor. The space allowed for customers to enjoy a band from upstairs, without being in the crowd below.

When he'd looked up at the balconies earlier, he hadn't seen anyone on them. The stairs might have been blocked.

Would Jasmine have known that detail? Or would they have shared that information with a new girl?

Jasmine had, beyond a doubt, drawn attention last night. She had been captivatingly beautiful, and she had played the runway perfectly, austere and yet with a sense of fun. She was perfect for the role she was playing.

The band, the models, the excitement… It had all been perfect for the setup. It was really a miracle that no one else had been hit.

He had thought that Jasmine was going after Josef Smirnoff when he had seen her lunge at him—getting close to see that the deed was done, that he was finished off if the bullets hadn't done their work. He'd never forget her surprise when he had tackled her…

Nor his own shock when she had thrown him off.

He was surprised to find himself smiling—he wasn't often taken unaware. Then again, while he'd known that MDPD had police officers working undercover, he hadn't been informed that one of them was working the runway.

A dangerous place.

But she worked it well. She had an in he could never have.

He pictured it all in his mind again. There had been multiple shooters but only one target—Josef Smirnoff.

Create panic, and it might well have appeared that Smirnoff had been killed in a rain of bullets that could have been meant for anyone.

Jacob paid his bill and headed out, walking toward Dolphin Galleries. He felt the burner phone in his left pocket vibrate and he quickly pulled it out. Dean Jenkins, his Miami office counterpart, was calling.

"You alone?"

The street was busy, but as Jacob walked, he was well aware that by "alone," Dean was asking if he was far from those involved with the Deco Gang.

"I am," he said.

"They're doing the autopsy now. Someone apparently had a bead on the bastard's heart. It's amazing that no one else was hurt. Oh, beyond cuts and bruises, I mean. People trampled people. But the bullets that didn't hit Smirnoff hit the walls."

"They only wanted Smirnoff dead. Kill a mobster, and the police might not look so hard. Kill a pretty ingenue, a pop star or a music icon, and the heat never ends."

"Yep. I wanted to let you know that I'm on the ground with the detective from the City of Miami Beach and another guy from Miami-Dade PD. Figured if I was around asking questions I'd be in close contact, and you could act annoyed and harassed."

"Good."

"You met the undercover Miami-Dade cops, right?" Dean asked.

"I did. We've talked."

"Good. The powers that be are stressing communication. They don't want any of you ending up in the swamp."

"Good to hear. I don't think I'd fit into an oil drum. Don't worry, we've got each other's backs."

"Have you been asked to move any money for the organization yet?"

"On my way in to the gallery now," Jacob said. "I expect I'll see someone soon enough."

"It may take some time, with that murder at the club last night, you know."

"A murder that I think they planned. I'd bet they'll contact me today."

"You're on. Keep up with MDPD, all right? Word from the top. Both the cops and our agency are accustomed to undercover operations, but this one is more than dicey."

"At least I get to bathe for this one," Jacob told him.

"There's a bright spot to everything, huh?"

"You bet."

He ended the call, slid the phone back in his pocket and headed toward the gallery.

The sun was shining overhead. People were out on the beach, playing, soaking up the heat. The shadow of last night's murder couldn't ruin a vacation for the visitors who had planned for an entire year.

Besides, it was a shady rich man, a mobster, who had been killed.

He who lives by the sword...

Jacob turned the corner. Ivan Petrov was standing in front of the gallery, studying a piece of modern art.

MOE, CURLY AND LARRY—or, rather Alejandro Suarez, Antonio Garibaldi and Sasha Antonovich—were upstairs when Jasmine arrived with Jorge at precisely 10:00 a.m. the next day.

Alejandro was at the top of the stairs. Sasha was at the door to what had once been Josef Smirnoff's office and was now the throne room for Victor Kozak.

Jasmine had made a point of greeting both Alejandro and Sasha. She presumed that Antonio was in the room with Victor, which he was. She saw him when the door to that inner sanctum opened and Natasha Volkov walked out.

The door immediately shut behind her, but not before Jasmine could see that Victor Kozak was seated at what had been Josef Smirnoff's desk.

The king is dead; long live the king, she thought.

This had shades of all kinds of Shakespearean tragedy on it. Apparently, Josef Smirnoff had known that someone had been planning to kill him—he just hadn't known who. Maybe he had suspected Kozak but not known. And he probably hadn't imagined that he'd be gunned down at the celebrity opening for the club.

She knew that Smirnoff hadn't exactly been a good man. She had heard, though, that he wasn't on the truly evil side of bad. He'd preferred strong-arm tactics to murder. He'd rather have his debts paid, and how did a dead man pay a debt?

Jasmine couldn't defend Smirnoff. However, she believed that Kozak was purely evil. It made her skin crawl to be near him. She had a feeling he'd kill his own mother if he saw it as a good career move.

"Ah, you are here! Such a good girl," Natasha said, slipping an arm around Jasmine's shoulder and moving her down the hallway. She turned back to Jorge. "You come, too, pretty boy. You are a good boy, too."

Jorge smiled.

Natasha opened the door into a giant closet–dressing room combo. There were racks of clothing and rows of tables with mirrors surrounded by bright lights for the girls to use. Before the show the day before, the room had been filled with dressers, stylists and makeup artists.

"So sad. Poor Josef," Natasha said, admitting them through the door and then closing it. She made a display of bringing her fingers to her eyes, as if she'd been crying. Her face was not, however, tearstained.

"We are all in shock, in mourning today," Natasha added. "So, let me pay you for last night and we will talk for a minute, yes? Maybe you can help."

"Definitely," Jasmine said. "Talking would be good. Mr. Smirnoff was so kind to all of us. It's so horrible what happened."

"Terrible," Jorge agreed.

"So." Natasha grabbed a large manila envelope off one of the dressers and took out a sizable wad of cash. She counted off the amount for each of their fees. When Natasha casually handed it over, Jasmine saw it was all in large bills. It seemed like a lot of cash to have lying around.

Natasha indicated a grouping of leather love seats

and chairs where models and performers waited once their makeup was complete.

Jorge and Jasmine took chairs.

"You—you were very brave," she said, looking at Jasmine. "I was behind the curtain, but I saw the way you protected Kari and tried to help poor Josef."

"Oh, no, not so brave," Jasmine said. "When I was a child... I was with my parents in the Middle East, and my father taught me to get down, and get everyone around me down, anytime I heard gunshots. It was just instinct."

"I tried to get to Jasmine," Jorge said, "because she's my friend."

"Of course, of course," Natasha said. "But you two and Kari were the ones who were out on the runway when it all happened. What did you see? Of course, I know that the police talked to everyone last night, but... we're so upset about Josef! Perhaps you've remembered something...something that you might have seen?"

Jasmine shook her head. "Oh, Natasha. This is terrible, but I was only thinking about saving myself at first. I didn't see anything at all." Jasmine wished that she wasn't lying. She could easily be passionate because her words were true. She wished to hell that she had seen something—anything.

She had just heard the bullets flying. And seen Josef Smirnoff go down.

"I'm so, so sorry," she said. "Of course, I suppose this means that... Well, if you need anything from me in the future, I'd be so happy to work with you again."

Natasha smiled. "Jasmine, you must not worry. We

will always have a need for you. We are a loyal family here! And, Jorge, of course, you, too."

"Thank you," Jorge said earnestly.

"But nothing—nothing at all?" Natasha persisted. "Tell me about your night, from the time you stepped out on the runway."

"It was so wonderful!" Jasmine said. "At first, I could hear the crowd. We were having a great time on the runway, and I heard people laughing and having fun... and then, that sound! I didn't realize at first that I was hearing bullets. And then...then it was as if I knew instantly. My past, maybe," she whispered. "And I went for Kari, and when I saw Josef down on the floor, I wanted to help... He'd been good to me, you know? Then that man—a friend of Josef's, I think—thought that I was trying to hurt Josef, and he...he tackled me."

"And you were angry, of course," Natasha murmured.

"Well, at first, of course, but it was okay after. He apologized to me. He told me he thought that I wanted to hurt Josef. He was very sincere. So apologetic."

"He saw to it that we got back to Jasmine's place safely. I liked him," Jorge said.

"And you, Jasmine? Did you like him?" Natasha asked.

"After we talked, of course. He was very apologetic. He told me that he's new to Miami Beach—new to Miami. He was working up north, but he got tired of snow and ice and had some connections to help him start up in business down here, and so...he was sad that his first time really heading to a fine event ended so tragically."

"So. He made moves on you," Natasha said softly. She wasn't pleased, and Jasmine recognized why.

Jasmine was now a commodity—one controlled by Natasha—even if she wasn't supposed to really understand that yet. This newcomer needed to go through Natasha—her and Victor Kozak now—if he wanted to have Jasmine as his own special escort.

"Oh, no, he didn't make moves," Jasmine said.

"He was a gentleman. Almost as if he was one of your security people. He just saw that we got home safely," Jorge said. He looked at Jasmine. "I thought maybe he liked me better."

"Oh?" Natasha said. "Interesting."

"No, no, Jorge—he didn't like you better!" Jasmine said. She knew that Jorge was smirking inwardly, and yet he was playing it well. They were both saying the right things in order to be able to stay close with Jacob as they ventured further into the world of Deco Gang.

They needed everyone in on this—Federal and local. Jorge had been right.

"You found him to be a nice man?" Natasha asked.

"Very," Jorge said before Jasmine could answer.

"Jorge, I am sorry, I don't think that he's interested in you," Natasha said. "He did express interest in Jasmine. But we shall see. Be nice to him, if he should see you or try to contact you. But if he does so, you must let me know right away."

"Of course," Jasmine said, eyes wide. "I know that you'll watch out for me."

"Yes, of course. We will watch out for you," Natasha said. She smiled. "We are family here. So, now, come with me. There will be another event soon enough. We will mourn Josef, of course. But so many are dependent on us for a living, we cannot stop. We will have a memorial or something this weekend on the beach. You will be part of it. We are family, yes? We don't let our people…down. For now, you will give Victor Kozak your…condolences."

Give him their condolences. If this had been happening just years earlier, they might well have been expected to kneel and kiss Kozak's ring.

She and Jorge both smiled naively. "Definitely," Jasmine said.

They rose; Jasmine led them down the hall.

Antonio and Alejandro were by the door to the office. Jasmine knew that Sasha Antonovich had to still be guarding the door.

Natasha tapped on the door to the office. Kozak called out, "Come in," and they entered.

He was alone, poring over papers that lay on the table before him.

"We're so sorry for your loss," Jasmine ventured timidly when Kozak didn't look up.

"The police are still in the club downstairs," he said, shaking his head. "They want to know about the balconies. I want to help them. I want to find the person who did this to our beloved Josef. But the balconies were closed off. Just with velvet cords, of course, but… Ah, Jasmine! We were all so enchanted with your performance," he said, looking up. "And you, too, of course. You were the perfect foil for the girls," he told Jorge.

"Thank you," Jorge murmured.

"I don't know who was on the balcony," Victor went on. "We'd said there would be no one on the balcony."

"Maybe the police have ways to find out," Jorge suggested in a hopeful voice.

Victor Kozak waved a hand in the air. "Maybe, maybe not. We'll keep up our own line of questioning. Anyway..."

He seemed to stop in midthought and gave his attention to them. "Please, I know that you were hired by Josef, but...it is my sincere hope that you will remain with us. We pay our regular models a retainer, which you will receive while we wait for this...for this painful situation to be behind us. That is, if you still wish to be with us."

"For sure!" Jasmine said.

"Retainer? Me, too?" Jorge asked hopefully.

Kozak glanced over at Natasha. She must have given him her approval with the slightest nod.

"Yes, you were quite the centerpiece for our lovely young girls. We have a reputation for always having beautiful people in our clubs. All you need to do is be around, available to us, and maybe meet some people we'd like to introduce you to. Please, we will be in touch. You may come in tomorrow for your paychecks."

They both thanked him profusely. Natasha led them down to the street.

As they were going out, Kari Anderson was just arriving. She threw her arms around Jasmine, shaking.

"I don't think I had a chance to thank you. You saved my life!" Kari told her.

"Kari, I just made you get down," Jasmine said, flushing and very aware that both Natasha and Sasha were watching the exchange. "Instinct!" she added quickly. "And we're all just so lucky…except for poor Josef."

"I know, it's so terrible," said the young blonde, her empathy real. Jasmine liked Kari. She was an honest kind person who seemed oblivious to her natural beauty. "Josef was always nice. It's so sad. Terrible that people do these things today! Terrible that poor Josef was caught in it all."

Naive—just like Mary, Jasmine thought. Not lacking confidence but unaware of just how much they had to offer.

"Come on up. We will straighten all out with you, Kari," Natasha said. "We will be all right. Victor will see to it," she added. "Now, you two run along and try to enjoy some downtime. Kari, come with me. We will have work for all of you—you needn't stress."

"See you, Kari," Jorge said, waving.

He and Jasmine started down the street while Natasha led Kari past Sasha and up the stairs.

"I worry about her," Jasmine said.

"I worry about all of us," Jorge said. "I was worried about the two of us unarmed during the show. We were taking a major chance."

"We knew there would be cops all over."

"Right. And Josef Smirnoff is dead and bullets were flying everywhere."

She couldn't argue that.

"So, tomorrow, we go back for our checks. Our retainer checks," she murmured.

"And you know we're going to be asked to do something for those checks."

"At least I don't think they're remotely suspicious of us," Jasmine told him.

"Not yet. We're still new."

"Kari came in just ahead of me," Jasmine said. "She…she was a replacement for Mary, I think."

"Here's the thing—what do we do when they want something from us that we don't want to do?" Jorge asked. "We haven't gotten anyone to admit to any criminal activity. If they ask you to be an escort, that's actually legal. So, you go off with someone they set you up with—and that guy wants sex. What do you do? Arrest the guy? That won't get us anywhere. And you sure as hell aren't going to compromise yourself."

"You may be asked first."

"I'm pretty—but not as pretty as you are."

Jasmine laughed. "Beauty is in the eye of the beholder, you know."

"Trust me on this. You'll be first. They'll tread a little more lightly with me."

Jasmine shook her head. "We have to get in more tightly, hear things and find something on them. You're right. They'll deny they have anything to do with illegally selling sex—I'm sure they've got that all worked out." She sighed. "I guess that our FBI connection will do a better job—he'll find out what they're doing with the money."

"How do we prove murder?" Jorge asked softly.

Jasmine lowered her head.

Jorge took her shoulders and spun her around to look at him. "We don't know that Mary is dead."

"I know," she whispered.

She was startled when her phone started to ring; it was a pay-as-you-go phone, one purchased in her cover name, Jasmine Alamein.

She looked at Jorge. "It's Natasha."

"Answer it!"

"Ah, Jasmine, my darling," Natasha said. "I'm so glad to reach you so quickly."

"Yeah, no problem," Jasmine said.

"We have a favor to ask of you. It includes a bonus, naturally."

"What is it?" Jasmine asked. Jorge was staring at her, wary.

"That friend of Josef's—Mr. Marensky. He is new in town. He has asked if you would be so good as to show him around. We'd be happy if you could do so— he came to us, instead of trying to twist our arm for a phone number. You will take him around town, yes? I said that wrong. He wishes to take you to dinner and perhaps you could show him some of the beach. And report to me, of course."

"Yes, for sure. Where do you want me to be when?" Jasmine asked.

"He will call for you at your apartment. Please, make sure your friend is not there when he arrives."

"What time?"

"Eight o'clock tonight."

"Thank you, Natasha. I will be ready."

"Wear something very pretty." Natasha didn't mean pretty. She meant *sexy.*

"I will. Thank you. Thank you!"

"My pleasure. Tomorrow morning you will come back in here."

"Yes, Natasha." Jasmine hung up. Jorge was staring at her. "My first date."

"I was afraid of this."

"She doesn't want you hanging around when my date comes for me."

"Like hell!"

"It's Jacob—*Marensky.*"

"Oh." Jorge breathed a sigh of relief.

"I'm just a little worried," Jasmine said.

"About Jacob?"

Jasmine laughed. "Not on that account—I'm not sure he's particularly fond of me."

"You were acting badly."

"I was not—"

"You were."

"Never mind. I'm just wondering what good it's going to do if we just wind up watching one another."

"Trust me. That man has a plan in mind."

"I hope you're right. I'm so worried."

"Jasmine, we just went undercover. You know as well as I do that often cops and agents have to lead a double life for months to get what they're after. Years."

"This can't take that long," she said softly. She didn't add the rest of what she was thinking.

If it did…they might well end up dead themselves.

Chapter Four

Jacob arrived at Jasmine's apartment at precisely 8:00 p.m. She was ready, dressed in a halter dress and wickedly high heels. The assessment he gave her was coolly objective. And his words were even more so.

"You know how to play the part."

"Hey, I'm just a naive young model willing to let a rich guy take me out for an expensive dinner," she told him.

"Jorge?"

"They told me not to have him here."

"What is he doing tonight?"

"Catching up on his favorite cable show," Jasmine said. "Playing it all low."

"At his studio?"

Jasmine nodded and turned away.

Her captain had gone along with this at her say-so. But the FBI seemed to know way more than the police. She was certain that Jacob Wolff knew all about her fake dossier and Jorge's fake dossier, and she felt woefully late to the party.

"Hey." To her surprise, he caught her by the shoulders and spun her around. "This isn't a jurisdictional pissing match, you know. The FBI started planning the minute we heard from Smirnoff. You didn't know because we didn't inform the cops until it was absolutely necessary they knew we were in town. We had no idea you were in the middle of an undercover operation— we've had an eye on these guys for a while. Smirnoff coming in was the opening we needed."

He was right; they'd both had separate operations going on. And she'd wanted this case. She'd talked her captain into it being important. The bodies in the oil drums had proved she was right. Provided they could link them back to the Deco Gang.

"I'm sorry," she murmured.

"I worked something like this in New York not that long ago," he told her. "The Bureau crew I wound up working with hadn't known about me. It's always like that. A need-to-know basis. Fewer people to say things that might get you killed."

"Yes, but now—"

"Now, we're in it together. And now we need to head out. Where would you like to have dinner?"

"Wherever."

He grinned. "I'm supposed to be a very rich guy, you know. Oh, and with the power to push ahead at any given restaurant."

"How rude!"

"Yes, absolutely. But we're playing parts. And we need to play those parts well."

"How have your people gotten to so many restaurants?" Jasmine asked.

"They haven't," he said. "No one will say it, but everyone is afraid of the Deco Gang."

"Ah," Jasmine said. "Well, then, we're in the middle of stone crab season. I say we go for the most popular."

"Sure."

As they left her apartment, he slipped his arm through hers. Jasmine stiffened.

"Play along," he murmured.

"You think they're watching?"

"I think they could be at any given time."

She didn't argue that.

"I didn't bring a car. Taxi or an Uber?" he asked.

"I'm fine walking."

"In those shoes?"

She shrugged. "Not my favorite, but we're going about seven blocks. Over a mile in these? I'd say taxi or Uber!"

They walked past T-shirt shops and other restaurants with tables that spilled out on the sidewalk. It was a beautiful night. Balmy. It had to be in the midseventies. Jasmine could smell the salt on the air, and, over the music that escaped from many an establishment, she could hear the water—or at least she could imagine she heard the waves crashing softly up on the shore. Here where they walked, the sand and water were across busy Collins Avenue; the traffic was almost always bumper-to-bumper. She knew young people often came just to cruise the streets, showing off their souped-up cars.

She didn't get it; never had cared for fancy cars.

People in all styles of dress thronged the sidewalks. Some were decked out to the hilt, planning to visit one of the clubs or see a show. Others were casual, out just to shop or dine in a more casual fashion. While the South Beach neighborhood of Miami Beach was trendy and filled with great deco places, boutiques and more, heading farther north, one crossed Lincoln Road, a pedestrian mall and beyond that, a lot of the more staid grande dame hotels from the heyday era when Al Capone and his mobsters had ruled, and later the fabled Rat Pack had entertained, along with other greats.

The beach was like a chameleon, ready to change for every new decade.

At an old and ever-popular restaurant, known for its stone crabs while in season, they did find they were welcomed by a hostess and discreetly—but far too quickly—shown to a table. Jacob had managed, even with the lines outside wrapping around the building, to get them a private table in a little alcove.

Jacob made a pretense of studying the wine menu. He had known, she was certain, exactly what he wanted from the beginning. He wound up ordering champagne—and club soda, as well. She knew as the evening progressed, the champagne would disappear into leftover club soda.

The waitress was gone—they had both ordered the stone crab claws—and he leaned toward her, taking her hand from across the table, rubbing his thumb lightly over her flesh.

"You talked to your people?" he asked softly.

She nodded. "This afternoon. The three men in the oil drums…one has been there, they estimate, about three years. One several months…and one maybe two weeks or so."

Jacob smiled lightly, his expression expertly at odds with their conversation. "Do you know who they might be? They'll be testing, checking dental records. But so far, they don't match anyone reported missing down here." He hesitated. "We're a land of promise, but… people take advantage of that. I recently worked a case in New York… Here's the thing, and the cause of half the world's problems. When you have nothing at all, you have nothing to lose. People from war-torn countries might be desperate and can be drawn in and then forced to do just about anything." He was quiet for a minute. "Some wind up in oil drums."

"And some," she said, "just want more and more—like Victor Kozak."

"So it appears."

"What do you mean, so it appears?"

"Kozak became kingpin. But when Josef Smirnoff came in to the Bureau, he didn't know who intended to kill him. He just…he was afraid. He ruled so much, controlled so much, and yet must have felt like an ancient king. Someone wanted his throne."

"Just like an ancient king—who could plan to overthrow him unless they had a right to follow in his line?"

"That's true. But… I can't get over how lovely you look in that dress," he said suddenly.

She saw that the waiter had arrived, bearing a large silver champagne bucket filled with ice and a bottle.

"You clean up all right yourself," she said softly. And he did. He was wearing a casual soft taupe jacket over a tailored white shirt. He was a handsome man, she thought—with a bit of the look of a Renaissance poet, except she was certain that while his appearance was that of a tall lean man, he was composed of wire-tight muscle beneath.

The waiter smiled and poured their drinks, and they acted like a couple happily out on a date.

Jacob leaned closer to her again, smiling as he lifted his glass to her. "Josef Smirnoff admitted to dealing drugs, arms dealing, prostitution and money laundering. He swore up and down that he didn't order murder."

Jasmine lifted her glass with a dazzling smile, as well. "And yet, one of those bodies discovered had been there a very long time."

"So, someone might have been getting rid of people without Josef Smirnoff knowing."

"And how could that happen?"

"I don't know. We weren't able to get to Smirnoff for more conversation before he was killed. This had all just sprung into being, you know. It's been a complicated case for us. Smirnoff managed to get hold of an agent in the Miami office, but they didn't have anyone down here that they were certain couldn't be compromised—wouldn't be known by anyone. They appealed to the head offices in Virginia. From there, they called on me. I spent a week immersed in everything related to the Deco Gang, and we were lucky that we could arrange paperwork so it appears that I—as Jacob Marensky—own the Dolphin Galleries."

"So, you didn't know Josef Smirnoff?"

"I can't say that I knew him. But I know what he

told people. And he was set up with the US Marshals' office—he would have disappeared into witness protection as soon as we had finished our investigation."

Their dinner was arriving.

"Do you really like stone crabs?" she asked him, hoping that her smile was flirtatious. "They're more of a local delicacy. And here's the thing—the crab lives! They take the claw and toss the crab back in. The claw regrows. That's why they're seasonal."

He lowered his head. His smile was legitimate. "Yes, I've had them, and I actually like them very much."

"Can I get you anything else?" their waiter asked. They had their crackers, mustard sauces and drawn butter.

"I think we're just fine," Jacob said.

"Lovely," Jasmine agreed.

The waiter left them.

"So, you think someone other than Victor Kozak arranged the murder? You know that the press—and half the people in the country—think he was caught in another act of random violence."

He nodded. "And we have nothing to say."

Jasmine cracked a claw. A piece of shell went flying across the table, hitting Jacob on the left cheek.

"Oh! Sorry!" she said, somewhat mortified.

He laughed. "Not a problem."

"These really aren't date food," Jasmine said. "But then again, we aren't really on a date." She frowned, then made a show of dabbing at his face and laughing. "So, if not Victor Kozak, who would have the power to pull off such a thing as the murder of Josef Smirnoff?"

"It might have been Kozak. If not, there's Ivan Petrov, bartender and manager."

"You think he's high enough on the food chain?"

"Depends on who is in on the coup."

"The only people as close to management as Ivan are the bodyguards—I like to think of them as the Three Stooges."

"On steroids," Jacob said.

"Yes, deadly Stooges," she agreed.

"So, Victor Kozak, Ivan Petrov, Natasha Volkov—and the Stooges," he said.

"I just wonder about the bodyguards. The others are all Russian or Ukrainian, but Alejandro is Colombian, and Antonio is Italian."

"Half Italian," Jacob told her. "His mother is English."

"You do know more than I do."

"They are equal-opportunity crooks," Jacob said drily. "Any group down here can find power else-where—even elsewhere around the country."

"Their bookkeeper is from Atlanta," Jasmine murmured.

"Good old Southern boy."

"Girl."

"Pardon?"

"Good old Southern girl," Jasmine said. "And yet…"

"Yet?"

"I don't think she really knows about the criminal enterprises. She gets money after it's been laundered. As far as paperwork goes, they're enterprising citizens, paying their taxes."

"Well, Ivan is deep into it all," Jacob told her. "He was waiting at the gallery when I went in this morning. We made arrangements for the sale of one of the paintings in the gallery."

"As a way to move money?"

"Yeah. He paid way more than the painting is worth. The funds will go into an offshore account. It's all setup."

"So they believe in you?"

"For now…"

He had been studiously cracking a shell. This time, his piece of shell flew across the table—catching Jasmine right in the cleavage.

"Sorry!"

She caught the shell quickly before he could. But the gentleman in him came through; he started to move but stopped. The two of them laughed together. Honest laughter, and it was nice.

"Not really date food," he said. "Unless I were more accomplished at this, of course."

"I don't think you could be much more accomplished," she muttered, afraid that a bit of envy and maybe even bitterness might have made it through in her voice. She caught his curious look. "You speak half a dozen languages," she explained.

He shrugged. "I was just lucky. My family—much like yours—is a mini United Nations. Everyone from everywhere. And I love language. It gets easier to pick up another, if you know the Romance languages, the Latin base always helps for reading, even if it takes a bit. But all languages have rules—well, except for English! It's the hardest. Luckily, it was my first."

"Still…it's impressive."

"You speak Spanish."

"Picked up from growing up in South Florida. Half of my friends are Cuban, Colombian or from somewhere in the islands or South America."

"Or Brazil."

"I do also know a bit of Portuguese," she agreed.

They both smiled again. "So…we're equal-opportunity law enforcement, dealing with equal-opportunity criminals," Jasmine mused.

"So we are," he said. "Let's wander on down Washington Street. We'll stop and have dessert and coffee somewhere else."

"You think we're being followed?"

"I think we're definitely being watched in one way or another."

He paid the check and they left.

"You're from here, right?" he asked her.

"You know all about me, right?" she returned, looking at him.

"Well, I do now. I swear, when I tackled you… I didn't."

"You knew there were cops on the scene."

"They didn't tell me that one of the cops was a woman—modeling as if she were accustomed to the runway. But then you are, correct?"

"You received a full dossier on me after the fact?" Jasmine asked. "I wish that the powers that be might have returned the favor."

"I'm an open book," he told her.

"I'll bet."

"I knew from the time I was a kid I wanted to be in the FBI," Jacob told her. "I had a great uncle who was gunned down—for having the same name as a criminal. He was killed by mistake. Anyway, I got into a military academy, served time in the army and immediately joined the FBI. I've done a lot of undercover work. I seem to blend in well with an accepted and ambiguous foreign criminal look."

"Or latent hippie," she told him.

He grinned.

"If you want to see some of South Florida, I can show you around," she told him.

He smiled, lowering his head. "Great. I grew up here. But you know South Florida better than I do."

She grinned. "I was born here."

"Oh?"

"We traveled a lot—but always lived here. Well, not *here*, but in Miami, in Coconut Grove."

"There are so many areas… An amazing city, really. I think, just four decades or so ago, the population of the area was about three hundred thousand. Now, we're looking at millions." He cast a grimace her way. "Populations always lead to crime," he added.

He could be incredibly mercurial. He slipped an arm around her shoulder and pointed to a café before them. "They're known for their crème brûlée. Shall we?"

"Crème brûlée," she agreed, frowning slightly.

He lowered his head close to hers. "We are being followed," he said, pretending to nuzzle her forehead.

"Ten o'clock, just down the street. Our dear friend Alejandro Suarez."

She was careful not to look right away, but let out a tone of delighted laughter and planted a kiss on his cheek.

"Let's have dessert," she said louder.

He took her arm and led her into the café.

"Well," she said as they sat close together. "I'm not sure if we've gotten anywhere, but the stone crab claws were delicious, and this is wonderful crème brûlée."

"Definitely better than some of the undercover work I've done before," he told her. He made a face. "Homeless detail. Sleeping in boxes—and for dinner, French fries out of the garbage."

"Yuck."

"You do what's called for."

"I would have…for this," she murmured.

"So, tell me about Mary. Tell me why you're on this case."

She stared up at him, startled. Somehow, he seemed to know everything. She hesitated and then shrugged.

"Our watchdog has stayed outside," he said softly.

She nodded. He was good at observation; she trusted him.

"Mary," she began. "The Deco Gang has been on our radar for a long time—they've operated out of restaurants, bars and even dry cleaners, moving on all the time. My usual cases keep me on the mainland. MDPD comes in on cases in many of the cities—Miami-Dade County is made up of thirty-four cities now, with more incorporating all the time. Not all the smaller cities have their own major crime divisions, and so we handle a great deal of it. South Beach does have a major crime unit, but the powers that be approved of us taking over this case. Miami Beach cops had a greater risk of being recognized, even undercover. It's not that they tried to hand off work—it was just a better plan. And honestly, until the bodies were found... I might have been the detective taking it the most seriously. Jurisdiction on this is complicated. The oil drums you saw were discovered up in Broward County, by a Seminole law enforcement official."

"There's the Florida Department of Law Enforcement. They could have taken over."

"And those guys are great. But going in on this, it fell to something Miami-Dade would do. We were investigating a disappearance. We were suspicious of the Deco Gang. And when it came to finding a way to slip in and be close enough, the models the clubs use all the time seemed a good cover. I approached my captain about it."

"You were in."

She shrugged. "In all honesty, I was afraid if I mentioned that a friend of mine had been working with the gang's models and then disappeared, it would be a strike against me in terms of being able to take the case. But it actually worked in my favor—I really knew her, I could talk about her and maybe get some information from the other young women working with them. And Mary, well, she's one of the nicest people you'd ever hope to meet. She looks for the good in everyone. Since I'm a cop, she thinks I'm jaded—though I actually think I'm pretty nice, too. Cops don't have to be asses."

"No, they don't," Jacob agreed, clearly somewhat amused.

"But Mary's problem is that she does look for the good. She has to be slapped in the face by bad to see that it exists."

"She probably is a very good person."

"Kari Anderson—the girl on the runway with me when Josef was shot—reminds me of Mary. They're both natural blondes with huge blue eyes and a trusting manner to go with them. Mary was working dinner theater, but not making much money. She saw the ad for models. She did a few shows with the group— Smirnoff's group is behind a number of entertainment offerings. They've been doing legitimate business, too. They own a bunch of other nightclubs. Anyway, Mary got swept up with Natasha and Josef and what she was doing…and saw no evil in it. And she was excited to get paid so well. Florida is a right-to-work state, so dinner theater may be a group requiring Actors' Equity, but then again, it may not be. She was thrilled. She paid her rent two months ahead with her paycheck from one show. And then there was the regular retainer just for being at the clubs, filling them with beautiful young people… It was easy money at first."

"Did she say anything to you about being nervous?"

Jasmine shook her head. "Never." She hesitated. "The last time I talked to Mary, she was excited. She was going to be a star attraction, working their next show. Which was the opening of the club the other night."

"The one you starred in instead."

"Yes. Look, Mary never said anything to me. She wasn't nervous, as far as I know. She just disappeared. A few weeks ago, she was supposed to meet me for lunch. She didn't show up. Mary's parents passed away when she was eighteen. She's on her own, an only child. She and I have been friends forever—we went all the way through grade school and high school together. We have other friends, but no one else has any other information about her. I don't even know how long she's actually been missing. After she missed our date, I called and called. We had an officer from Missing Persons go in to talk to Josef and Natasha, and they both appeared mystified—according to the officer."

"Have you gotten anything?"

"Not yet. The girls are still getting to know me. No one expected what happened to Josef. But apparently, we're all on retainer. Including Jorge."

"Retainer," Jacob murmured.

"I'm not sure what's next. Jorge and I can go in for checks tomorrow."

"Good. I'll stop by at some point." Jacob leaned back. "Well, I believe I'm supposed to walk you back now."

She nodded, oddly sorry that the evening was ending. It was work. Dangerous work.

Work to find Mary.

"You think we're still being watched?" she asked.

"I do."

He paid, stood and drew out her chair. He very politely took her arm and opened the door for her as they exited the café. He slipped an arm around her shoulders.

"Alejandro still around?" Jasmine asked.

"I think he was sitting at one of the outside tables... that's the back of his head behind us. Nope, he's rising now. I'd say he's going to make sure that I take you home and then leave—not overstepping my bounds."

They walked at a lazy pace, his arm around her but with all propriety.

"Interesting," she murmured.

"What's that?"

"How I'm going to discover that they keep control. I mean, as far as they know, I'm just a girl trying to get ahead in modeling. What if I just liked you and wanted to be with you?"

"I don't know. But if I went outside the rules..."

"I'm wondering if we'd both wind up in oil drums. I can see how they'd blame you. You're officially on the inside. But—"

"You're just an innocent. Well, in their eyes."

They'd reached her apartment. She was in a charming place, ground floor, almost in front of the pool. He walked her to the door and then paused. She wound up with her back against the wall by her door. He had a hand on the wall and was leaning against her.

He lowered his face toward hers and gave her a slow careful kiss. She allowed a hand to fall on his chest, and she wished that she didn't feel that there was absolutely nothing wrong with him. His scent was clean and masculine, mixed with the salty cool ocean air. His chest was vital and alive and yet like a rock. His lips were...

He drew away from her.

"I think that was just right. You might want to smile and laugh and then go in."

"Alejandro is watching?"

"He's right out on the street."

"Lovely, what a lovely night," she said, letting her voice carry.

"I'm sure we'll see each other again," Jacob said. "If you're willing…"

"I just have to check my work schedule."

"Of course." He stepped back, and she turned and let herself into her apartment.

She swung the door shut and slid the locks. And then, she stood there for a long, long time. She brought her fingers to her lips. They felt as if they were on fire.

Chapter Five

"You will pay Mr. Chavez twenty-five thousand for the painting," Victor Kozak told Jacob.

They were seated in the office at the rear of the gallery Jacob was pretending to own. Jacob nodded sagely to Kozak. They had already been through the niceties. They both sat with little demitasse cups of espresso. Kozak had admired the shop. Jacob had expressed his appreciation for Kozak's patronage.

"I don't know this artist," Jacob said.

"Trust me. He is excellent."

"And my commission?"

"Fifteen percent."

Jacob let that sit. He smiled at Kozak. "No disrespect. Twenty percent." He was pretty sure that in all such haggling—legal and illegal—Kozak had a higher limit than the figure he'd started with.

"Eighteen," Kozak said.

"I'm looking forward to working with you. Seeing that wonderful art arrives in our country. But if we're to go forward in the future, I believe we need a set rate now. I will be an excellent gallery to procure all the right artists—but I need to survive. The overhead here is quite high," Jacob told him.

Kozak was thoughtful. "All right, then. Twenty percent."

He rose; their dealings were complete. Jacob stood as well and the two men shook hands.

"Have the police come up with anything as yet regarding the shooter? Or shooters?" Jacob asked.

"No, nothing they have shared. You said *shooters*. You think that more than one man was involved?"

"We both know guns," Jacob told Kozak. "Yes, the shots were coming from at least two angles, maybe three."

"Accomplices," Kozak said, shaking his head. "So much violence in this world." He sighed as he lowered his head in sorrow. "Josef was a good man." He shrugged, a half smile on his face. "A good man—for all that we are. He was simply a businessman, and he had integrity in what he did."

Drugs and prostitution, if not murder. But sometimes, even criminals had their ethics.

"All the security," Jacob said, "and still—"

"Don't worry. What the police don't discover, we will," Kozak assured him.

"Naturally," Jacob said.

"I'm so sorry that this happened. Josef…was your friend?"

"We had a few business deals years ago. Art, you know, is always in the eye of the beholder. He'd commissioned a few pieces through me in my galleries before. When I wanted to come south—no more chipping ice off windows, you know—I looked down here and saw that Josef was opening a club. It's always prudent to establish relationships before opening a business anywhere," Jacob said.

"Josef told me about you." Kozak smiled. "And we do nothing without checking out references. I know that Josef trusted you. But now…his body will be released on Friday, they tell me."

"And there will be a funeral?"

"Yes, it will be at a little Russian Orthodox church in the city, not on the beach. A private affair. But you will be invited."

"I appreciate the honor and privilege of saying goodbye to an old friend," Jacob told him. "And with your permission, I will be by this afternoon with a small token for our new friendship."

"That will be fine. The club will reopen Friday night, but invitation only. A very small group to begin. We must show the world that we're now a safe place to be."

"This violence… It can happen anywhere. Lightning doesn't usually strike the same place twice. I believe the club will be fine."

Kozak gave him a rueful grin. "Sometimes, such events make a place a curiosity. Think back to the '80s. Paul Castellano and Thomas Bilotti were gunned down in a hit ordered by Gotti in front of Sparks Steak House in New York. The restaurant is still going strong. Down here, Al Capone was often in a suite at the Biltmore Hotel in Coral Gables. The suite is very expensive, and people still love to take it—even though Thomas 'Fatty' Walsh was gunned down at the hotel, supposedly over a gambling dispute." His smile deepened. "The hotel did go down after hurricanes and the Depression. It became a veteran's hospital. It was empty—and very haunted—but it's back to being very chic today."

"Let's hope we don't all have to go down first."

"Not to worry about us. Josef created a strong group of business associates. We will be fine." With that, Kozak took his leave.

Jacob walked him to the door. They both smiled at Jacob's "assistant," who was busy behind the old art nouveau desk that served as their register and counter. Katrina smiled back and waved.

She was a perfect choice for this role. Katrina Partridge had been with the Bureau for nearly twenty years. She was in her midforties, attractive and able to carry off both charm and a completely businesslike demeanor. She also knew the art world backward and forward.

When Jacob was gone, she shook her head, indicating they shouldn't talk in the gallery. She pointed to his office, and he followed her there.

"He was walking around a long time. I think he touched a few of the frames, and… I could be wrong. But he could have planted some kind of a bug."

"Good observation, thank you. So, we're being given our first commission," he told her.

"But that's not enough," Katrina said.

"We could bring him down," Jacob told her. "But there will be a work of art, and who is to say what a work of art is worth?"

"Someone who knows art," she said drily.

"But art is subjective."

"So true. Yes, you're right."

"We're after killers," he said softly. "That's what we want to nail them on."

"I know," Katrina said. "And hey, what's not to like about this assignment? I don't have much going on yet—I'm enjoying my downtime. Sand, beach, lovely weather..."

"Still, be careful, Katrina. We can never know when something may slip. They gunned down a man in a room full of cops and security."

"I'm always careful," she said. She smiled, indicating her back.

She was dressed in a fashionable skirt and blouse ensemble with a handsome tailored jacket. Despite the tailoring, he could see—when she indicated her back—that she was not without her Glock.

He smiled his acknowledgment but found himself worrying about Jasmine Adair.

Modeling. There was no hiding a weapon when dressers were around, making sure that a gown was being worn properly. And she was into it on a personal level—something that was dangerous from the get-go.

He had no right to interfere; her operation had begun before his and they were now required to work together. He had no problem working with police.

It was just that he was attracted to her. He didn't think it possible not to be. She was unique; elegant and a bit reserved, and yet when she smiled, when she laughed, she was warm, vibrant and sensual.

He turned his mind from thoughts of her.

"I'll bring the caviar over in about an hour," he told Katrina.

"All ready, in the container in back. I've dressed it up beautifully, if I do say so myself."

"I'm sure you did," he told her.

They moved back into the gallery. Jacob made a point of informing her that they were commissioning a piece, one that had a buyer already, who was in love with the artist's work.

She made mention of a local up-and-coming artist the buyer might like, as well.

A real customer sauntered into the room. Jacob returned to his office but found himself sitting and doing nothing but thinking.

He had to find a way in that was tighter; he had to be close to Jasmine.

He was still wary, of course. She hadn't turned him into a fool.

Maybe she had. Jacob hadn't felt such an instant attraction…almost a longing…in years.

Not since Sabrina.

"Ah, you are so beautiful, even in mourning," Natasha told Jasmine, admiring the way the draped black dress fell in sweeps to the floor. "Remember, at this, you will be quiet. You will help our guests with their drinks and food but keep a distance. Victor has ordered that this be a solemn occasion. You understand?"

"Yes, Natasha," Jasmine assured her.

Natasha looked over at Jorge, handsome in a conservative black suit. "You two will do well, I believe."

She called to the little seamstress who hurried over. "I don't think that the hem needs to come up, but at the waist…a half an inch?"

"Yes, ma'am, of course," the seamstress said. She poked and prodded at Jasmine for a minute, pinning the waist and then nodding.

Jasmine thanked her. The tiny woman helped her slip out of the dress, and carried it away.

As Jasmine reached for her jeans and T-shirt, she was aware that Natasha was assessing her again—as she might assess meat in a market.

"So, last night, you were charming?"

"Yes, he took me for a nice dinner, and I told him about the beach."

"Very good. He likes you."

"I believe so."

Natasha turned away. "You could be asked to do much worse," she said, almost to herself, rather than to Jasmine. "So, now…jeans and a T-shirt. You must dress more…ah, how do I say this? Much prettier, to come in here."

"Business clothes."

"No, the halter dress you wore last night. Very pretty. And heels. No sneakers."

"Definitely, whatever you say."

"Victor would like to see you. I wish there was more time…time for you to go home. Ah, what am I thinking? I still have clothing from the show!" Natasha beamed, and caught Jasmine's hand. "No, no. Don't put your jeans back on."

"Oh…okay."

Natasha left her standing on the little podium where dresses were fitted and headed back to the racks of clothing that remained hanging in the massive closet space. She searched through the racks until she evidently found something that pleased her.

When she returned, she had hangers that bore a sleeveless silk blouse and a red skirt. "These will do," she said.

The skirt was short. Very short.

Jasmine donned the clothing. She smiled, hoping to show that she was feeling friendly with Natasha. "I don't think that the sneakers go with this so well."

"Ah, but of course not! You're an eight and a half, American size, in shoes?"

"Nine," Jasmine told her.

A very large shoe size, apparently, in Natasha's opinion. "Ah, well, you are tall."

She was five-ten. Natasha would be appalled by Jasmine's mom—just five-eight and she wore an eleven.

Natasha brought shoes—four-inch stilettos. "These will be beautiful," she said.

Jasmine slipped on the shoes. She was well over six-feet, now.

"So, come. Victor is happy with you." She turned to Jorge. "You—you will come on Friday evening. The service is at two. Josef will be interred after, and then we will be arriving here."

"Yes, ma'am," Jorge said.

Natasha studied him for a minute and then smiled. "We may have more work for you soon. Showing people Miami Beach—and all its pleasures."

Jasmine knew Jorge well. He didn't miss a beat. "Thank you," he said.

"And, now, you..." Natasha took Jasmine's hand. "Come and see Victor."

"For sure, a pleasure," Jasmine said.

"I'll wait here," Jorge said cheerfully.

"No, Jorge, you are done for today. Antonio will see you out."

Antonio was standing at the door to the large dressing room.

"Call you later!" Jasmine told him cheerfully.

She wasn't feeling so cheerful; she was caught here with nothing, no backup—and she was off to see Victor. She wasn't worried for her life. If she was going to be taken out, they'd have gone after Jorge, too.

Had she done too well with Jacob "Marensky"? Was she now going to be asked to entertain another of their associates?

There was really no choice but to play it out. She had to wonder if this was where Mary had stood—right before she had disappeared.

With a smile, Jasmine watched Jorge go—and she accompanied Natasha to Victor Kozak's office.

Victor Kozak was not alone.

There was a man in his office. A tall man, he wore a designer suit in charcoal gray. He was perhaps in his midfifties, with iron-gray hair and mustache and watery blue eyes.

They'd both been sitting; Victor behind the desk, the new man in one of the upholstered chairs set before it. They stood politely.

"Ah, Jasmine. I'd like you to meet Mr. Connor," Victor said. "He's visiting from England and knows nothing about Miami Beach. He's hoping you will show him the beach, and to the finest hotel."

JACOB WAS ALREADY on his way to the club when his phone rang. He glanced at the number; he hadn't saved any in his contacts, but rather memorized the last four digits of those he needed to know.

Jorge Fuentes was calling.

"Where are you?" Jorge asked.

"Heading to the club. Why?"

"Head faster. I think they've taken Jasmine in to entertain a client. I mean, she can handle herself, but this is happening way too fast."

"Picking up the pace," Jacob moved forward quickly. "I'll be back in touch as soon as possible."

He didn't run; he might have been observed. But he could walk fast as hell and he did so. He came to the corner of Washington Street and rounded it, heading to the employee side entrance to the club.

This time, Antonio was leaning against the wall by the door, smoking a cigarette, watching the day.

"Those things will kill you," Jacob said.

"Mr. Marensky. I don't believe we were expecting you."

"I have something for Mr. Kozak. He was just in the shop, you know. I need to get right up there."

Jacob didn't wait for Antonio to respond but hurried past him in a way that meant the goon's only action could be to physically accost him, and the man would still be trying to figure out if Jacob was important enough or not to get through.

Suarez was in the hall.

Jacob made a point of striding past him with a huge grin on his face. "Present for Victor!" he declared, lifting the ice chest filled with caviar that Katrina had so beautifully decorated with multicolored ribbons.

He burst into the office before he could be stopped.

Kozak immediately stood, reaching toward his jacket—and the weapon he surely carried there, Jacob thought. But he didn't draw the weapon.

Good. Jacob was trusted.

Jasmine was there, outfitted like the very expensive and exclusive call girl she was apparently expected to be.

A man had just been leaning over her—either inspecting her or seeking a better look at her cleavage. He was tall and solid, though his face was lined—perhaps from years of worriedly looking over his shoulder. His eyes were a strange, cool blue. Like ice.

"Victor! A present. Forgive me for interrupting. My source delivered this just this morning, and after we spoke—" He paused. "Excuse me, sir. No disrespect intended. I was in a rush— Jasmine!" he said, breaking up his own run of words. "Hello, and thank you again for last evening. You were a wonderful tour guide."

"I was conducting business with Mr. Connor—" Kozak began.

Jacob brought a frown to his face, and then allowed himself to appear deeply disturbed. "No, sir," he said, addressing Connor.

Connor straightened and stared at Kozak. "Kozak, I want—"

"I'm afraid I already have an interest," Jacob said softly.

"She's just a woman," Kozak muttered beneath his breath.

Jacob was glad that Jasmine appeared not to have heard the words. "Forgive me, but, Mr. Kozak, you're a very busy man. This arrangement was made. Yesterday. And at the show, before he was killed, I received promises from Josef Smirnoff."

"Smirnoff is dead," Connor said.

"But not forgotten," Jacob said.

Kozak was, of course, in a tight position. If he hadn't murdered Josef Smirnoff and was taking over as a natural progression, he had to respect promises made by his predecessor.

"Not forgotten, no. And honored," Kozak murmured. Jacob had given him an out—and he was glad to see that the man wanted his "business" and was willing to take the out.

Jacob turned to Connor.

"I'm new, but… I understand this. Miss Alamein and I had dinner last night and arranged for a sightseeing tour this evening. I had forgotten to tell Mr. Kozak about my tickets, but I'm afraid that I did specify this… young woman."

"I can make even better arrangements for you, Mr. Connor," Kozak said. "You must understand, we are in mourning right now. And in honor of Josef, I must follow through on all his promises."

"Fine. Call me when you have found a suitable companion," Connor told Kozak. He was looking at Jacob. Sizing him up. Apparently, he determined that the companionship of a certain woman was not worth a battle. He turned and left without another word.

"So, before you came to me... Josef had promised you this woman," Kozak said.

Jacob didn't look at Jasmine. Knowing her as he was coming to know her, he was amazed that she was managing to just sit still.

"When I saw her on the runway," he said, his voice husky, "I knew I wanted her at that moment. I believe she might have been his last promise."

"Then I will make no other arrangements. But you must remember, Miss Alamein is in my employ. And she will appear when she is needed."

"That is understood."

Kozak walked over to Jasmine. "You will honor this arrangement?" he asked her.

Jasmine stood. In the heels she was wearing, she was eye level with Kozak. She smiled sweetly. "As you wish, Mr. Kozak."

"Fine," Kozak said. "Just remember, you work for me," he added softly.

"Always," she told him earnestly. Jasmine's smile deepened. "And thank you, sir. Thank you. Mr. Marensky and I were able to have the most delicious dinner last night. Far more easily than I might have ever imagined!"

Even Kozak seemed caught by her charm. "My pleasure. So, I believe that Natasha wanted to talk with you one more time. And…" he gave his attention back to Jacob "…Miss Alamein will be ready for you tonight, for these tickets you have."

"I'll wait and escort her home now," Jacob said. "Sir, if you have a minute, the present I brought… I believe you will enjoy it immensely. It is Almas, from the beluga sturgeon—supposed to be some of the finest caviar. I must admit, I am not an expert, but I have been assured by those who are that this is delicious."

"Then you must sit and enjoy it with me," Kozak said. He waved a hand at Jasmine. "See Natasha, see what she needs from you."

Jasmine was dismissed. She left the room.

Jacob looked at Kozak. "I thank you for respecting me—and Josef's memory," he said. "And I would like to do more."

"Oh?"

"I am not without certain skills. I would like your permission to look into Josef's death myself."

Breathing was difficult.

Jasmine's heart was pounding. She'd been so sure of herself, even in Kozak's office with the very strange *Mr.* Connor all but pawing her, that she'd been figuring out ways to handle the situation herself. Alone with the man, she'd have figured out something…

And blown her cover. And all hope of finding out what had happened to Mary.

She hurried down the hall—smiling at Sasha, on duty there now—to the dressing room. Natasha was at one of the tables, studying her face in the mirror.

She looked at Jasmine, and as she did so, Jasmine had to wonder if the woman's eyes could stretch out of her head, or if she had ears that could extend down a hallway.

Natasha already knew what had happened.

"It's not good," she said. "It's not good at all. One man should not become so possessive."

Jasmine shrugged. "Does it matter?" she asked. "Does it matter if the money is the same?"

"Ah, child, you're new to this," Natasha said.

"Yes, I am. And I am ignorant but willing to learn."

Natasha seemed pleased with her reply. "He will start to think that he owns you and that he would be better off just spiriting you away somewhere. You must be careful and declare your loyalty to us at all times, do you understand?"

"Yes, Natasha. And I am loyal, I promise you."

"And," Natasha added, "you like this Jacob Marensky?"

"He's clean and he smells good. And he is younger."

Natasha waved a hand in the air. "Yes, he is clean and young and smells good. And young can be good. Old men, with their hopes and their prayers and their pills... They have no idea how often those they think they control sit there and do nothing but laugh at their faulty efforts." She shook her head; Jasmine had the feeling she had experienced the worst and earned her way out of it.

"So then, you may have your jeans and your T-shirt. Apparently, Mr. Marensky is a more casual man and you are going on a sightseeing tour." She shuddered as if a sightseeing tour might be akin to torture.

"Thank you," Jasmine said. "I must admit, the shoes...the heels are a lot."

"They make you very tall. Then again, Mr. Marensky is very tall." She waved a hand in the air. "Josef admired the man. Victor believes that he is an admirable man as well, who understands our business but demands that we respect his. You will, of course, report to me."

"Yes, I will."

Jasmine heard voices. A few of the other girls had arrived.

Kari Anderson came into the room, carrying a bundle of clothes. Behind her were Jen Talbot, Renee Dumas and Helen Lee. They were like a palette of beauty—Kari so pale, Jen olive-skinned, Renee almost ebony and Helen extraordinary with her mix of Eurasian features and lustrous long black hair. They were beautiful on a runway.

They had also been hired to please all tastes.

Thus far, though, she hadn't seen any of the women forced into anything. Just pretty girls with an understanding that they could be paid well for their company. She had sat silently herself as Victor had introduced her to Mr. Connor and informed her that he needed a guide and an escort for the evening. What if she had protested?

Had Mary protested?

"I'll just grab my things and change and get out of here," Jasmine said. "And hang these up."

She fled over to the hangers, finding that her clothing had not been hung—just folded as if with distaste and left on the shelving above the racks. She eased out of the shoes and slid out of the skirt.

Kari walked in. "I'm going to need that skirt, I hear," she said.

"Oh?" Jasmine handed her the skirt on its hanger and shimmied the blouse over her head.

"I'm going to go see Mr. Connor," Kari said. She sounded slightly nervous.

"Are you afraid of him?" Jasmine asked in a whisper. "If so—"

"No, no. He's supposed to be very nice."

"I thought he was new."

"No. Mary went out with him. Just dinner. She said he was very nice. Oh, sorry, you didn't know Mary. She was great, but... I guess this wasn't for her. Me, I want the runway. And if it means dating a few losers..." Her voice trailed. "Dating," she repeated drily. "Okay, having sex with a few repulsive specimens... Well, I managed to choose a lot of losers on my own! Might as well have it be worth something in the end, I guess."

"Kari?" Natasha called.

"Excuse me," Kari said to Jasmine. "I have to run!"

Jasmine caught her hand. "Kari—please. Will you call me tomorrow and let me know that you're all right?"

Kari seemed surprised. "Of course, I'll be all right. But thank you. And I will call you— we can maybe have lunch or something?"

"I'd love to have lunch," Jasmine assured her. She hesitated. "It's allowed?"

"Oh, yes. They like us to be friends. Sometimes..."

"Sometimes?"

"Kari!" Natasha called again.

"Later!" Kari told her, and with a swirl of blond hair, she was gone.

KOZAK HAD OPENED a bottle of his special "very Russian" vodka to go with the caviar. Jacob was careful to pretend to sip as much as the crime tsar but imbibe as little as possible.

His time with the man was proving to be very interesting.

Kozak talked about growing up in Russia—about the KGB coming for his father in the middle of the night.

"That must have been very hard on a child," Jacob said.

Kozak shrugged. "My father, he was a killer. When it all broke apart, though…everyone was running. The kind of crime was brutal, from all manner of directions. My mother, bless her, got us out. I never understood. Business is business, but…"

He paused and looked hard at Jacob, very sober despite the vodka he had all but inhaled. "You think you can find Josef's killer?"

Jacob weighed his words carefully. "There have been certain…events in my past that required me to take a closer look at them. I have a talent for uncovering things." He paused. "You really have no idea who killed him?"

Kozak frowned.

"No disrespect," Jacob said quickly. "I liked Josef. We did very good business together. But perhaps, something was going on with the group that was dangerous to all."

"You're talking about the bodies discovered in the Everglades," Kozak said. "There is talk of little but that and the shooting on the news these days. We have even ceased to care about politics, eh? When people are scared…"

He paused and shrugged again. "We had nothing to do with those bodies. Not Josef, not me. And I do not know who killed him. Me, I have kept my boys close— Sasha, Antonio and Alejandro. I have played the game, I have become the king. But you are a newcomer. Down here, that is. Josef trusted you. You know how to stand your ground. You tell me—who killed Josef?"

"I don't know, but as I said, with your permission, I will find out."

"You have my permission—and my blessing. What else do you need?"

"Permission to speak with your boys. And Ivan and Natasha. Whether wittingly or not, Victor, one of them helped the killers."

There was a tap at the door.

"It's me, Mr. Kozak," Jasmine said in a small voice.

"I will see her home," Jacob said, rising and heading to the door. "And I will begin tomorrow. I will find the killer, I promise you."

"Then most definitely, the woman is yours—along with my gratitude," Kozak told him.

Jacob nodded and opened the door. And capturing Jasmine's hand, he hurried down the stairs, Jasmine in his wake.

Chapter Six

"I should have gone with him," Jasmine murmured.

The look Jacob gave her could have turned her to stone. She supposed, in his mind, he had managed not only to save her from a fate worse than death—or actual death, for that matter—but to keep up their undercover guises, as well.

"No, no," she amended quickly. "You were wonderful, magnificent. I mean, you pulled that off, and normal circumstances—"

"Just wait. Wait until we reach your apartment," he said. "At this point, I'm pretty sure it's okay if I come in."

"Are we being followed?"

"Maybe. You never know."

She was surprised when he pulled out his phone. He had such a grip on her with his left hand that she could hear the voice of the man he was calling from his phone in his right hand.

"You got her out?" the voice asked.

Jorge.

"Yes." Jacob glanced her way. "I need tickets, fast. Some kind of sightseeing trip. First available."

"Call you right back."

"Tickets?" Jasmine murmured.

"Tickets."

They were almost to her apartment when the phone rang again. This time, Jorge was speaking more softly.

"Lincoln Road Mall," Jacob relayed.

"We can walk it," Jasmine suggested.

"Then keep walking."

He was angry; she hadn't had a chance to explain yet what she'd meant about wishing she'd gone with Mr. Connor. And on the street the way they were, unaware of how things might go, despite the stand Jacob had just made, he clearly didn't want her talking.

His pace was urgent; she had long legs, and she could trek it, but he was moving fast. They were some distance from the club on Washington Street when he finally seemed to slow—perhaps having burned off some of his energy.

She managed to retrieve her hand from his hold and slide an arm through his, drawing herself close and speaking softly, as if she whispered a lover's words.

"I may have found out how Mary disappeared—and with whom," she told him.

He turned and frowned at her.

"I finally got a second with Kari. She's probably going to wind up going off with this man, Connor. Jacob, Mary met with Connor. She met him—and then she disappeared."

"And you were willing to take that kind of a chance?"

Jasmine swallowed, leaning on his shoulder. "That's what I'm here for. But I didn't find out until after you came and got me out of the room. I saw Kari when I went back to get my own clothing. That's when she told me…and they're going to send her in to be his escort. Jacob, we have to find a way to follow that man. Maybe Jorge—"

"No, Jorge still has an in. And they'd wonder what he was doing. Let me call my office. They'll get someone on it."

He pulled out his phone again. They'd reached Lincoln Road Mall—a pedestrian walkway that offered dozens of shops and restaurants, fun places to dine and enjoy a coffee, a drink, entertainment or an evening.

"It's a private tour company," Jacob said, pointing to a spot by the theaters on Alton Road. "They'll pick us up there."

He veered in that direction, speaking quickly to someone on the phone and giving them the information they had on Connor. Jacob described him to a T. But Jasmine knew he had little else to go on.

She heard rapid questions in return, and then assurances.

"I believe that's ours," Jacob said, pointing to a limo with a sunroof.

The vehicle made a U-turn and pulled to the corner. The driver, a young man in a suit, hopped out and offered them a broad professional smile. "Marensky?" he asked.

"Yes, thank you, Jasmine and Jacob," Jacob said, sliding his phone back into his pocket.

"I'm David Hernandez, your guide for the day!" he said cheerfully. "I'm at your disposal. Now, I understand you're new to the beach, so I'll give you a few suggestions. My first pick is the Ancient Spanish Monastery, but that's north on the beach, so..."

"That's fine," Jacob said quickly. "Is that okay, honey?" he asked Jasmine, and then he told their guide, "Jasmine knows the place. Me, I'm new."

"I love the Spanish Monastery!" she said. "But I'm not sure I'd be the best guide."

David looked at his watch. "Well, if we move, you can have a couple of hours there. Your assistant ordered a driver and guide until midnight, so—"

"We'll start with the Spanish Monastery," Jacob said.

They slid into the car. With the beach traffic, it was going to take them a few minutes to reach what Jasmine considered to be one of their most intriguing destinations.

"I grew up here, but not on the beach," Jasmine told David.

"Cool. I grew up in the city, by the old Flagler Dog Track—Magic City Casino now," David told them. "People say Miami is young, no history. But we've got tons of it. I could go on forever. But—"

"Please, do, go on forever," Jacob said.

He leaned back in the plush seat of the limo, closing his eyes for a minute. It was the only indication Jasmine had seen that his world could cause him pressure.

He had come in, guns blazing, for her.

She leaned back, as well. She really needed to talk

to Captain Lorenzo and give her report. Lorenzo could get cops out after Kari and Connor.

"Of course, South Beach itself is a tourist attraction," David said. "Did you know that it was the original area that was populated? Believe it or not, the beach started out as farmland. The City of Miami itself incorporated on July 28, 1896. Julia Tuttle, our founding mom, had sent an orange blossom to Henry Flagler, convincing him to bring his railroad down—we were almost always frost free!

"The City of Miami Beach was incorporated on March 26, 1915. Now, Miami Beach is comprised of natural and man-made barrier islands. In 1870, Henry and Charles Lum—father and son, by the way, bought a lot of the bracken, sandy, nothing land that's worth billions today. There was a station to help shipwreck victims up north of where you're staying, closer to where we'll be today. They started off with a coconut plantation, but that didn't go so well. Enter some rich Yankees, and the beach started developing.

"Collins Avenue is so named because of an entrepreneur called Collins. He mixed up the crops and got things going. Then with Miami up and running, the railroad coming down and Government Cut created, people were on their way to thinking it would make a great resort area. Enter the Lummus family, who were bankers, and Carl C. Fisher from Indianapolis, who worked with the Collins and Pancoast group, and by the beginning of the twentieth century, Miami Beach was on its way."

David had a great voice—informative, interesting

and soothing. Jasmine hadn't realized she had closed her eyes, too—until she opened them and discovered Jacob was looking at her.

"We're on it," he said softly. "The Miami office will speak to your captain and see that the police are aware of this new player."

"I just…" Jasmine paused, looking to the front.

David was going on, talking about the development of the area for tourists. The entrepreneurs had started off developing their crops—avocado, for one—and taking tourists on day trips from the City of Miami. Then came food stands and finally, the Browns Hotel, which was still standing.

"What if this man, Connor, is…a killer?" Jasmine asked quietly. "One of those men who can only get off if he strangles or stabs a woman. What if…?"

"He'll be followed and watched, Jasmine. And, they'll do the same with him as they did with me— just a date, first. Just a date. We'll find out about him, and Kari will be all right."

Kari would be all right. And that meant so much. But what about Mary? She'd been gone nearly a month now.

Jacob started fumbling in his pocket. She realized his phone was buzzing. He answered it in a quiet voice.

David kept speaking. "Collins needed money. He got it from the Lummus guys. He started construction of a wooden bridge. The beach areas went through a number of different names, but you can still find those founding fathers in street names here—and of course, we have Fisher Island, a haven for the very rich. If you really want to find a lot of these founders, we can do that another day.

"You should see the old Miami City Cemetery across on the mainland. It was north of the city limits in 1887 when it was founded. Julia Tuttle is buried there, and oh! If you like Civil War history, we've got some Confederates buried just feet from some Union guys—friends by then, I would think, since they died long after the war. Friends in death, if nothing else."

Jasmine looked at Jacob. He smiled tightly at her. "We have two guys on it. They're trying to dig up something on Connor, but we don't even have a first name for the man."

"He's English. He definitely had an accent."

"I told them that. Jasmine, they're watching Kari. She's at her apartment right now."

"She's an innocent… She's a Mary. She isn't worried about…about anything he might ask her to do. She said she's been with dozens of losers and might as well improve her career chances by going with men chosen for her by Kozak or Natasha. I'll never forgive myself if she gets hurt. I could have gone with Connor."

"She's going to be all right."

Jasmine nodded, taking a deep breath.

David talked on, telling them that when the South Beach area had fallen into a slump, Jackie Gleason had helped to change things doing his famous show from the beach, along with more entrepreneurs who saw the fabulous artistic value of the art deco hotels and buildings.

They were finally nearing their destination.

"The Ancient Spanish Monastery, known officially

as the Monastery of St. Bernard de Clairvaux, is really—well, ancient. Construction began in northern Spain in 1133, in a little place near Segovia called Sacramenia. It housed monks for somewhere around seven hundred years, and then there was a revolution and it was sold and became a granary and storage and…not a monastery.

"It came to be here because, in 1925, it was purchased by an American—you guessed it—entrepreneur, Mr. William Randolph Hearst. For a long time, it was known as the world's biggest jigsaw puzzle, because it was shipped to the US as thousands upon thousands of stones.

"Well, then Hearst had some financial problems. He'd wanted to rebuild it at San Simeon, but some of what he'd purchased of the monastery was sold off. The crates—about eleven thousand of them—were in storage in New York. Not to mention there had been an outbreak of hoof-and-mouth disease in Segovia, which meant the packing hay had to be burned and the crates had to be quarantined.

"And then poor Hearst died! More entrepreneurs invested, and all the crates were taken out of storage. Took about a year and a half, they say, to put all the pieces back together. Two businessmen bought them, had them put together and then couldn't afford the fact that the monastery didn't make it right away as a tourist attraction. Financial difficulties again.

"In 1964, it was purchased by Bishop Henry Louttit, who gave it to the diocese of South Florida, which split into three groups. Then it was owned by a very rich and good man, a billionaire and a philanthropist, Colonel Robert Pentland, Jr. He went on that year to give the cloisters to the Bishop of Florida, and voilà! Finally, a church and a tourist attraction. And now, while the monastery is still a great tourist attraction, it's still also an active church. I love going there. It's like stepping back in time."

They arrived. David quickly arranged for their tickets, and Jasmine and Jacob were in, admiring the old stone cloisters and hearing about the historic instruments that were often used in services, seeing some of the artifacts that had come with the monastery—and the carved coats of arms and other relics that had come from other monasteries and venues around Spain.

Then they were out in the gardens, arm in arm, and Jacob was back on the phone again.

"I did get the autopsy information on Smirnoff from my Miami counterpart," Jacob told her as they strolled.

"I realize autopsies are important, but I'm pretty sure I know how Josef Smirnoff died—bullets," Jasmine said.

Jacob nodded. "Yes. But I guess he didn't know he had cancer—colon cancer. According to the ME, Smirnoff must have had it for some time without knowing. He wasn't looking at a long life, even if he'd gone for treatment."

"So, someone murdered him for nothing," Jasmine said. "Kozak was next in line anyway."

Jacob was quiet.

"You don't think it was Kozak?"

"He would just be so obvious. And he denied having anything to do with the bodies in the oil drums."

"Have they finished those autopsies?" Jasmine asked.

Jacob nodded. "They are still waiting on testing. They've gotten fingerprints on the most recent body, but the two other corpses were too decomposed. They think one of the bodies has been there several years."

"I'm assuming they're also trying to trace the oil drums and whatever remnants of clothing they can find?"

Jacob nodded. "They don't have much hope on the oil drums. They were apparently dumped by a major oil company years ago. They were headed to the closest landfill, I imagine. Nice, huh? Anyone could have picked them up."

"But you said they got fingerprints off the most recent corpse?"

He smiled. "As soon as I know, you'll know. Easy now that I've staked my claim on you."

"It does make communication between us a lot easier," Jasmine murmured.

"And hopefully keeps the wolves from baying at your door—and forcing you to show your hand." He grinned at her. "I can appear to be extremely possessive."

She was afraid that her smile was a little fluttery. Because something inside her had fluttered, as well.

His phone rang. He answered and listened intently. "Okay," he said, hanging up. He looked at Jasmine. "Apparently, Mr. Connor doesn't believe in being fashionably late Miami Beach–style. He's at Kari's apartment now."

"So, they're heading to dinner now. We should get back down there—"

"Jasmine, agents are on it."

"I know, but—"

Her phone rang then. She glanced at the number; it was the number that Captain Mac Lorenzo was using for the operation.

"Checking in—and watching out for a valuable asset," he told her.

"I'm fine," Jasmine assured him. "I'm touring the Ancient Spanish Monastery."

"I've spoken with Jorge. We're not pulling either of you out yet. But I also have strict instructions from way high above not to endanger an FBI operation."

"We're not endangering it."

"And you're not to endanger yourself," he reminded her.

"Never, sir," she told him.

"Just make sure you remember the FBI has taken the lead on this, and they're calling the shots."

"I understand." She was careful to keep any remnant of emotion from her voice.

"You're doing all right with interagency communication?"

Jasmine glanced at Jacob. "We're doing just fine, sir."

Jacob must have heard. He arched his brows in a question and reached for the phone.

"Captain Lorenzo, how do you do? Jacob Wolff. We're working on this together well. I don't think we could have planned this out any better."

Jasmine didn't hear what Captain Lorenzo said after

that. Jacob handed the phone back to Jasmine and she quickly hung up.

"Thank you for that," she told Jacob.

He shrugged. "I think we are working well together."

"Yes, I guess we are."

"Hey, I'm pretty sure I would have liked you one way or the other. And I do admire your swing. That was a hell of a punch you gave me the other day."

"I didn't know—"

"Maybe that was better. That's the thing with undercover, really. Check in only when you need to or when you need help. Work everything on a need-to-know basis."

He was right, and she knew it. And she could have said she liked him, too. But suddenly, doing so seemed to be a very dangerous part of the operation.

She liked him too much.

Liked the deep set of his eyes, the tone of his voice... the way he touched her. She'd liked the feel of his lips on hers far too much... That brief touch was still a memory that lingered and haunted.

"I still think we should head back," she said.

He looked around. "It's beautiful here. Not just the monastery, I mean South Florida."

"Yeah. But how often do you get down here?"

"I go where they send me," he told her.

She nodded and turned away. Even with the undercover operation underway, they were ships passing at sea. It was disturbing that she was coming to care about him, and almost humiliating the way that she felt...

With him, she would have gladly taken a feigned relationship anywhere.

It was one thing to discover she found him attractive. More, even. Compelling, sensual…a man with the kind of masculinity that moved beyond sense and logic and simply reached into the very core of her being.

It just didn't work to be craving his touch while on the job.

"Well, we've checked in, Jorge knows I'm all right," she said, "and Connor will have Kari on the beach somewhere soon. I'd like to get back to South Beach."

"We can do that," he said.

He took her arm and they headed back. David Hernandez was waiting for them by the limo. Jacob told David he was great, and they would use him in the future, but for the moment, they'd decided just to head back to the hotel. They were going to wander the sand by night.

Hernandez thought that was fine, and he was grateful they'd call on him again. Of course, the man would be pleased. He had the night off now with full pay.

Jasmine and Jacob were both quiet during the drive back. When they reached the cute little boutique hotel where Jacob was staying, Jasmine admired the old lobby.

"You've never been in here before?" he asked her.

She grinned. "When I was in high school, we used to come out here and prowl a few of the clubs and maybe have soda or coffee at a few of the hotels. But I think I've only stayed out here a few times. I'm a native, but that doesn't mean I know every hotel."

"It's nice. Not a chain. And the owners seem to love the deco spirit of the place. I can have coffee on the balcony every morning if I want. I can hear the sound of the surf and watch the palm trees sway—before the rest of the world wakes up and the beach becomes crowded with bodies."

She smiled. "You will see some of the most beautiful bodies in the world out here, you know."

He was quiet for a minute.

"You disagree?"

He smiled awkwardly and shrugged, and then looked at her at last. His light blue eyes seemed to caress the length of her.

Her heart, her soul, her *longing* seemed to jump to her throat.

But he quickly changed moods. "Then again, it's not just perfect bodies. You know that, of course."

"You mean old and wrinkly? We'll all be there someday. I hope when I'm older and drooping everywhere, I still love the beach."

He laughed. "I'm with you on that. I hope when I'm creased and drooping everywhere I can still sit on the sand and watch the sway of the palms and not worry that someone is judging me. I believe everyone has to do what is comfortable for them—and that's part of what I love.

"Yes, there's beauty. Yes, there's the ridiculous. And there are quiet times, when the sun is rising, when you can look out and feel you're in a private paradise. And then you turn around and the neon of the hotels and the rush of the world comes on in. This place is ever changing, plastic in so many ways and yet real when it comes to the feel of the salt air and those moments when you're in the water, and it's just you and the waves and the sea and the sky."

"Yes," she said softly.

"So, let's take a walk," he said.

They headed out to the beach. Jasmine doffed her sneakers and Jacob rid himself of his shoes and socks, too. They left them by a palm.

Jacob's phone rang.

He listened, and then he told Jasmine, "Connor has Kari out to dinner. He took her to Joe's Stone Crab. They're fine."

"I'm afraid for when they leave. What do we do now?"

"Wait," he said.

"So hard!"

He laughed. "I've been undercover for months at a time. Watching, waiting. And for this case, well, the watching and waiting is a hell of a lot better than usual." He was quiet for a minute. "I recently worked a case where immigrants were brought in and used horribly. It was long on my part, but when it broke, we moved quickly. This may be the same. Thing is, right now, we could get them, or Ivan at least, on money. Then again, they can employ the best legal team known to man. So, we have to take them down big-time—with evidence that prosecutors can take to court."

Jasmine muttered, "So…we wait."

"And play the part," he agreed.

Nightfall was coming in earnest. The sky was fighting darkness and the sun was shooting out rays that seemed to be pure gold and magenta.

Jasmine wasn't sure what got into her. She suddenly broke away from him and ran down the beach, turned and kicked up a spray of the waves that had been washing over their feet.

She caught him with a full body splash, and he yelped and laughed with surprise. Then he came after her.

She squealed and turned to run, but he tackled her and bore her down to the soft damp sand. He leaned over her, looked down into her eyes and then murmured, "Good move. I just saw Sasha up on the boardwalk. We are being watched."

He eased closer. "Can I kiss you?"

Role-playing...

She tangled her fingers into the richness of his hair, pulling him in, and he kissed her.

And then he broke away, laughing, and pulled her to her feet. "I think we gave Sasha a good show, eh?" he asked softly.

"Oh, yeah," she whispered. Once again, her lips were burning.

As they retrieved their shoes and decided on a restaurant for dinner, she couldn't help but wish that the FBI had sent down a much less attractive agent.

Chapter Seven

"His full name is Donald McPherson Connor," Jacob told Jasmine. "He's living at that grand old place down from the club just off of Washington Street—a quiet and dark intersection. The whole sixth floor is his apartment."

They were at her place. He'd done a thorough search for bugs and hadn't found any, and with the way this gang seemed to work, he was pretty sure he wouldn't find anything. In Kozak's words, Jasmine was "just a woman."

Jacob had a feeling that Kozak might be pretty surprised.

Just a woman. In any kind of a fair fight, Jasmine would take Kozak.

But for them, at this moment, it bode well that Kozak and the members of his gang still seemed to live in an archaic world of chauvinism.

"And what else?" Jasmine asked.

"Born in Yorkshire, and he has dual citizenship."

"How does he make his money?"

"He inherited a nice sum and knows how to invest in the stock market."

"So, an older Englishman-turned-American, rich, with nothing to do. Wife? Kids?"

Jasmine had changed from her salt-spray-and-sand-covered clothing to a dark silky maxi dress. She'd come to perch on the sofa by him, hugging her knees to her chest as she looked at him.

"Wife died about ten years ago. They had a daughter but I can't find much on her."

"Criminal past?"

"Nope."

"Any hint of anyone disappearing when he's around?"

"He's been living in Savannah. He's just been down here about two months. They're still looking into him."

"And the agent saw him take Kari back to her apartment and then leave?"

"Yes," Jacob said.

He didn't have to read from his phone; one of his assets was his memory. He could retain what was told to him, which was probably why languages came to him easily. Then again, he loved languages, and all the little rules and differences and nuances within them.

He wished at that moment, though, that he was reading. Because he was left to meet her eyes.

He'd been right that first day, when he'd seen her from afar. Her eyes were green. A brilliant beautiful green, like twin emeralds in a sea of gold. Her face was so perfectly molded he was tempted to reach out and touch it, as he might be tempted to reach out and touch a classic sculpture. Her hair was free, freshly washed and tumbling around her shoulders, still damp. And in the maxi dress, she seemed exceptionally alluring—though he was sure she had donned the article of clothing because it covered her entire body. It felt like a reaction to the skimpy outfit she'd been forced to put on for the "date" with Connor.

"But according to Kari, Mary did escort him," Jasmine pointed out, "and then she disappeared."

"You're going to need to get closer to Kari."

"Well, we're both supposed to report to Natasha tomorrow—Kari and I."

"And I have an excuse to go in. I've gotten Kozak's permission to investigate Smirnoff's murder."

"Have the cops gotten anything? I guess not. I'm pretty sure that, even though the FBI has lead, I'd know about it if anyone had been apprehended for the murder."

"From what I've heard, they're still pretty much in the dark," Jacob said. "Trajectory shows the bullets were fired from the balcony. But everyone working there swears the balconies were closed off. Someone is lying, of course. But no one knows who."

"No guns were found, no casings…no nothing?"

"Nope. And the gunmen—two to three of them, best estimate—entirely disappeared."

Jasmine leaned her chin thoughtfully on her knees. "We could see all the major players when it happened. You were out there with Kozak, Ivan Petrov and the goons, Sasha, Antonio and Alejandro. And Natasha was backstage."

"The killers were hired, obviously. And they were guaranteed a clean getaway. We dusted for prints on the rails and so forth, but there are hundreds of prints. Workmen were there, of course, before the grand opening. Anyone who so much as delivered pizza might have left a print. Smirnoff, from what I understand, loved showing off the place and brought everyone out to those balconies to let them see how they looked down at the floor and the main stage."

She shook her head. "So, we're nowhere."

"No. We're moving forward. You're just impatient."

"I guess so. I mean, I have worked undercover before. But often just for a day or so, getting into the right place, talking to the right people. I admit—it was never anything like this."

"We just keep moving forward."

She nodded. "I guess… I guess I need some sleep."

"Go on."

"You're staying here?"

"I believe I'm entitled now—and I don't want to disappoint anyone by not taking my full measure."

"Ah." She stood, almost leaping away from him. "Pillow and blankets. If I'd known I was having nightly guests, I would have asked for a two-bedroom." She smiled awkwardly and hurried into her bedroom. A moment later, she was back. She plopped down two pillows, sheets and a blanket. "Not sure if you need the blanket, I don't air-condition the place too much. But… Anyway, all right. I'll see you in the morning. Start coffee if you're up first!"

She spoke quickly, almost nervously. It wasn't like her.

"Good night," he said softly.

She left him, and he wished he wasn't playing a role. More than that, he wished he wasn't working. She'd closed the door between them, but he could still see her in his mind's eye.

See her laughter as she kicked up the salt spray.

Feel her beneath him when he tackled her in the sand.

He could see the emerald of her eyes as she'd looked at him before she pulled him in for that blistering kiss.

And he couldn't help but wonder, in his misery, if she just might…just might…be wishing a little bit herself that they had met under different circumstances.

He spent the next hour reminding himself he was a special agent, he loved his job and he had made a difference… They were professional. They played their parts. They brought down the bad guys.

He thought he'd never sleep. He wondered why the hell he had stayed. She could take care of herself. She was trained.

But despite the logic, despite what he knew, he was afraid for her.

He could have returned to his apartment. He knew being here had nothing to do with being professional. If it came to it, he'd give anything to save her life if it was threatened in any way.

Why? He'd worked cases with so many beautiful women and never done more than acknowledge that fact.

Jasmine was different. She had touched something else in him. Something that was more than attraction, even desire.

She was…everything. Everything in a way he hadn't known in over a decade. Not since his wife had died.

JACOB WAS UP when Jasmine emerged in the morning.

She'd spent the night…waiting. She'd thought the door to her bedroom might open at any time. She couldn't decide if she wanted it to or not.

But it did not, and when she finally rose, she found him already awake. He'd brewed coffee and was sipping a cup, leaning thoughtfully against the refrigerator.

He looked at her as she emerged, his eyes fathomless.

"Three more bodies last night," he said softly.

"What? Where?" she asked. Three bodies. Was one Mary?

He must have seen the fear on her face. "Three men again," he said quickly. "And they weren't found in oil drums. This time, they were found south of the Tamiami Trail. Miami-Dade County, on Miccosukee tribal land."

"Three. Maybe the hired gunmen? If they weren't in oil drums, if they're new… It's possible it isn't related. Will we get identities soon?" Jasmine said.

He hesitated. "No. The bodies are missing heads and hands."

"Oh."

"Cause of death?"

"Unknown, at this point. In my mind, logic suggests they were shot in the head."

"Logic?"

"Execution-style—then the heads were removed. Dumped them in the Everglades." He hesitated. "From what I've been told, they were well ravaged by the animal life. Among other creatures, the vultures had a feast."

"There are few better places to dispose of a body than the Everglades," Jasmine agreed. "But they were definitely...male bodies?"

"Yes, definitely male bodies."

She wandered to the coffeepot and poured herself a cup. She was shaken, but she didn't want to be. She was a detective in a major crime division. But this was personal.

Maybe she shouldn't have been working this investigation. But there had truly been no one better suited to the task of getting in with the Deco Gang.

Jacob came up behind her and placed a hand on her shoulders. "Jasmine, I believe the men found might well have been the shooters. If whoever planned this wanted to make sure no one talked, they had to get rid of the people who actually carried out the deed."

"Yes, that's my gut feeling on it, too," she said. Her hands were still trembling slightly as she held her coffee cup. And she was ridiculously aware of him, right there behind her, the heat of his body, the scent of him.

She had to spin around, composed and determined. "So, today, you start questioning everyone?"

"Today I start questioning everyone."

He had barely spoken when there was a knock on the door.

"Excuse me," she murmured.

As she headed to the door, she was aware Jacob had already showered and dressed completely for the day. He had his hand behind his back, ready to draw his weapon if the guest at the door intended to offer any danger.

No danger was forthcoming; she looked through the peephole. It was Jorge.

She let him in quickly. "Hey."

Jorge glanced at Jacob. He seemed to accept the man's presence as normal.

"I was bringing you the latest news. Captain said he didn't think you should be calling in, even on the burners. Too easy for one of them to catch the phone and check out numbers and get suspicious when nothing on you had an easily trackable number. But I imagine you've gotten the latest?"

"The bodies in the Glades?" she asked.

He nodded and looked at Jacob. "Who do you think did it? Is it Kozak? Natasha? Ivan?"

"I don't know. But I intend to find out." Jacob smiled. "Breakfast first. Somewhere obvious. Somewhere anyone who wishes can see the three of us—me and my escort, provided for me with their blessing, and you, my new love's best friend. Plenty of places in the area. Let's go for a walk and find good food."

"Okay," Jorge said slowly, frowning.

"Then Jasmine needs to check in with Natasha and assure her of my happiness and her own satisfaction with the arrangement—and I get to question the goons."

"And…" Jorge pressed. "Me?"

"I think it's fine if you come in today, just a cheerful dude happy to be with a friend."

"It's a plan," Jorge said.

IT WASN'T DIFFICULT for Jacob to pretend to be out with friends. He liked Jorge very much and thought he was probably a damned good cop. He knew how to fit in to what he was doing, and he didn't need to take the lead. He'd set up the tour for them yesterday in minutes flat and had managed to introduce him and Jasmine on the floor opening night at the club—at the end of a spray of bullets—without giving things away. Jacob also just liked the man.

And as for Jasmine...

He had to be careful.

When they were seated, Jasmine and Jorge were talking about Miami, and Jasmine was telling Jorge about their tour guide.

"He was a great guy—a super guide, knew his stuff," Jasmine said. "Friendly and informative without being annoying."

"Hard to imagine this place as a coconut plantation," Jacob said.

"Hard to imagine the whole south of the state as a 'river of grass,'" Jasmine said.

Jacob noted that there was a man seated at a far back table, eating and reading a newspaper. Watching them.

Jacob picked up his coffee cup and said softly, "Antonio Garibaldi is at the back of the restaurant."

"We were followed here," Jorge said casually.

"And here's the thing," Jasmine said, running her fingers up Jacob's arm and smiling sensually, "we don't even know who else might be in the employ of the new boss, be he Kozak or even someone else."

Jacob leaned closer to her. "We need to find out who

is calling the shots." He planted a quick kiss on her lips and looked at her lingeringly. Then he stood. "Think I'll visit the restroom."

He headed to the back of the restaurant and the restrooms. But he made a pretense of stopping, as if surprised and pleased to see Garibaldi.

"Hey! I guess I did choose a good place, if you're here," he said. He pulled out the chair on the other side of the table and sat.

"Yeah, they do a great breakfast," Garibaldi said. He was a big man with dark hair and a solid physique, built as a good bouncer should be. His eyes were quick and dark. His smile was pained.

"I'm really loving South Florida," Jacob told him. "And getting to work with Kozak. Of course, I'm as sympathetic as anyone over Smirnoff. He was a good man. What the hell do you think happened? I mean, forgive me, I know you guys are good at your jobs. But how the hell did shooters get up on the balconies?"

Garibaldi looked uncomfortable—he was on the spot. Then he leaned forward. "Hell if I know. Seriously. From the beginning, it was planned that the balconies be roped off. Crowd control. And that day... Smirnoff was giving us our orders. I was watching the front, Suarez had the stage and Antonovich was moving through the crowd. There were cops all over, hired for the occasion. I'll be damned if I can figure it out, and I've tried. Thing is, I was given my orders. The other guys were given their orders. We never saw anyone get up there."

"There has to be an entrance from the offices," Jacob said.

"Sure. There's a door across from Smirnoff's office. That way, when he chose to, he could be in his office, and when he wanted to be part of the crowd, he could come out on the balcony. The cops were all over it. But here's the thing. The door is kept locked. There's a key. And when the cops were all over the place right after the shooting, the door was still locked. Smirnoff kept the key."

"Duplicate keys can be made. I'm sure the cops checked on that," Jacob said.

Garibaldi shrugged. "Whoever may have had a duplicate key, I don't know."

"It was obviously well planned."

Garibaldi appeared to be honestly confused. "You know, sure, it could have been planned. But it seemed like one of those bad things, you know. Some disturbed person just out to hurt anyone—and getting Smirnoff."

"You don't believe that, do you?" Jacob asked.

Garibaldi's voice was soft and low. "I want to believe it," he said.

"But you don't."

"Kozak told us last night that he'd given you permission to question us, see if you couldn't figure something out. I'd like to help you. What do I know? I was in my position. And the shooting started. I was—well, hell. Hate to admit this. I was scared. I think I managed to get people out, get them down. But I got the hell out as fast as I could myself."

"You were armed?"

"I was. But the best gun in the world doesn't do you a bit of good if you don't know what you're supposed to be shooting at."

He seemed to be telling the truth. Jacob never took anyone at face value, but he also noted the man's expressions and body language. He'd have bet that he was being honest.

Garibaldi looked at him and seemed to judge him, as well. "I'm not in this for violence," he said softly. "The money is good…" He shrugged. "I mind my own business and don't care where it comes from. Drugs… People are going to buy them somewhere. The girls… They do what they choose. Natasha talked to Jasmine, and you all had an agreement. Cool. She seems to really like you. So, is that a crime? As for me, I do what I'm told and I keep my nose clean and stay out. I'm just security."

"So you're just supposed to report on us today?" Jacob asked him.

"Yeah. And it's cool. It's obvious you two have more than a business relationship going. That's the way Josef Smirnoff always rolled. Kozak said that it will be business as usual. Of course, he's scared now. Whoever killed Smirnoff could be gunning for him. That's probably why he said you could talk to people. Though, I already told the cops what I told you. The truth."

"Sure. Hey, next time you're watching us, just join us." Jacob shrugged. "She's a cool girl and I like Jorge, too."

"That wouldn't be the way the game is played," Garibaldi said.

"No, I guess not." Jacob stood. "You're a good-looking man with the right stuff. There are tons of other places on the beach that need bouncers, security. If this whole scene is too much for you."

Garibaldi shrugged. "I screwed up once. Didn't check an ID the way I should have. The girl's parents caused a stink. Josef gave me a job. Said I didn't need to ID anyone." He laughed suddenly. "Garibaldi. Nice Italian name. I was born here, my parents were born here and my grandfather came over from Naples to run a tailor shop. No mob ties whatsoever. He was in Worcester, Massachusetts. And didn't even have to pay anyone for a safe working environment.

"Alejandro Suarez, his family came over in the late 1880s. They were cigar makers up in Ybor City, Tampa area. And even Antonovich, he's a third-generation American. We're not…we're not mob. We're not mob-related. I'm here because I have a job. And I do it. Long hours, maybe, but so far, I haven't been asked to do anything other than protect people, watch people and break up fights."

"And what if you had to do something that was illegal?"

"It would depend on what that thing was." Garibaldi hesitated a minute. Then he said quietly, "Hey, man, you're buying art—that you haven't even seen. And we all know about your past."

Jacob nodded. "Yeah. But I play it the way Smirnoff played it. I don't go in for murder. Gets messy—and gets the cops on you."

"Yeah," Garibaldi agreed.

"Sounds like you're a good man. One I'd like to have on my side," Jacob said.

"Thanks," Garibaldi told him.

Jacob left him and returned to his own table. Jasmine and Jorge were having a conversation about the best spas in the area. When he sat down, Jasmine played it perfectly, stroking his arm.

He wished her touch didn't seem to awaken every ounce of longing in his body.

NATASHA WAS WITH Kozak when they arrived.

Jacob was allowed admittance to Kozak's office. Jasmine and Jorge were directed to the dressing room, where they were alone.

Jorge found a stereo system and turned on music. Phil Collins, "In the Air Tonight." Fitting. Shades of the old *Miami Vice* that had really put the area—and many myths about it—on the map.

"Natasha is sleeping with Kozak," Jorge said softly. "She might have been sleeping with Josef Smirnoff, too. At any rate, she was with him for years and years. Trusted. She could have gotten the key and had a copy made."

Natasha came sweeping into the room. She saw Jorge and frowned slightly, then shrugged. "I suppose you say anything in front of Jorge," she said. "Oh, by the way, Jorge, a man has been courting our business, one who may need some entertainment."

"Ready when you are," Jorge said.

"Now, Jasmine, about Mr. Marensky…"

Jasmine smiled and then decided to go another step. She walked over and hugged Natasha.

The woman was not used to hugs. She didn't push Jasmine away, but she didn't hug her back. She awkwardly patted her shoulders. "So, all went well," Natasha said.

"He's lovely," Jasmine said. "Best way to make some money I've ever known!"

"Yes, I believe you. You're very lucky such a man is so captivated by you. It's not always the case, but for you… Yes, I am glad that such a striking man—one whom Josef approved and Victor seems to admire, especially—has taken such a shine to you. But you must realize, my dear, he may tire of you. And move on."

"I know that," Jasmine said. "But for now…he's fun. He wishes to please me."

"And he is far from repulsive in bed, I imagine," Natasha said.

Jasmine didn't let her smile slip. "Oh, so, so, far from repulsive."

"Ah, she's a lucky one," Jorge said.

"Then you will continue as you have been doing. Don't forget… Friday night. Friday is the funeral. And at the funeral, you will be a hostess here, and you mustn't cling to Mr. Marensky at the gathering after the ceremony. After tomorrow night, the club may reopen. The workers will have cleaned up. No bullet holes will show in the walls by the ceremony. Now, you do understand about Marensky, Jasmine? First, we need you to be working. Second, it's important he remembers that he is graced with your company through us."

"Definitely," Jasmine said. "Understood."

"Then you are free for today. You may go. You, too, Jorge." She handed them each an envelope. Their paychecks. They had no choice but to thank her and leave.

As they walked, they noted they were being followed. It was Alejandro Suarez on their tail this time.

"So, straight to my place, I guess," Jasmine murmured.

"I don't think they're following me."

"What about phones?"

"I have a new one."

"I need to know about Connor. About Connor…and Kari."

Jorge sighed. "Jasmine, we have to trust our fellows. They saw last night that Connor left Kari at her apartment. No sex, nothing. She was fine."

Aware of their follower, Jasmine laughed as if Jorge had said something great and grabbed his arm in fun—as a friend might do. In contrast to her actions, her whisper was intense. "But what are they doing about him?"

"Watching. And waiting," Jorge said. "Jasmine, you knew this wasn't going to be an instant fix, that we'd be out of the loop much of the time. And—"

They had only come a half a block from the club when Jasmine saw Kari headed their way. She released Jorge's arm and cried out with delight, running to see the other girl.

"Kari!" She hugged her. She pulled away and asked softly, "All is well?"

"Fine, it's lovely. Mr. Connor is an absolute gentleman. I'll be seeing him tonight." Kari grinned and said, "Oh, he isn't young and hot like Marensky. But he's fine, very nice. Polite and courteous in a way I haven't seen in years. Happy to have some arm candy while he's out on the town, you know?"

"Good. Well, I guess you knew that, from what Mary said."

"I miss Mary. She was the sweetest!"

"Did she ever say anything to you," Jasmine asked, "anything about going away or even...even about being afraid?"

"No. She was just with us, and then one day she didn't show and didn't come back. Natasha was very upset. She was very fond of Mary, too. Speaking of Natasha, I've got to get in. She wants to see me." But suddenly, Kari gripped Jasmine's hands. "I'm telling you, Mr. Connor is so kind and caring, wanting to know my every wish."

Jasmine realized then that it was the man's very kindness that actually frightened Kari.

Someone so nice. What happened when he wasn't? What might he really want?

Further determined, Jasmine smiled. "Great, Kari," she said loudly. "I guess Jorge and I are going to go home and binge on repeats of *Desperate Housewives*."

"Have fun!"

"You're welcome to join us!"

Kari waved and headed off.

Jasmine headed back and grabbed Jorge's arm. "Something has to be done," she said firmly. "Before tonight!"

Chapter Eight

"I have had that door rekeyed," Kozak told Jacob. "The police asked about it, but it was locked. There was no sign that anyone had forced it. But...how? How did someone get through the balcony without being seen? There were dressers here, makeup artists... But when the show began, everyone was downstairs. Natasha was with the girls backstage. The band members were all downstairs. I didn't have the key! No one had the key—except for Josef Smirnoff."

"Someone obviously copied it," Jacob said flatly.

Kozak shook his head. "I have the only key now. No one knows where I keep it. And I don't intend to tell anyone. Including you. No offense or disrespect intended."

"None taken," Jacob said.

"You are free to look around, but I have to go. Josef's body is at the funeral home. I will make sure he is given the send-off such a man deserves."

"Where will the funeral be?"

"A small Russian Orthodox church, up the way on the beach. And then we will come here." Kozak hesitated. "Will you make the arrangements for it with me today?"

"I thought that I should stay here. We want to know what happened to Josef," Jacob reminded him.

"We do." Kozak sighed deeply. "Yes, you must speak with Antonio, Alejandro and Sasha. The thing is…"

"What is it?"

"They have their place. We work carefully. Of course, they are aware… But we never give them facts. They know people, they know who is important, but we have never given them much on the clients."

"They might have seen something," Jacob said. "Something they don't even know they saw. I've spoken with Antonio. You didn't tell me about the door and the key."

"I didn't. I had to make sure. Josef brought you in, and he assured me you were solid, that you were a powerful man with a long history. I had to come to know you myself." Kozak shrugged. "The police checked the door. They remain with nothing."

"But you know someone within your own ranks had to be involved."

Kozak looked unhappy. "Yes. But whoever did this, they were clever. They hired out. A man doesn't guard what he doesn't see to be in danger."

"No," Jacob agreed, trying to read Kozak.

"You must do what you will. I have hidden nothing on Josef's murder from the police. I will not hide it from you. But I must prepare to bury an old and dear friend."

It was evident that Kozak wanted company while he

made arrangements at the funeral home. Perhaps it was even important to go with him.

"I will go with you," Jacob agreed.

As it turned out, Kozak didn't want a driver with them. He had a big black Cadillac sedan, and he asked Jacob if he would do the driving.

"You don't want one of the guys to come along?"

"A bodyguard?" Kozak asked. "I think you will do."

They took Collins Avenue north and reached the funeral home. They were greeted by a solemn man in a suit, Mr. Derby, the current owner of Sacred Night Final Rest Parlor.

Derby expressed his condolences, offered them water or coffee and then tactfully suggested they needed to choose a coffin. The coffins ranged from a few thousand dollars to just about enough to buy a house—at the least, a nice automobile.

Jacob was surprised to see tears in Victor Kozak's eyes. He had either really cared for his friend, or he was able to pull off a feat many a Hollywood actor could not.

Then again, business was business. He could have loved the man—and still arranged for his death.

"What do you think, my friend?" Kozak asked Jacob.

"Personally?" Jacob asked. "I believe in a greater power, but I don't believe the body is anything but a shell. It makes no difference if a man is laid to rest in the finest mahogany or the cheapest pine, or if he's cremated and his ashes thrown to the wind. But if you're worried about the funeral, about our show of respect... then I'd say this."

Mr. Derby, the funeral director, was eyeing Jacob

with anything but kindness. Still, he seemed to perk up when Jacob pointed out a fairly expensive coffin, one that was both handsome, staid and possessed just the right amount of ornamentation.

"Perfect," Kozak said quietly. "This one is it, sir."

"All right, nice choice," Mr. Derby said. "Now, as to the wake—"

"No wake," Kozak said. "You will bring the body to the church. Closed coffin."

"Sir, my people have done an extraordinary job. You may have a wake. Mr. Smirnoff's face was not impacted, and his suit will cover—"

"No wake. No open coffin," Kozak said. "Josef will be honored and buried."

"As you wish, sir. As you wish. This is a painful time for you as a friend. I do suggest that you consider a viewing, for other friends—"

"No," Kozak said. "Our business is quite complete. We have our own cars for the services. You will bring Josef as arranged to the church. And arrange for the transport from there to the cemetery."

"Yes, Mr. Kozak. Arrangements have been made. He will be brought from the church to the cemetery. Now, the cemetery is over in Miami. You will need police officers for the journey as friends follow for the last services, something which, of course, we take care of for you."

Kozak waved a hand in the air. "Do what is needed."

He was anxious to leave; Jacob held back and assured Derby, "Someone will be by with the final check."

He then followed Victor Kozak back out to the car.

The man waited by the passenger's side as Jacob clicked the door open.

Kozak was trembling when he sat. Jacob hurried around to the driver's seat. He didn't have to push; Kozak appeared ready to speak.

"It's not real—I was there. I was there for a hail of bullets. I watched my friend fall, I saw the blood. And yet, it's not real. Not until you see he is laid into the ground. Yes, it is indeed a hard time. You know this. You have laid a wife to rest."

Jacob was still a moment.

A deceased wife was in his fake dossier. It was always best, when creating such a lie, to incorporate many details of life that were real. That helped an agent live the lie that was being created.

"It was a long time ago, right?" Victor Kozak asked.

Yes, a lifetime ago. He'd fallen in love with Sabrina Marshall the minute he had seen her. It had been tenth grade. They'd quickly become an item; he, a high school jock, Sabrina the smart one. They'd married and gone off to college together, and even after graduation when they'd planned their perfect life, talked about starting a family...

The cancer had found her. It had cared nothing about youthful dreams.

"It was a long time ago, yes," Jacob said softly.

A long, long time ago. Many women in between; savvy, bright women, some in business, some in politics, but none in law enforcement.

None like Jasmine, someone he had seen from afar

who had nevertheless seemed to enter into his soul. He barely knew her. Maybe, though, he knew her enough.

Maybe, when this was over… When this was all over, Jasmine would no longer be playing a role. She would go back to her passion, being cop in a major crime unit. And he would go where the Bureau sent him, because he was good at what he did, and he did believe, no matter what unbelievable things were going on in the world, that what he did was right. One good man, or maybe many good men, could make the world a better place.

Sabrina had believed that, too.

"I'm sorry," Kozak said.

"So am I," Jacob said softly. "So am I."

"But now, this woman, this Jasmine—she means something to you?"

"Yes," Jacob said simply.

"When Natasha brought her in, I knew, too, there was something about her. Women…most often, they are just part of business, and that's how it must be. So few have that inner fire. But, now and then…one enchants the mind, eh?"

"Yes," Jacob agreed. "This one in particular…there is something that appeals to me on many levels."

"She's all yours," Kozak said.

Jacob lowered his head. He was pretty sure he knew how Jasmine would feel about being granted to a man as payment for his friendship.

Heading back to Washington Street, Jacob cut down Meridian Avenue. As they neared the Holocaust Memorial of the Greater Miami Jewish Federation, Kozak made a little sound.

The memorial was a heart-wrenching, well-conceived artwork, created by survivors, respected and honored by a community. Statues and plaques told a story that tore at the human soul.

Jacob had been there several times through the years. His own past was a checkered piece of all manner of peoples, from the free world and from areas of great subjugation; his Russian mother had a background that included royalty, his Israeli father had parents who had barely made it out of Germany. Jacob was eternally grateful they had chosen the United States as a place to raise their own family—he knew he'd had a relatively easy and privileged start to life.

He was surprised when Kozak asked him to stop.

"You want to get out and walk around?" Jacob asked.

Kozak shook his head. "I just want to look."

Jacob sat next to him in silence.

"World War II. A brutal business. Hitler wanting to exterminate a race of people. Stalin…twenty million Russians were also killed, you know, between the enemy and Stalin."

"Yes, I am aware."

"Young people these days…they don't always know."

"Education is everything," Jacob murmured.

One of the sculptures at the outdoor memorial was especially poignant. It depicted a body, as many bodies had been found. Prisoners had not just gone to the death camps to be gassed and cremated; they'd gone to be a work force, and they'd been all but starved as they worked.

The body was skeletal and depicted in bronze. They

were a distance from the sculpture and couldn't see it completely. But Jacob had seen it before. And he knew that Kozak had, too.

Kozak turned to Jacob. "My grandmother survived by hiding in plain sight in Berlin. My grandfather was a Russian soldier, hiding the fact that he was also Jewish. When the Soviet Army closed in on Berlin, my grandfather found my grandmother, who was terrified. She had been in living with a Christian German couple who were appalled by the death and terror around them. She'd been told, however, there was less torture if you quickly admitted what you were. When he found her, she said, '*Juden.*' But you see, my grandfather said, '*Juden*, yes, I am *Juden*, too.' They were married, and they stayed married for the next forty years. They died in the same year. I believe he died of a broken heart when he lost her, because she passed away first."

"They had years together. It is still a beautiful story," Jacob said.

Kozak turned to him. "I have told you this story because maybe it will help you believe me. I don't kill people. I don't torture, and I don't kill."

Jacob couldn't help himself. Looking at Kozak, he said, "I beg to differ—slightly. Drugs kill."

Kozak waved a hand in the air. "Drugs kill, but people have a choice. But we do nothing where others have not made a choice. The addict must choose life. The drugs exist with or without my participation. We may as well get rich. Am I a good man? No. Am I a cold-blooded killer? No. Take what you will from that. But I did not kill my friend Josef."

Jacob nodded slowly.

Neither spoke for a moment.

He put the car back into gear and drove back south, to Washington Street and the club. They hadn't been away long.

"So, now," Kozak said, "you will find out what happened to Josef, yes?"

"I will do my damnedest," Jacob said.

JORGE REALLY DID put on a Netflix marathon of *Desperate Housewives*.

Jasmine nervously paced the room. "We should be doing something," she said.

"Jasmine, here's the thing. We are doing something," Jorge told her. "Okay, so, you're not a fan. What should we watch?"

"I can't. I can't sit still."

"You stink at this."

"Sorry!"

"All right," Jorge said. "I'll check in with Captain Lorenzo. Will that help?"

"Maybe."

He took out his phone and called. Jasmine watched him as he spoke, assuring Lorenzo they were both fine and they were proceeding with the work and their relationship with the FBI was moving along smoothly. Then he asked if anything else had been discovered, listened a while and then thanked Lorenzo and promised he'd be the one in touch.

"Well?" Jasmine demanded, burning with impatience.

"There's a Miccosukee village where they sell hand-made clothing, arts and crafts—and have alligator shows," he said.

"I know. It's out on Tamiami Trail, just west of Shark Valley."

"There's a fellow who lives not far from the village. He raises alligators, sells them to various venues for alligator wrestling. Handles them from the time they hatch." Jorge stopped speaking.

"And?"

"One of his young alligators died, and he didn't know why, so there was a necropsy done on the gator."

"And?"

"They found a hand. He reported it. And it's been brought in to the medical examiner, and they believe it belonged to one of the dead men found out there. They're hoping to get an ID. I don't know a lot about alligator stomach acids, but…well, they're still hoping to get something."

"I know what they're going to find," Jasmine said. "There won't be a match. I'm willing to bet that whoever is doing this is clever enough to have hired undocumented newcomers to do the deed."

"Maybe. Someone desperate and grateful for any work that doesn't go on the books."

Jasmine nodded. "Jorge, what do you think of Natasha?"

"She's all business."

"Yes. And she was in charge of the models. Of the show. And we all suspect she is sleeping with Victor Kozak, but—"

"Maybe she slept with Josef, too. And maybe she

was sleeping with Victor because Josef tired of her,
and maybe—"

"Maybe!" Jasmine said. "If only we had a definite."

She started to pace again, thinking, trying to remember every move Natasha had made on the day of
the show.

Jorge groaned and turned back to *Desperate Housewives*.

"HEY," JACOB SAID to Alejandro Suarez. He was on guard
downstairs, at the door to the club offices and staging area.

"Hey," Suarez said. He studied Jacob. He was puff-
ing on a cigarette, leaned against the wall. He grinned
suddenly. "Are you some new kind of enforcer?"

"I'm just an art dealer."

Suarez studied him. "Sure. But hey, I just work here.
Kozak said you were going to talk to us."

"Do you remember anyone—anyone you didn't
know—at the grand opening?"

Suarez laughed. "Anyone I didn't know? What? Do
I look like I rub elbows with the rich and famous reg-
ularly?" There must have been something ominous in
Jacob's look, because he quickly sobered up.

"Did you see anyone upstairs?" Jacob clarified. "We
know that the killers were on the balcony."

"Yeah, that's what the cops said." Suarez sighed,
reaching in his jacket pocket for another cigarette. He
lit it with his current smoke. The man was a few years
younger than Garibaldi and maybe a few inches taller
in height. "I came in through the upstairs. We all re-

ported to Josef, who said the balcony would be closed off. That would leave all of us down on the floor with the hired cops—you don't do anything that big without hiring cops."

"Right."

"When I checked in, the girls were all getting dressed. The band members were in the green room, making cracks about the girls. I guess they planned on having them in to party later. That idea went all to hell, huh?"

"You saw the band, Josef Smirnoff, Natasha and the girls. Anyone else?"

"Ivan was already down at the bar. The caterers were never allowed upstairs. Oh, Victor Kozak was downstairs already when I came in, seeing to a last-minute check on the place. When I joined him, he pointed out that the balcony stairways—there's one set near the entrance on both sides—were roped off with velvet cords. They didn't want people up on the balcony. There's only one door up on the second floor, but it almost leads right into the office, and they didn't want anyone going up because of the office. And he didn't want anybody trying to grab selfies with the girls or the band or anything. If anyone headed toward the stairs, we were to politely stop them. And if they tried again, we were to politely escort them out."

"But no one tried to get up the stairs?"

"There were big signs attached to the velvet cords that said No Admittance. I think most people honor signs like that. Hey, it wasn't supposed to be… It was supposed to be a cool grand opening. No one expected any violence. If anything, we'd have had to throw out a drunk."

"But you saw no one. Nothing?"

Suarez shook his head. "No! I mean, I could have told you before the cops did their investigating that the shooters had to have been on the balcony. But there was a stampede. You know that. I admit, I froze for a second. Then I went to work getting people out."

"Was anyone on the back door—where we are now?"

"I'm assuming it was locked up tight. We were all on the main floor. But…"

"But?"

"I don't know what weapons were used. I was thinking that whoever was up there… Well, if they pocketed their weapons, in all the confusion, they might have come down the stairs and run out with everyone else. Or…" Suarez paused, shaking his head.

"What?"

"They could have come out the back, out of this door. But you see, I don't understand how that would be possible. Cops were already in here. They were crawling all over the area within minutes. I can't believe they wouldn't have seen three men with guns run out this door." Suarez seemed as mystified as Garibaldi had been.

Two down; one to go.

They were great liars—or they had planned their stories well.

Jacob thanked him, then turned and hurried back up the stairs. He found Sasha Antonovich outside the door to Kozak's office. Like Alejandro Suarez, he seemed at ease—bored, probably—as he stood by the door.

"My turn, eh?" Antonovich asked him. He shrugged. "We just look stupid. Kozak said you were going to try to do what the police seem be failing at. So. What can I tell you?"

"What *can* you tell me?"

Antonovich was older than both Suarez and Garibaldi. Remembering all the info he had been given, Jacob knew Antonovich had been with Josef Smirnoff the longest—well over a decade. His hair was beginning to gray, just at the temples. Fine lines were appearing around his light brown eyes, and he wore a weary look.

The man shook his head, his expression grim. "What do I know? That it wasn't just a random shooting? That someone was after Josef? I'm sure you believe that, too. How the hell did they get in? They had to have been on a guest list. I don't know who they were, what they looked like… There were hundreds of people here. They could have been with the caterers, they could have gotten in with the off-duty cops. The cops came from all over the city. Some of them, the Miami Beach guys, were naturally on duty, but in here… Josef wanted lots of security, so we hired people from all over the city. I've been thinking about it, too."

"A dirty cop? Is that what you're thinking?"

"Maybe. Or just someone dressed up like a cop. The other guys might not have known—they came from precincts all over the city. I keep thinking, though, that the guys investigating the shooting had to have thought of all this."

"I imagine they have. I would think they're working all angles."

"Three bodies found down off the Tamiami Trail—no hands, no heads. Sure as hell sounds like a hit to me."

"I agree. I'll bet just about all of law enforcement would."

"Definitely not just a domestic disturbance," Antonovich said, not amused at his own attempt at humor. "The door up here... I was the first one to check it, along with one of Miami Beach's finest. It was locked. If they came through that way, they had a key."

"It's been rekeyed."

"Yeah."

"Well, thanks," Jacob said. He started to walk away.

Antonovich called him back. "Hey," he said softly. "You get that son of a bitch. You get whoever killed Josef. He was all right. Yes, he sold drugs, he sold arms, he sold...women. But he was an okay guy, you know?"

"Sure," Jacob said quietly. He didn't agree that Smirnoff was "an okay guy," but he did believe that a murderer should be brought to justice. Antonovich seemed passionate about catching Smirnoff's killer.

"You're going to the funeral?" Antonovich asked.

"Yes, course."

"I want to go over to the cemetery. It's old—and pretty big. Angels and archangels...and small mausoleums and large mausoleums."

"Places for a shooter to hide?" Jacob asked.

Antonovich nodded grimly. "I'll be checking it out," he said.

"Good. And good to know."

Jacob turned away. He knew the cemetery, on Eighth Street, or Calle Ocho, in the city. It was a beautiful cemetery. Gothic archways, handsome landscaping… and dozens of places for a shooter to hide—if Kozak was next in line, and there was still someone making a power play.

Antonovich appeared to be bitter about Smirnoff's death, as eager as any to pinpoint a killer. But Jacob just couldn't be sure what he felt he'd learned.

Either the goons were just hired muscle…or they had put together a trio of stone-cold killers, just waiting for the right moment to sweep in.

Which would mean that Victor Kozak was scheduled to die, as well.

Chapter Nine

Jorge left Jasmine's apartment at about 4:00 p.m. "I don't think I'm supposed to be hanging around here forever," he told her. "Despite the amount of fun and entertainment you're providing me, I've just got to go."

"What are you going to do?" Jasmine asked.

He smiled. "Hole up in my room with computer files. I'd rather hang around the beach. Check out the scene, hear what I can hear. But I guess that will be nothing. Rats. Guess I'll be hanging out with my computer."

"You don't think that's dangerous?"

"No, Bernie in tech helped me out. I hit a key, and only a genius could find my erased history or files or anything. I'll be okay. You'll be with a hot guy—I won't." He grinned at her.

She didn't grin back.

He walked over to her and hugged her. "Partner, I can feel it. Mary is going to be okay. And you're going to be okay, and I'm going to be okay. Okay? Oh, and pretty man is going to be okay, too."

That one, at last, made her grin. "I'm sure. Fine, go work. And I'll—"

"Keep pacing."

"Yep, I'll keep pacing."

Jorge was gone; she was alone.

She found herself pondering Jacob Wolff. He seemed to know everything about her. Of course, he was with the federal government. She was MDPD—not any lesser, but still, a total difference in privileges and responsibilities. She was, however, sure that if the operation had been planned differently, she'd know much more about him. She didn't even know anything about the fake man, much less the real Jacob Wolff. She was probably lucky she knew his real name.

He probably even knew that her parents were working with a charity rebuilding houses down in Haiti.

She was working up a fair amount of aggravation by the time Jacob Wolff arrived at her apartment; she didn't notice at first that he seemed worn and weary when he walked in.

"Anything? Do you have anything at all?" she asked. "I believe that Connor will be with Kari again tonight— and I'm very afraid for what will happen to her after that."

"We've got field agents watching Connor. They can find nothing to suggest that he's a murderer."

"Oh, really? So, in your usual line of work, people advertise the fact that they're murderers?"

The way he looked at her, she wished she could swallow the words back.

"I don't know anything yet. I have a firm belief that the men just found in the Glades were the killers. I believe they worked for someone who copied the key to the balcony, and they didn't bother to escape that way—they just blended with a panicked crowd that was trampling one another. I actually don't believe Kozak called the shots, but I can't be sure. What have you got?"

"Why do you believe Kozak is innocent—of murder, that is?"

Jacob was looking straight ahead, at the television. "I think he would do a great deal to make money, but I think he's seen enough of death."

"What makes you believe that?"

He turned to look at her. "He has a past very much like my own. My father was born in Israel to parents who barely escaped the Nazis. My maternal grandfather made it out of one of Stalin's purges. I was lucky. I was born here. Almost right here—Mount Sanai. But my parents had to work hard. We were always just scraping by. We were here several years, and then in New York. I went to high school in Manhattan, and on to Columbia University with tuition assistance through the military—and then after my service, the FBI. I've been under the direction of great men with the Bureau for years, always FBI, but recently, FBI in conjunction with Homeland Security—and I've seen what's really, really ugly. So, I allow myself to be wrong. But I talk to people. I try to hear what's beneath what they say. I'm not perfect. I have been fooled now and then, but not often."

"So, you're the only one with a tough past, huh?"

He didn't reply. He looked away. "We'll need a place to go to dinner. We're definitely being watched, and while I'm not worried about our three stooges—who aren't all that stupid, I don't think—we're being watched by someone else, as well. I'm itching to get to the cemetery, but I know I have to trust others. I've called ahead. Miami field agents will be in the cemetery, in the mausoleums, around every angel high enough to cover a man. So, for us, for now..."

She sat next to him. He looked over at her.

She hesitated and then said, "I'm sorry. My past was a piece of cake. My parents are as sweet and kind as a pair of over overgrown lovebirds. I wanted to be a cop because my dad was a cop, and he was influential in catching a serial rapist at work on Eighth Street near Westchester. He somehow managed to teach us about the evils of the world and see the beauty in it, as well. He never whined about me becoming a cop because I was a woman, and neither did my mother. I never wanted for anything. I was helped through college. I... I'm sorry."

He reached across the sofa and took her hand. And they weren't playacting for anyone, because no one was in the room.

"I know," he told her. He grinned. "I've seen your file."

"And I haven't seen yours. I don't even know... Are you married?"

"I was."

"Divorced?"

"No."

"Oh. I'm...sorry."

"It's been a long time," he said.

"Still."

He shrugged and smiled. "You would have liked her."

"I'm sure I would have," she said softly.

He was studying her, to a point where she flushed. "What?"

"I'm a classic case—that's what an analyst would say, I'm pretty sure. Married young, the sweet love of youth, lost that love, plowed into work, kind of a loner. Way too much time undercover for serious relationships…"

She was definitely blushing by then.

"So I've read your file, but there's nothing in there that explains the you that Jorge knows—and told me all about."

"I'm going to kill him."

"Don't. He's your partner. And he loves you."

"Okay, so I don't have a haunted history. And I didn't lose anyone. I mean, I didn't lose a husband or a lover. I just…"

"Well, if you don't go out, you don't meet anyone."

"Seriously, I'm going to kill Jorge."

He grinned. "I really like Jorge. So?"

"Okay, I don't often work undercover. But I do work major crimes. And even though you have shifts with other officers and you work with other agencies, there are times you have to be dedicated to the case instead of getting to know the people you're working with. When you're the one a loved one of a victim is depending on, or you're the one who's gained the trust of a young witness, or…"

Her voice trailed. His elbow was angled on the couch and he was smiling as he watched her.

"Many men find female police detectives to be intimidating," she went on. "And many of those who don't are a little scary themselves. It's not that I don't go out, or I don't believe in going out—"

"Just haven't found the right guy?"

She shrugged, rising nervously. She hadn't expected the evening to turn into a tell-all, especially when she sure as hell couldn't tell the truth about her feelings regarding him.

She walked over to the door. "I guess we'd better go to dinner. Let's see…where haven't we been?"

He stood and met her at the entry. "I don't know. Where do you suggest?" They were facing each other, ridiculously close.

And then, they both heard a shuffling sound, just outside.

"Someone following you?" she mouthed to Jacob.

He carefully looked out. "Maybe," he mouthed back. He drew his gun. He checked the door, and she saw that he had double-bolted it.

To her surprise, he threw the door open.

Night was falling. But the way the apartment building had been laid out, the pool and patio area faced the west, and while the night encroached, the lowering sun created a sky of bold beauty. Soon, the radiant colors would be gone, and it would be the darkness that reigned.

"Ah, what a lovely night. Maybe later…" Jacob said, his voice carrying. And then, still speaking with a full rich voice, he turned to her. "On second thought, why don't we order in tonight?" he asked.

Was there someone out there? A figure, to the side in the shadows, hunkered down in a lawn chair?

The door was fully open. They were on display, and he was looking down at her with his brilliant blue eyes, so handsome and so startling against his dark hair and bronzed face.

Jacob pulled her into his arms and kissed her. And this time, he pulled her close. His mouth came down on hers while his arms encompassed her, his hands sliding down low against her back, drawing her ever closer, his tongue parting her lips and slipping deep within her mouth.

The door slowly closed behind them while they backed inside the apartment, locked in the passionate embrace.

He was still kissing her as he eased one hand away, once again double-bolting the lock. She heard the sound as the bolts slid into place. And only then did his hold ease, his lips part from hers.

They were still so close. He looked down at her, and she could still feel the dampness of her lips, burning as they seemed to do when he touched her.

"I think…" she murmured, and he leaned closer, as if to hear her. His lips were almost upon hers again, his body was all but touching hers. To her amazement, she almost smiled, and she said softly, "Oh, screw this!"

She moved back into his arms. She was tall, but she moved up on tiptoe, the length of her body against his. She moved her mouth that one inch closer, found his lips and kissed him, parting his mouth, delving deep within it with her tongue, initiating all. She was stunned by her own movements, but more so by the depth of the longing and desire that was sweeping through her.

The kiss deepened and deepened. She pressed closer to him, flush against him, and felt his hands travel down the length of her body. The kiss broke, and he eased back slightly.

She felt she was panting like an idiot, and he had moved away. A flush of heat broke over her, and her limbs began to tremble. She had to force herself to bring her eyes to his, but when she did, she saw he was still watching her, intensely alert. He smiled slightly and said, "Ummmm." He was still holding her, and then he arched a brow and whispered, "Oh, screw this."

He swept her up, higher, into his arms. His mouth found hers again, but he moved as he kissed her, across the floor, toward the apartment bedroom. In seconds, they were lying down together on the bed. He braced himself over her, and said softly, "Only if it's what you really want."

She smiled. His pausing to question her, to be very sure, added to her sense of attraction and desperation.

She reached out, drawing his face down to hers again. She replied with her hands on his face, caressing his face as she drew him to her. "Yes. So much." They kissed again…just kissed, and then he straddled above her, doffing his jacket. The Glock he carried was evident then, and he reached back for the gun and holster, leaning over to set them on the dresser.

He looked down at her a moment.

"Mine's inside the bedside drawer, to the left," she

told him. Now they both knew where to reach if they were threatened in any way at any time.

That solved, he struggled from his shirt; she rose up to help him. He was still in trousers, socks and shoes. He halfway rolled from her, divesting his clothing, and she slipped out of the cool knit dress she'd been wearing, as well as her bra and panties.

To her surprise, he suddenly made an urgent sound, almost like a growl, rising to meet her again.

Naked flesh against naked flesh, he whispered, "So wrong of me. I knew the moment I saw you on the runway that you were extraordinary, you were grace and laughter and beauty, and I wanted you, but I didn't know what it would mean when I knew you..."

When his mouth found hers again, she felt the burn that had teased her lips become something of a raging wildfire that snaked down the length of her body. She allowed herself to roam free with her hands, loving the curve of his shoulders, the clench of muscle in his shoulders and down his back. She felt his body harden against her own, and she couldn't wrap herself tightly enough to him, to be both almost in his skin and touch him just the same.

They fell back on the bed together and she lay on top of him, landing kisses on his neck and his shoulders, the hard planes of his stomach, and moving lower against his body.

His hands grabbed her back, and they flipped in the bed. His mouth fell upon her throat and her breasts and lingered and teased and caressed. Those kisses continued downward, and she arched and writhed against him, finding his flesh and returning each touch of passion and hunger and longing.

She thought she would burn to a cinder, she was so alive, burning with a need unlike anything she'd ever known, wanting the play to go on forever, yet desperate that something be touched, that he be within her, as well.

And then he was, and they were moving, and moving, and moving…

They rolled, their lips melded together again and the rock of his hips was incredible. The sense of him within her was almost more than she could bear, the absolute sweetness, the rise of that fire, that longing to be ever more a part of him. Rising…and bursting out upon her like a flow of liquid gold.

The night seemed to sweep in all around her for long moments as she felt little bits of ecstasy shoot through her, ebbing bit by incredible bit, until she felt the damp sheen of their flesh, still so taut together, the rise and fall of her breath, the rock-hard pounding of her heart. And him, still holding her, still clinging in the darkness to the awesome beauty of what had been. So real, flesh and blood and pulse and their gasps for air…

They didn't speak at first; they just breathed.

And then he whispered softly, "I don't think I'll be putting that in the report."

She smiled and turned to him. "I understand you're often by the book. Forgive me."

"Forgive you?" He straddled her again, catching her hands and leaning low, his eyes alight with humor and tenderness. "Ah, my dear Detective Adair. It is I who must ask forgiveness. On second thought, no. Can't ask forgiveness. This was—"

"Incredible," she whispered.

"More than incredible. I don't know the words… Maybe there are none."

She pulled him back to her, and the kiss they shared was sweet and tender, and still, she knew, could arouse again at any second.

He pulled away and got out of bed suddenly. Light from the living room swept into the bedroom and she could see the full leanly muscled perfection of his tightly honed body in the doorway. He wasn't self-conscious as he padded out to the living room. Curious, she rose up on an arm.

Then he was back, every movement sleek and fluid, and he fell down beside her again. "Checking the door," he murmured.

"There's still someone out there?" she asked.

"Sitting by the pool. We'll order in," he told her.

He moved toward her and she jumped back suddenly, stricken. She'd been so enraptured with the man she'd been lucky enough to come to know that she had all but forgotten this wasn't an ordinary job.

She was looking for Mary. And even though Mary still seemed beyond her reach…

"Kari!" she exclaimed. "I'm worried, Jacob. What about Kari—and Mr. Connor?"

"I'll call in," he assured her. He found his jacket where he'd flung it earlier and dug his phone out of the pocket. After a minute, he had the info.

"Kari is back at her apartment."

"She's all right? And they're back inside?"

"Just Kari is back at her place. Connor took her out for a steak dinner and then a moonlit stroll on the beach. Then he brought her home. He left shortly, a smile on his face."

"Oh," Jasmine said. "Jacob, you don't think she'll be in any trouble with the gang for...for not sleeping with him?"

"No, I don't think she'll be in trouble."

Jasmine was still unsure. "He's being watched, Jasmine. Kari will be okay. Someone will get to Connor soon enough."

"Kari was worried though. I think she felt something was off. And I can't forget about Mary..."

"We'll find Mary. I swear it," he told her.

She believed him. And miraculously, she could move forward with her own night, grateful that the young blonde woman was all right. For now.

And there was nothing they could do. Not for the night.

She moved forward, catching his face, looking up into the dazzling blue of his eyes. "Thank you."

He kissed her again, that tender kiss... But the kiss deepened, and then it began to travel, and he was kissing her breasts again, affording each the most tender caresses, and her belly and thighs, bringing that erotic fire with every touch.

She let the night seize her again, and she returned his caresses, unable to stop seeking more and more of him, know the taste of his skin, the taste of him.

They embraced tightly, and he was within her, and

they rolled, and she was atop him, and this time they laughed and teased and whispered.

And then they lay together again, just breathing, still afrire, savoring the beauty of the darkness of the night, the coolness of the sheets beneath their bodies.

She was the one to sit up and straddle him this time.

He smiled, catching her hands with his. "Leave it to a cop to always want to be on top." He rolled her over, covering her with his body.

"And leave it to a Fed to think he must be in control."

"This Fed," he said softly, "is just happy to be with you."

She smiled back at him, wishing that the night would never end; that this was all they needed in reality and that the world would go away.

It could not.

He rolled from her, standing. "Food—we need to order food."

"I am hungry," she agreed.

She leaped out of bed, reaching to the foot of it for the caftan robe she kept there. He found his boxers but bothered with nothing else. He was already out in the living room, his phone drawn from his pocket. He looked at her. "I have a delivery service so, Chinese, Indian, Italian… Steaks? Seafood? What's your pleasure?"

You are my pleasure! she thought.

She managed not to say it out loud. "I'm easy. Foodwise," she added quickly. "Anything."

"Wow. I found one with pizza and champagne. Now there's an interesting combo. But I don't think that champagne… Not tonight."

"Not tonight," she agreed.

It was one thing to be drunk on desire when you were supposed to be drunk on desire. But quite another to have anything that might alter the mind with a goon outside on the porch.

"I don't believe we're in any danger, but I've seen things change quickly," he told her. "Ah, Thai food!"

"Perfect."

She stood near him and looked over his shoulder as he went through the offerings. They decided on one noodle dish and one rice dish.

Jasmine suddenly felt extremely awkward.

"Coffee!" she said. "I should make some coffee."

She started to walk into the kitchen. He caught her arm and pulled her back to him, holding her there, looking into her eyes. "Please, don't go away from me," he said softly.

She knew he didn't mean she shouldn't go into the kitchen and make coffee.

"I…it sounds like a line," she told him, "but I've never…in my life…just done this so quickly… I guess I don't know how to act."

"And I hope you believe me. I've always drawn a line. Until tonight."

She stood on her toes and kissed his lips lightly. "I won't go away," she promised.

She made coffee; Thai food arrived. Jacob made a point of answering the door still clad just in his boxers. He was careful to double-bolt the door again, and then to bring his Glock back out to sit on the table while they ate.

"You know, I'm a damned good markswoman," she told him.

He smiled at her. "I'd expect no less." He picked at a strand of the noodles. "Oh, by the way, Kozak gave you to me today." His smiled deepened as he saw her stiffen. "Sorry. All in a role."

She hesitated. "But in truth, I give myself where I choose."

"And so do I," he told her.

She laughed softly. Much of the Thai food went uneaten; they wound up laughing over a noodle they had both chosen.

And then they wound up in one another's arms again.

THERE WAS A knock on the door.

Jacob rolled out of bed, instantly awake. He grabbed his trousers and then his gun. Jasmine followed him out of bed in a flash, slipping on a robe, going for her own weapon.

He took a quick glance at the clock on the nightstand: 9:00 a.m. He headed out of the bedroom quickly, with Jasmine on his heels.

But one look out the peephole had Jacob unlocking the door. "It's all right. A friend," he told her.

Jorge stepped in, looked at both of them and then smiled.

"Method acting!" he said. "I like it. Just wondering what the hell took you two so long."

Chapter Ten

The funeral service was long. Speaking in Russian, the priest delivered the service with all respect and care—while the man might have known about Smirnoff and his deeds, he didn't judge when it came time for a man to meet his Maker. It was actually beautiful, though Jacob was sure many in the congregation had no idea what was being said.

Victor Kozak gave an emotional speech about his friend, and he did so in English for the benefit of the mourners who had gathered.

Many had come out to pay their respects—not so many would be invited to the celebration of life that would come later, at the club. Equally, not so many would travel with the funeral train that would follow the hearse to the cemetery.

Jacob had spoken with his Miami counterpart, Dean Jenkins. He knew agents were already waiting at the cemetery.

It would be a fine day for an attempt on Victor Kozak's life.

Jenkins also filled him in on what was happening

with events at the morgue, and with the local crime scene technicians.

"They identified one of the dead men, from the hand they got out of the alligator's gullet. Ain't technology great? Although, to be honest, it wasn't fingerprints or anything like that. One of my guys working in Little Havana recognized the ring.

"The victim was Leonardo Gonzalez—an undocumented Venezuelan immigrant. He and a few of his fellows had traveled through Mexico and, according to our agent, onto a cruise ship and into Miami. He'd been a contract killer at home and was looking for work in Little Havana. He was happy to work for anyone but was looking for connections in the Little Havana area because he didn't speak any English.

"Anyway…according to our sources, he was the kind of really bad guy taking serious advantage of the criminal activity going on down there right now, but he might have crossed another crime lord, meaning it was time for him to get out. But he had his own little gang. I'm working under the assumption our other two headless bodies are associates of his."

"Thanks— Anything new on Donald McPherson Connor?"

"We followed him. He was a perfect gentleman with the young lady. And he left her at her door. An agent is still outside. He could have followed Connor, or he could have kept his eye on her. He chose to protect the one we know to be an innocent. Anyway, we have a new crew out on the streets today. Oh, they're check-

ing in at your art gallery, too, making sure that Special
Agent Partridge is doing okay."

"Thanks. Hey, should I be getting a new phone?"

"Not to worry, I'm listed as a local artist. You any
closer?" Jenkins asked him.

"I don't know. I'm going to see what happens at the
funeral."

They ended their call, and Jacob joined the mourners, making himself one with Ivan Petrov and the three
goons.

Jasmine was not invited to this part of the day; she
would be at the club, preparing to work with the food
and drinks that would be served. He tried not to worry.
He knew she was an accomplished policewoman, and
he believed she was an excellent markswoman. She
was also vulnerable, though he had warned her that
she should be wary at all times—and armed if any way
possible.

She knew that, of course.

Kozak hadn't asked Jacob to drive to the cemetery;
he wanted him next to him in his car, behind the driver,
who would be Antonovich.

Jacob couldn't help but wonder if Kozak was afraid
that Antonovich could shoot them both if Jacob was
driving—he'd be easy prey for a man sitting behind
him.

They arrived safely at the cemetery. It was just west
of the downtown area known as Calle Ocho. The cemetery had recently joined with two different companies that had been offering funeral arrangements and
grave sites since the 1850s back in Cuba. It was at the

edge of a neighborhood close to downtown known as Little Havana.

But like most of Miami, anyone and everyone might be here.

They entered through Gothic arches. The grounds were sweeping, well tended and beautiful. Trees cast shady spots everywhere, and the park stretched for long blocks. They drove around a winding trail until they reached the canopy that stood over the area where the body of Josef Smirnoff would be laid to rest.

The cars parked; Jacob got out and waited for Kozak to emerge from the car, as well. He looked around. A lovely marble angel stood guard over a nearby family lot; a small family mausoleum stood about fifty yards away. Another, about a hundred yards farther out.

They were under a gracious old oak, near to a grouping of military headstones. Down a bit farther was a large concrete memorial to a man who had been a Mason and with the Mahi Shrine. His memorial gave witness to the fact that he had spent forty years as a Shriner, dedicating his time to raising funds for the children's hospital.

Probably a great guy. Right now, Jacob had to be certain that his memorial wasn't hiding a sniper.

He continued his scan of the area. The large mausoleum with its beautiful stained-glass windows, known to house many, many bodies, was perhaps a hundred yards behind them. A great place for a sniper to hide.

He reminded himself that the Miami agents knew this cemetery, where to be and where to watch.

And still he was on high alert.

"There, Mr. Kozak," Antonovich said, coming around to Kozak's side. "The chairs in front, sir. Those are for you and those who were close to Josef."

Sticking to Kozak's side like a piece of lint, Jacob led the man to the chairs.

Josef Smirnoff might not have been a cold-blooded killer, but he sure as hell had been a criminal. Victor Kozak had taken over from him, and while he might not be a cold-blooded killer either, he was also a major criminal.

But the showing of respectable people at the cemetery was large enough; the local news media brought trucks to the winding road that led through the very large cemetery—another place for a shooter to hide. Politicians and other respectable citizens arrived to say goodbye to Smirnoff.

Jacob sat back as the priest gave the graveside prayers. He had to have faith in his fellow agents. But just as he had settled—still alert and ready—a latecomer arrived at the grave site.

It was the man who so disturbed Jasmine.

Donald McPherson Connor.

THE CLUB WAS a bustle of activity when Jasmine arrived, even though it was early. The catering company personnel included two chefs, two wine stewards and six members of a cleanup crew.

Jasmine and Jorge reported right away to the dressing room. The servers were suited out appropriately—men in tuxes, women in similar versions with short skirts instead of pants—and shown the various food stations and the additional bars.

"Remember, today, you serve quickly, politely and quietly. We honor Josef," Natasha instructed. "You all understand? Behavior is beyond circumspect."

Stopping by one of the makeup tables where Jasmine had just harnessed her own hair in a braid at the back of her neck, Jorge told her, "Five City of Miami Beach cops, all aware to watch for trouble—hired on by Kozak." He lowered his head to her, pretending to smooth back a piece of her hair. "The chef at the first table is a plant—FBI. We have representation from MDPD as well—Detective Birch. You've worked with her. She'll be on the arm of one of our young politicians."

"Sounds good," Jasmine murmured. "Then again, how many cops were prowling the show when Josef was killed?"

"There's a cop at the balcony door. If anyone is going to start shooting, it won't be from the balcony." He leaned closer still, pretending to flick a piece of nonexistent lint from her brow. "FBI is crawling over the cemetery, too. Thing is, the killer must know. Unless he—or she—is really an egotistical bastard, nothing will happen today."

Nothing would happen. This would go on...

Jorge grinned suddenly. "You look different."

"I don't dress this way often."

"No, it's the way your eyes are shining."

"Jorge."

"It's nice to see you happy."

She looked at him and then lowered her head, rue-fully smiling. "I'd like to see you happy."

"Hey, you may. I'm not watched, not the way you are," he told her. "I had some dinner out last night. Sat on the beach."

"Jorge, you have to be—"

"I was careful. Trust me."

He grinned, and she knew it was the truth.

"Jorge, I need you!" Natasha called. "Now, you will take the large silver tray—you have nice long arms. Move through the crowd but offer up the food. Do not interfere with people who are talking. You let them stop. Think of yourselves as courteous machines."

Jorge moved on. Jasmine saw Kari at the next dressing table and she stood, heading over to her.

"Need help with anything?" she asked.

"Nope," Kari said, looking up. "I never can do false eyelashes right, but Natasha says we shouldn't wear them today."

"They're miserable things anyway."

"I agree."

"So, how are you?" Jasmine asked her softly.

"Good. Great, really."

"Great?" Jasmine asked.

Kari smiled. "I know that he's old, but honestly, if I were, say, forty-five instead of twenty-two, well… He has such a great accent. He talked to me about books and plays and he told me so much history about this place that I didn't know… He's kind, Jasmine. So very kind."

"Great to hear. I thought he made you a bit nervous. Are you okay with him now? When do you see him again?"

"Tonight. Later, of course. I told him—and I'm sure Natasha told him—that the club models were working the funeral, and we wouldn't be available until the entire celebration of life came to an end. He told me that, no matter what the hour, he'd like to see me." Kari hesitated a moment and then whispered, "I don't know why I was worried. Jasmine, we had the best dinner. Such a lovely night. He's truly so well educated. And then I thought he would want more. I thought he would want me to sleep with him. Oh! And he talked about Mary. He said she was such a lovely person—he was sure she went on to resume her education. They had talked about school and always having a backup to modeling or acting. He believes she might have headed out to California."

California? Or the pit of an alligator's stomach, somewhere out in the Everglades.

"I guess he's worked with or been a client of these people for a while," Jasmine said.

"Not so long. He told me that the group here—well, Josef Smirnoff first, and now Victor Kozak—knew how to find the most cultured women. He likes to go to the theater and the opera and art shows, and…he needs the right escorts."

"How nice."

"He loves music and musicals, voices!"

The opera…or screams as a woman died beneath a knife?

"Jasmine, he's really such a gentleman. I thought he

might be the type to immediately demand that we sleep together, that…"

"What?"

"That he might want me to do weird things." Her voice dropped to a whisper. "You know, weird sexual things. Scary things." She swallowed. "You know…autoerotic asphyxiation, or maybe not even scary things, just disgusting things. But he didn't even press sleeping with me." She paused, seeming a little uncomfortable, then went on quietly. "We're not specifically *ordered* to sleep with the clients, but there's an understanding that they get what they want if they're paying the price. And that trickles down to us in money and…in prestige on the runway. It's no secret that Natasha's highest earners get the best gigs. But…this guy, no pressure. I'm babbling. I guess I am still maybe a little nervous."

"Kari, you have my number, right? If not, I'll make sure that you do now."

Kari pulled out her phone and Jasmine quickly gave her the number to her burner phone.

"We're having lunch, right?" Kari asked.

"Lunch, yes, but keep your phone near. If you're afraid at any point, you call me immediately!"

Kari frowned, but then smiled. "You can call me, too, you know, except that… Well! You seem just fine, and I imagine…" She broke off and laughed suddenly, leaning forward. "I might have been willing to pay some big bucks myself for that blue-eyed wonder who chose you."

Jasmine smiled weakly.

"You're okay, right?" Kari asked. "I mean, with him."

"Yes, I'm just fine," Jasmine managed.

"What is he like, that Jacob? Those eyes of his... If he ever looked at me the way he looks at you, wow. I'd be putty."

"Putty," Jasmine repeated. "That's me."

"Girls!" Natasha called. "Time to take your stations. Sasha has called—the services at the grave site are ending. We will be ready, the most gracious of hosts and hostesses."

And so, they were on. They all trailed out of the dressing room.

Natasha was by the balcony door; it was open for them to head down the stairs.

Jasmine smiled as she passed Natasha. Only Kozak was supposed to have a key. But Victor wasn't here. And Ivan was downstairs, setting up the main bar, giving orders to the catering company.

Jasmine hurried downstairs along with the others. She knew that somehow, she would get that information to Jacob.

Lightning didn't strike twice...

Unless sometimes, it did.

No BULLETS RANG out at the cemetery.

The priest, resplendent in his robes, carried through the service. Women had been given roses; they walked past the coffin to drop them down upon it.

"I need a moment," Kozak told his companions.

He was at the coffin alone, except for the four cemetery workers who waited discreetly to see that the coffin was lowered six feet under. The hearse was preparing to leave. Antonovich, Suarez and Garibaldi waited while other mourners filed out to their cars.

Donald McPherson Connor was starting to walk away.

Jacob was a distance from Victor Kozak as it was; he wouldn't be any farther from the man if he walked toward Connor. He excused himself to the trio of bodyguards.

"Mr. Connor!" Jacob called out.

The man stopped walking and looked back at him, eyeing him distastefully. Jacob noticed that he was lean but fit.

Probably plenty strong. Certainly strong enough against a slim blonde girl.

Connor was evidently irritated at having been stopped—by Jacob, at any rate. "Yes, Mr. Marensky, what is it?"

"Well, I just wish to apologize, and I hope that we don't keep bad blood between us. I was, in fact, hoping that you found Miss Anderson to be up to your expectations."

"Miss Anderson is a truly lovely woman. I am enjoying her company."

Jacob forced a smile. "Excellent. She is quite beautiful."

"Not as intriguing as Miss Alamein though," Connor said. He was an oddly dignified man—soft-spoken. "So, Mr. Marenksy, what exactly do you do in relation to the Gold Sun Club?"

Then again, Jacob had seen some of the most innocent and soft-spoken men and women possible turn out to be vicious and as cold as ice.

"We have shared business interests. I run an art gallery," Jacob said.

"So I hear," Connor said, his British accent a little clipped.

"I'd welcome you for a visit. See if there's anything that catches your eye. Just what is your enterprise, sir?"

The man's smile tightened. "No enterprise—other than the stock market. Now there, sir, is bloody criminal action from the get-go, and yet quite legal."

"Ah, I believed that you had worked with Josef—and now Victor."

"I simply require a certain kind of companion."

"I see," Jacob said, still smiling. Just what was it that he required? "Well, sir, I shall see you at the club. I just wished to clear the air between us. Please understand, my arrangements had been made first."

"Oh, yes, I understand perfectly, Mr. Marensky." Connor was still looking at him with watery blue hatred.

"Jacob?" Kozak was calling to him.

"Excuse me," Jacob said, spinning around to return to Victor Kozak's side.

"We must be leaving now," Kozak said.

"Yes, of course."

"You and Connor are good then?" Kozak asked him softly.

"Oh, as good as we can be, Victor. As good as we can be."

"Please, then…" Kozak indicated the road through

the cemetery; theirs was the only car that remained. "Sasha, you will drive."

"Yes, sir," Antonovich said, sliding into the driver's seat.

Garibaldi took the front seat by him. Kozak slid into the back, between Suarez and Jacob. The car rolled out of the cemetery, onto Southwest Eighth Street and then headed for I-95 and the extension out to South Beach.

The funeral itself had gone off without a hitch. Now, all they had to do was make it through the reception—the celebration of life where the mourners would come together and Smirnoff would receive his last honors.

Smirnoff, Kozak and their peers really were criminals. Jacob had seen one too many a decent person cajoled into and then hooked on drugs. And abusing the trust of hopeful girls was reprehensible. But Jacob wanted Kozak prosecuted and locked away—not on a slab with a bullet in his head.

As the car rolled up to Kozak's special parking place at the back of the property, Jacob felt Kozak's hand wind into a vice on his arm.

The man looked at him, and there was fear in his eyes, quickly masked as Garibaldi came around and opened the door.

Jacob got out.

"My friend, I know you will change things!" Kozak said. He caught Jacob's arm again, turning to show him where they were. "Cops—down there, at the end of the block. That guy with the long hair and the beggar's cup at this end? A cop." He pulled Jacob along to show him the men to whom he was referring.

And then he whispered to Jacob, "Here. This is where they will try to kill me. Somewhere here, at the club."

Chapter Eleven

It always amazed Jasmine to see the people who came out for such an event—the last rites for a man they had to have known conducted criminal activities. She was also certain many people on the guest list had not sat through the long religious ceremony at the church, nor attended the final graveside services.

The club was busy within minutes of the door opening.

Ivan stood at the main doors dressed in his best designer suit. Natasha was at his side tonight, ready to greet everyone as they came in; she had finished her busywork, prepared her various crews and was ready to be the grand hostess.

Jasmine had been given a tray of canapés to carry around, and she did so smoothly and easily. Though maintaining her demeanor as a courteous robot was not as easy as it might have been—Kozak and the goons and Jacob had yet to come into the club.

When they finally did, she breathed an inward sigh of relief.

She tried to maneuver herself around to Jacob's position casually, making it part of her regular sweep of the room. When she made it to an area near the street entrance, he was still standing with Kozak and the bodyguards.

"Gentlemen," she said quietly, offering up her tray.

The bodyguards quickly reached for the little quiches. Jacob inclined his head slightly and took a canapé, as well.

Kozak turned to her. "What I need is a drink, Jasmine. Will you get me a vodka? I'm sure that Natasha has seen to it that our hired bartender knows what is my special reserve."

"Yes, of course," Jasmine said.

But Natasha swept by at that moment, giving her a serious frown. "Jasmine, you are to move among our guests."

"Yes, Natasha," she said.

"Natasha," Kozak said softly. "We have many people working the floor. I would like Jasmine to go and get me my drink."

"Victor, I can do that for you," Natasha said.

"You are the hostess. Let Jasmine go," Kozak said. "It's time that I...that I welcome our guests and give my little speech here, eh? But one vodka first!"

Jasmine headed off to the bar. The man there gave her an appreciative look and she smiled in return. "I need a drink for Mr. Kozak—his special reserve. He believes you'll know what it is."

"Yep," the bartender said. "I've been given the bottle and serious instructions. It's a unique vintage from Russia, not sold in the United States." He grinned at her, reaching beneath the bar for the bottle. He got a glass and said, "Just two ice cubes. Rich men and their drinks."

"Thanks," she told him.

"I live to serve. Come see me again!"

She nodded and started to hurry away but turned back. "Did you meet with Mr. Kozak before this event? Did he give you the bottle?" she asked.

He shook his head. "I met with the praying mantis. Oh, sorry—the entire catering company met with Natasha. She gave us strict instructions."

"And the bottle of vodka?"

"No, it was here where she said it would be when I came in. Hey, sorry, I hope she's not a friend of yours— I'm an actor and this catering company keeps me in cash while I'm pounding the pavement. I'm sorry. Please, I didn't mean to be offensive."

"You need to be a lot more careful."

"Please, don't get me fired."

"I won't, but… Never mind. Thank you."

Once again, she turned away, but then something about the situation seemed disturbing. "Would you mind? Give me four more drinks, just like this one but with regular vodka. Something good, just not Kozak's special reserve."

"Anything for you."

She smiled. And prayed that she and Jacob had come to know one another in their undercover roles as well as they had come to know one another personally.

Kozak and Jacob, with Garibaldi, Suarez, and Antonovich behind them, were heading toward the stage.

Jasmine took a step back, her heart pounding, wondering if she was wrong and if she might just cause the entire operation to implode—and put them all, including the guests, in serious danger.

But her hunch was strong. She had seen Natasha with the key.

Natasha was definitely sleeping with Kozak—but had she been sleeping with Josef Smirnoff before? Was she part of what came with taking over the business because she wouldn't be ousted herself?

Jasmine walked toward the men.

"Special for Mr. Kozak, and gentlemen, I believe it was a long day for you, as well. I hope I have not displeased you, Mr. Kozak."

She looked at Jacob, just lowering her eyes at the glass he was to take, and gave the barest shake of her head. He shouldn't drink it. He would know—surely, he would know!

Jacob's striking blue eyes fell on hers. Before Kozak could answer, he said, "That was very thoughtful of you."

"Nice, sweet, as always," Antonovich said happily, and he looked at Kozak.

"Definitely. One vodka, boss, eh?" Suarez asked.

"One vodka," Kozak agreed.

Jasmine dared look around as the men took their drinks. An up-and-coming beach politician was entering with a lovely young news reporter on his arm. Natasha was doing her duty and greeting them.

"I must get to the stage," Kozak said.

"I'll get you there swiftly," Jacob assured him.

Jasmine flashed a smile to all of them. "I'd best get to my canapés," she said. She started to walk away.

"A second?" Jacob asked, looking at Kozak for permission, as well.

"Yes, then you will walk with me, stand by me, at my back," Kozak said.

Jacob smiled and stepped away with Jasmine. She had her chance. "Natasha had the key tonight," she said. "Might be important. Kozak wasn't here. I don't think they plan a shooting."

"Poison in the vodka?"

"I could be wrong."

"Thanks. You gave it to me."

"You knew!"

"I knew," he assured her, and then he squeezed her hand and stepped back.

"To the stage," Kozak said. He seemed very nervous.

As he should be! Jasmine thought.

As he walked away, Kozak took a sip of his vodka. He frowned instantly. The man did know the taste of his special reserve.

And that wasn't his special reserve.

But Jacob guided him toward the stage. Jasmine saw Jacob casually and discreetly set his own glass down on a waiter's tray.

The waiter was Jorge. He looked across the room at her and nodded.

JACOB STOOD JUST behind Victor Kozak as the man took the microphone, thanking everyone for coming, and for honoring Josef Smirnoff. He told a few tales about his friend and talked about the way Smirnoff had loved Miami Beach and how the club had been a dream for him.

"Sparkling like the Miami sun!" Victor said. "He was my business partner. He was my friend. In his honor, we will rename the club—it will be *Josef's* when it opens to the public tomorrow night. While we faced senseless violence and his death here, we are a powerful people. We are South Floridians, whether we were born here or we were lucky enough to enter this country and find this paradise as our home. We are strong. And, in his name, we will prevail!"

As Kozak spoke, Jacob kept his eyes on the room. He also mused that Kozak didn't think that peddling escorts or drug dealing were really bad things to do. Illegal, but not bad.

He saw the police—in uniform, and undercover—and the agents in the room. And he knew each of them was watching for the first sign, so much as a hint, of the barrel of a gun or someone reaching into a pocket.

But he was pretty sure Jasmine was right; guns would not be blazing. A killer must right now be waiting for whatever poison might have been in the special reserve to work.

"Make it quick," Jacob managed to whisper.

Kozak took heed. He quickly asked the crowd to honor Smirnoff's memory and enjoy his dream. Then Jacob took his arm and led him from the stage.

"Tell your men you feel sick," he said. "That I'm going to get you upstairs."

Kozak heeded him once again. "I am unwell! Sasha,

you will watch the east stairs. Antonio, you will watch the west. Alejandro, you will take between them. I am… I must sit down. Alone. The day… It has been too long. Mr. Marensky will see me upstairs to my office. Tell Ivan and Natasha they must remain the finest hosts."

"Yes, sir," Garibaldi said quickly.

"Hurry, and stumble as we walk up," Jacob said quietly to Kozak.

Antonovich nodded to the policeman at the base of the stairs; the man noticed Kozak, nodded in return and unlatched the velvet barrier. Jacob set his arm on Kozak's back and they headed up the stairs. Halfway up, Kozak pretended to stumble.

"Good, good, we keep going," Jacob murmured.

They passed the expected security. They made it to the door, and Jacob passed through it quickly. A cop met them in the hall.

"Getting Mr. Kozak to his office," Jacob told him.

The cop nodded.

They opened the door to the office—despite the massive security, Jacob entered first.

The office was empty. He had expected it would be. The killer would be waiting for Kozak to fall downstairs.

And everyone would think the day had been just too difficult for Victor Kozak. The man drank, he liked his cigars, and maybe he liked some of his smuggled product, too. His heart could just give out, after a day like today.

And the poison wouldn't be found during an autopsy,

since such substances would not fall into the realm of regular tests.

Kozak sat behind his desk and sighed deeply. "I really could use a drink!"

"I'm sure you keep something in here. Then again, I'm sure there are others who know you keep something in here," Jacob warned him.

"So. I will not drink. What do I do?" Kozak asked.

"We wait here. We see if someone comes. Maybe we call an ambulance. We let the crowd know you're in the emergency room, barely hanging on."

Kozak drummed his fingers on his desk, smiling. He stared at Jacob.

"You are not an art dealer, are you, Mr. Marensky? As a matter of fact, your name isn't even Marensky, is it?"

THE NIGHT SEEMED VERY, very long.

Jasmine moved about the floor as she had been directed, watching the stairs now and then. She saw Jorge with one of the catering crew, an FBI plant, and knew the vodka was probably already on its way to be tested.

But the bartender, she was sure, had just been hired on for the night.

She saw the other girls milling about the room, doing exactly what they had been told to do. They were pretty and silent and moving like robots. She watched the stairs. And to her relief, people began to leave.

While the club had been open and music—soft, somber music, much of it Russian—had played through the night, there was no dancing. After the speech, after the food and free-flowing alcohol, there was little else to do.

People murmured about coming when the club was up and running again. Big names in music had been booked before Smirnoff's death—they were probably still on the agenda.

She was doing her last round with coffees and coffee liqueurs when she saw the man, Donald McPherson Connor, stop Kari Anderson and talk to her. Then he slipped out the door.

A moment later, Kari followed.

Jasmine walked back to the bar quickly, ready to dispose of her tray and head out.

But there was a man at the bar. A little man with big glasses, a nerdy smile and wild bushy hair. "Don't," he said softly, then called to the bartender. "Another, my friend!"

"Pardon?" Jasmine asked, setting her tray down. She didn't care what he was saying; Jacob had Kozak upstairs. Things were coming to a head. And Kari was leaving with a man who just might be a very sick murderer.

"No, we're on it," the little man said. He spoke more loudly. "I mean, man, you're not just a beauty, lady, you are really cool looking. Those eyes of yours—emeralds!" He lowered his voice while pretending to study her eyes. "Special Agent Dean Jenkins, working in association with Wolff. We have a man following Connor and Miss Anderson. Keep your cover."

"That's very nice of you, sir," she said. "I work for the club. We don't date customers."

Garibaldi came up behind her. "Is there a problem?" he asked, glaring at the man who had just identified himself to her as FBI.

Dean Jenkins lifted his hands. "No, sir. No problem. I'm totally a hands-off guy, just complimenting beauty."

"He was very sweet. No problem at all," Jasmine said quickly.

To her relief, Garibaldi ambled away.

Jasmine turned with her tray of coffee cups and coffee drinks.

Natasha was standing there. "All is well?"

"Yes, of course."

"Have you seen Mr. Marensky?" Natasha asked her.

"I believe he went up with Mr. Kozak. He wasn't feeling well."

"They are upstairs? Still?"

Jasmine didn't have to answer. She heard the sound of an ambulance screaming through the night. People began to chatter nervously.

"Oh, my God! Victor!" Natasha cried. She turned and raced for the stairs. She was stopped by Garibaldi, with whom she argued. But this time, Garibaldi had apparently been given strict instructions by Kozak himself.

The wailing sirens stopped.

Natasha kept arguing with Garibaldi. Ivan was coming to join her, a strange look on his face. Was he frowning…or was that a look of satisfaction?

No one was near Jasmine at that moment. She heard a soft whisper at her ear.

Dean Jenkins was standing just behind her. "Jacob

is with Kozak. They're heading to the hospital. Word will be out that he collapsed and that they're afraid of a heart attack."

Jasmine let him know she had heard him, nodding slightly, watching along with the others. She moved away from him. As she did so, she felt her phone vibrate in her pocket. She quickly made her way close to the bar, behind a structural beam, and answered it, halfway expecting Jacob.

But it wasn't Jacob.

"Jasmine!"

It was Kari Anderson.

"Jasmine, I need to tell you—"

"Kari, what? Kari?"

Jasmine looked at her phone; the call had ended. The line was dead.

"So, I WILL DIE. Or I will go to prison for the rest of my life," Kozak said, sighing softly. He shrugged. He was lying in the back of an ambulance. Comfortable.

It was a real ambulance. But they weren't real paramedics manning the vehicle, though they would really take Kozak to the hospital, where he would really be admitted.

Jacob had feared that Natasha or Ivan might have made their way upstairs before he'd managed to get Kozak out, but the ambulance had arrived just in time— and Kozak had been shoved right in and the vehicle had taken off into the night. Within moments of closing the ambulance doors, Jacob had revealed to him that he was FBI.

"Victor, the whole operation has to go down," Jacob told him. "I'm sure if you give the district attorney any help you can, he'll make the best arrangements possible."

"I can give you cartels. Names of the men who come and go with drugs and drug money."

"I'm not the DA," Jacob said.

"And I discovered that I do want to live, however long that may be," Kozak told him. He sighed. "My friend, will you do one thing for me?"

"This will be out of my hands now, Victor."

But Victor smiled. "This is a small thing. Before I am locked away, will you see to it that I get just one more…"

"One more what?"

"Shot of my good vodka!"

"I will do my best, Victor. I'm sure you have an attorney, and… I don't know. But for now, your best service is to give us the men who did put those bodies in the oil drums and who left the headless men in the Everglades."

"They want me dead."

"All the more reason we need anything you have to find out just who is calling the shots."

Jacob felt his phone vibrating in his pocket.

Jasmine? She had saved the night, somehow suspecting there might be poison in the vodka. But her cover might be jeopardized…

He answered the phone quickly.

It was Dean Jenkins. "She's gone after Connor, Jacob. Your detective associate."

"What? How? When?"

"The commotion started with the siren. She disappeared. And she saw Kari take off after Connor. We have a man on him, of course, and I'm on my way out, but—"

Jacob leaped up and hurried to the front of the ambulance. "Stop, let me out—quickly!" he said.

"Yes, sir. But—"

"Proceed, get him to a room, guards all around," Jacob said.

"Will do," the driver promised.

The ambulance jerked to a halt. Jacob jumped out and began to run. He had blocks to run, blocks filled with tourists, diners, children...

But at least Connor's apartment was north of the club. At least...

Jasmine was a cop; a good cop. She'd be all right. She'd think it out.

She was also emotional. She was afraid Mary had disappeared because Connor had done something horrible to her. Afraid that same horrible thing might happen to Kari...

"Hey!" a man protested.

Jacob just nudged past him and quickened his pace.

THANKS TO DEAN JENKINS, Jorge and all the other police and agents working the case, Jasmine knew where to go. Connor's room. She knew the street, the hotel complex and the number.

Naturally, it was on a side street—one that was poorly lit, for the beach. One that was a bit austere, where the rich came to stay, unburdened by the noise and ruckus of the average working-man tourist.

She ran up to the building. She could see the lobby through the plate-glass windows that surrounded the handsome interior. It was an old deco place redone— velvet upholstered chairs and a check-in reception that wasn't a counter but a desk. She could see a man with a newspaper in the lobby, watching the door.

FBI. The man watching Donald McPherson Connor? If so, he was nowhere near close enough.

Jasmine hesitated, taking a deep breath. One more time—one more try.

She pulled out her cell and dialed Kari's number. It rang once and went straight to voice mail.

She pocketed her phone and tried for a regal and non-chalant manner. She waited for the clerk to walk back into the office behind the desk.

Then she sashayed through as if she belonged there, despite her elaborate if dignified waitress uniform. She didn't know the man with the newspaper; he didn't know her. She offered him a brilliant smile and saun-tered on through to the elevator.

She realized, in the elevator, that Connor had taken the penthouse; a floor all to himself. She was surprised when the elevator let her choose the top floor without any additional security.

The doors opened into a charming vestibule, rather than a hallway. It was as if she had arrived at some-one's grand house. Handsome double doors led into the apartment itself.

She tried knocking, her heart beating a thousand

drums a second. It would be illegal for her just to enter.
She certainly couldn't force it open.

She waited…and no one came. The door might well
be unlocked in such a building—in a good neighborhood, with security in the lobby.

And if she said she entered because she thought she
heard a cry…

Just as Jasmine reached for the handle, the door
opened.

Connor stood there, a gun in his hand.

"Ah, Jasmine," he said. "We've been waiting for
you."

AS HE RAN, Jacob envisioned every manner of horror.
His breath was coming hard; his calves were burning.

He knew he had made the right choice, running. It
was the weekend on the beach, cars were bumper-to-
bumper. For some reason there was an element of local
society who thought it was cool to drive down Collins
Avenue and show off their cars, some elegant, some
souped-up, some convertibles, and some…just cars.
Some with music blaring, and some discreetly quiet.

He was moving far faster than the cars.

And still…

He pictured Jasmine, bursting in on Connor. And
Connor, ready for her, shots blazing before she could
enter the room; Jasmine shooting back, maybe even taking the man down, as well. Injuring him, maybe killing
him, but then lying there in a pool of blood, dark hair
streaming through it, almost blue-black in contrast to

the color of blood, eyes brilliant emerald as she stared into the night, and yet…sightless.

He had to stop thinking that way. He wasn't prone to panic; he'd have never survived his past.

His phone rang; he answered it anxiously, still running. It was Dean Jenkins.

"Natasha, Ivan, and the trio have headed to the hospital. I was just escorted out of the club. It went into lockdown. I found a place behind a dumpster by the cars. They all left together in the limo."

"Thanks. But no one goes in to see Kozak. They can be herded into a waiting room. They can't be near him. They can't know he's not really poisoned."

"We've got a 'doctor' ready to talk to them. As far as they'll know, Kozak is being airlifted to a trauma center where they're fighting to save his life."

"Thanks, Jenkins."

"Anything on your end yet?"

Apparently, Jenkins couldn't hear the way that he was panting. Just one more corner…

"Almost there."

He turned the corner and saw Connor's building, grand touches of Mediterranean-style along with the fine art deco architecture.

He ran through protocol in his mind—there was no right way to burst in on the man. This was a small part of what was going on; they didn't know who had killed Josef, who had tried to kill Kozak. The operation was in a crisis situation at the moment—and he needed to keep his cover.

He ran to the front, stopped briefly for a long breath

and to gather his composure. He saw the agent with his newspaper—and the tiny dolphin tie tack that identified him. A clerk in a handsome suit sat at the desk.

There was no time; Jacob entered the lobby, headed over to the man he'd never met, and greeted him. "Henry, how are you doing?"

"Great—fine fishing today. The kids come in tomorrow. We're going to take them over to Key Biscayne to see the lighthouse and then back to the Seaquarium— let them swim with some dolphins."

"Sounds like a plan. I've done the dolphin thing myself…" Jacob watched as the clerk headed to a back room. "How long?"

"Connor—just twenty minutes or so. Kari Anderson—fifteen. And then, another woman, just a matter of minutes."

Minutes…

Jacob headed for the elevator. It only took seconds for a bullet to find its mark. But as he reached the elevator, he realized the other agent had leaped to his feet to join him.

"I'm here now," Jacob said. "If I need backup, you'll know. If I'm not down—"

"Wait, there's just something you need to hear first," the agent said.

CONNOR NEVER HAD a chance to use his weapon.

Jasmine judged her distance—and the awkward way the man was holding the gun. She ducked low and took a flying leap at him, catching his legs, toppling him.

She'd been right; he was no gunslinger himself; he

was completely inept. His gun went flying and he let out a yelp that made him sound like a wounded kitten.

She straddled him, pinning him down. "Where's Kari? What have you done with her?"

"What have I done with her?" He seemed stunned.

"You bastard, what have you done with her?"

It would be unethical, but...she was still playing a role. She'd taken him, and she meant to get the truth from him, beat it out of him if she had to. She could get away with this—one high-class escort worried about another, attacking a man...

But just as she was about to deliver a good right to his jaw, she heard her name called.

She looked up.

Kari was standing in the archway to the next room.

At the same time, she felt strong arms wrap around her waist, drawing her off of Connor. She twisted and fought and turned—

Jacob!

Jacob, stopping her, when she had the man down...

"Let me go!" she demanded furiously.

"Jasmine, Jasmine, it's all right, you don't understand!" Kari cried. She rushed over to Connor, going down on her knees and trying to help the man up.

Astonished, Jasmine turned to Jacob. "What in God's name is happening?" she demanded, wrenching free from him. "Has everyone gone mad?"

Jacob turned and closed and locked the door and then looked at her.

For one moment, she felt extreme panic. Were they

all in on it? Was Jacob a turncoat, had he somehow tricked the federal government, was this all…?

No! She believed in him, she knew him, knew this couldn't be.

"I admit, I don't fully know myself," Jacob said. "But we need to give Mr. Connor a chance to explain."

Connor was up on his feet, standing next to Kari—who was protectively holding his arm. "What is going on?" Connor asked.

"You first," Jacob told him.

"I'm just a citizen," Connor said. "Trying to…do the right thing."

Kari spoke up then, passionately. "Donald's daughter came to Miami Beach and wound up modeling with the group." She let out a long breath. "She was found dead on the beach. Drug overdose."

"I hire them to get them out," Connor whispered.

"But…but…" Jasmine began.

"Nan, my daughter, talked to me. She was frightened. She said that she couldn't forget what she had seen, and she was afraid that someone knew she knew about the cocaine, and…then she was found dead. She wasn't an addict. She didn't do drugs. I called the police—there was an investigation, and it went nowhere. The officers tried, but Nan wasn't found anywhere near the club, she'd been out with friends, she'd said she was leaving, and…they killed her. I know they killed her. And I couldn't get justice, so—"

"Donald made arrangements for me to get away—far away. Hide out, and then start over," Kari said softly. "I wanted to get ahead so badly, be rich and famous…

be loved. I did things I'm not proud of. And I couldn't see any way out. But… Donald is a savior!"

"I need some kind of proof," Jacob said. "And if this is all true, Mr. Connor, I am so sorry and, of course, so grateful, and you're a fool, as well. You're risking your own life."

"My life does not matter so much anymore," Connor said flatly. "I have proof—our airline tickets. I was taking Kari to London tonight and then on to Yorkshire, to settle her with my family there."

Jasmine stared at them all, incredulous. And then it hit her. Connor's daughter…dead.

"Mary," she murmured.

"Mary?" Connor said. "Mary Ahearn?"

Jasmine stared at him.

Connor smiled. "Lovely young woman. She tried to help me find out which one of those horrible people was responsible for Nan's death. She tried to find out what was going on."

"So, you gave her a death sentence, too," Jasmine whispered.

He shook his head, looking a bit confused but still smiling. "Mary is alive and well. She's at my estate in Yorkshire, happily working on a play she's been longing to write. Of course, she'd love to be acting, and she's very fond of British theater, so she just might want to stay on. I asked her not to contact anyone from her former life until we were sure she was safe."

Jasmine would have fallen over. She felt Jacob's strength as his arms came around her.

He was staring across the room at Connor. "We will

have to verify your information. And I hope you're telling the truth. If so, I swear to you, we will get justice for your daughter. I'm setting you up with an agent to get safely out of the country. I don't think you'll be bothered tonight—there's too much else going on right now."

"Why did you call me? Why did you hang up?" Jasmine demanded of Kari.

"My—my phone died! I figured I'd call you and let you know I was leaving as soon as possible," Kari said. "And then we were getting my things, and Donald promised he'd come back and get you out, but he thought you were safe, that Jacob might be a criminal, but he'd be watching over you and then somehow, he'd get to you and—I'm so sorry!"

"One thing, please," Connor said.

"What?" Jacob demanded.

"Who the hell are you people?" Connor asked.

Chapter Twelve

It felt odd that it had just been that afternoon that Josef Smirnoff had been lain to rest. The ceremony at the club had taken place, and Jacob had ushered Kozak out in an ambulance, pretending the man was at death's door.

While Jacob and Jasmine were at Connor's suite, Kozak had gone into the hospital—and then out another door. He had immediately been ushered out to a FBI facility out west in Miami, in a little area with scores of ranch houses built in the 1970s, heading west off the canal that bordered the Tamiami Trail all the way across the south end of the peninsula to Naples, Florida.

Agents watching the hospitals—the beach hospital where Kozak had first been taken and the county hospital with the trauma center where he'd supposedly been brought later—had kept up with Jacob; Jasmine had been in touch with the MDPD who had in turn been in touch with the Miami Beach department, and everyone was on alert in case another attempt was made on the life of their new informant.

The entire inner core of Kozak's circle had arrived at the beach hospital, only to be assured that everything was being done, but that no one could see Victor Kozak. They had left together, but now Ivan and Natasha were back at the club with only Antonovich to watch over the doors. Natasha had been a mess, so Jasmine and Jacob were told—and had to be sedated when she was told that Kozak was on the verge of death.

Jacob had received many calls from both Ivan and Natasha, but he had told them both that he also had been kicked out of the hospital for having grown too insistent on seeing a man when an intensive care crew was busy trying to save him.

It was well after midnight by the time Donald McPherson Connor and Kari Anderson had been escorted to the airport—and safely onto their plane. Jasmine had gone from being ready to rip the man's throat out to being his best friend—they'd wound up talking and talking.

Kari had told her she'd wanted to say more, but she couldn't. She'd been afraid of what Jasmine might say or do, not at all certain that Jacob wasn't on the rise through the gang—or that Jasmine wasn't already completely beneath his control.

Connor had spoken about his own grief and then about dealing with it in the most constructive way he could.

"You really took chances," Jacob had told him.

"Not so much. I wasn't in on anything. I was just a client. Not someone making money—I was someone giving them money." He paused and shrugged. "And money is something I have. But it means nothing when you don't have the ones you love to share it with."

Jacob had to admit, he was a bit in awe of the man himself. Grief and loss often destroyed the loving survivors; Connor had channeled his resources and himself into saving others.

Naturally, Jacob hadn't immediately trusted what he heard, but with the information Connor gave him, the FBI offices were able to verify his story. The man did own a huge estate in Yorkshire. In truth, he had a title. He also held dual citizenship and spent as much time in the States—recently in the pursuit of saving the lives of young women—as in Great Britain.

And so it was two in the morning when Jacob and Jasmine returned to her apartment. She didn't seem the least bit tired. She was keyed up and alive, filled with energy.

"She's all right, Jacob! Mary is fine. She's in England…and I've been so, so afraid!"

He was sitting on the sofa, wiped out. She'd been all but flying around the room. In her happiness, that flight took her to fall down on his lap, sweeping her arms around him, her smile bright and her eyes as dazzling an emerald as could ever be imagined.

Her touch removed a great deal of his own exhaustion.

"She's alive, and you have to meet her. Oh, Jacob, to think I wanted to skin that man alive, that I thought he was part of…" Her voice trailed off and she frowned.

"What?" he asked, reaching out to stroke back a long lock of her hair.

"We're no closer to the truth. Nan Connor was afraid because she was a witness to a huge cocaine deal. But we don't know who saw her, and there's no way we can find out. We're pretending that Kozak is dying, but none of the gang has risen up to try to take over."

"Jasmine, as far as I know, they wouldn't dare do so. They don't believe that Kozak is dead as of yet, and they won't dare play their cards until they do."

"Where do we go from here?"

"Everything is in motion. I don't even call the shots from here on out. I'll go out tomorrow to interrogate Kozak, but it's going to be up to men with much higher positions than mine to determine what our next steps are. Kozak was grateful just to be alive." He paused, looking at her. "That was an amazing save tonight—the poison in the vodka. How did you know?"

"When he talked about his special reserve, it occurred to me that he'd be the only one drinking it. I'd hoped I'd find out who had brought the bottle and handed it to the bartender, but the guy was from the catering company and he said the bar had been set up when he got there, with the instructions that the special reserve stuff was for Kozak and Kozak only."

"Impressive." He smiled, watching her eyes. "You are a veritable beast. I thought you were going to rip Connor's head off. We're lucky you didn't shoot. He had a gun, right? You need to slow down—you could have gotten yourself killed."

"I could see he didn't know what he was doing with the gun," Jasmine said. Then she frowned. "How did you know that he wasn't going to kill anyone?"

"The agent watching him, Special Agent Daubs, Miami Criminal Division. He'd overheard Connor and

Kari talking. And he watched them. Said he was a pretty good judge of men, and I guess he was."

"I'm glad," Jasmine said softly.

"So now, once again, we wait. Tomorrow, I'll spend some time out with Kozak. And you and Jorge and others will be on the beach, waiting, ready to move if anything does break—play your part. But don't go anywhere near the club."

"I still have my uniform."

"If they call you, let me know right away. And for now—"

"Tonight?" she asked seriously.

"Sleep would be on the agenda."

"Ah, yes, sleep."

"Perhaps some rigorous exercise to speed the process," he suggested.

"We are still playing roles," she murmured.

"Jorge did say we were method actors."

"We can always work on method," she whispered.

Jacob wondered vaguely what it was about a special woman, that her slightest whisper, the nuance in her words, her lightest touch, could awaken everything in a man. There was no one in the world anything like her, he thought.

She stood, reaching for his hand. He rose, smiling. In the bedroom, they both saw to their weapons first. They barely touched, shedding their clothing in a hurry.

He went down on the bed, patting the mattress, and for a moment, she stood, sleek and stunning as a silhouette in the pale light from the hallway. She moved with grace, coming to him, and then she was next to him, in his arms, and if anything, they were more frantic that night to touch and to tease and to taste one another. To make love.

Later, when they should have been drifting off to sleep, she rose up on an elbow, looking at him, empathy in the ever-brilliant sheen of her eyes. "Forgive me, but..."

He knew what she wanted to know. So, he told her about growing up in Miami at first and moving to New York. Falling in love with Sabrina in high school, college, the service...

"Going off to the Middle East," he said. "She was always so worried about me. And she was vibrant. Full of life. We were happy. I'd done my service and I knew I wanted to head into the FBI Academy. I was certain I'd make it. We never thought... Well, she was diagnosed, and three months later, she was gone."

"I am so, so sorry."

"It was over ten years ago now," he told her, rolling to better see her face, stroke her cheek. "But you... hmm. Can't figure how you manage to be unattached. Of course, Jorge told me that you do have a tendency to shut a guy down before he can ask you out."

"Jorge talks way too much."

He laughed softly and pulled her into his arms. "That's all right," he told her. "I'm not an easy man to shut down."

She grinned, indicating their positions. "I didn't try very hard to shut you down."

He laughed and she was in his arms again.

SHE WAS NO good at waiting. She would never make it full time in undercover work.

Jasmine actually tried to sleep after Jacob left. His phone had rung far too early, letting him know that a car was coming to take him to the safe house where Kozak was being guarded. But sleep was impossible. She made coffee, washed and dried her hair and was tempted to try to do her own nails, since she had a rare moment of downtime. She reminded herself how incredibly happy she was—how grateful.

Mary was fine, alive and well. Kari was fine, too. They'd met a man who was trying to prevent future wrongs.

Still, someone within the gang was truly cold-blooded. At least eight people were dead because of the person within who considered murder to be a stepping-stone to criminal power.

If only Jacob were there to bounce her theories off of. They worked well together. Even when they were just playing roles. But the roles had become so much more. She'd found someone who seemed to really care about her, who could be with her, for all that she was, for what she did.

These roles would come to an end. That didn't mean they had to stop seeing each other, but her life, her work, was here. And his life and work were in New York.

It was foolish to think about the future. In the middle of this, she couldn't even be certain that either of them had a future. She had faith in herself and faith in him and all their colleagues—but no one entered into law enforcement without recognizing the dangers.

Worrying about the future was not helping her keep from crawling up the walls.

She couldn't call a friend and go out. She was still undercover. And Jacob had told her not to go near the club.

She was on her third cup of coffee when she realized that she could call Jorge. She was so antsy she'd probably annoy him, but Jorge never seemed to mind. As the thought occurred to her, she felt her phone ring.

"Jorge!"

"Hey, gorgeous, whatcha doing?"

"I was about to call you. I'm waiting. Doing what I was told to do. Climbing the walls. Being such a desperate cop I'm ready to watch a marathon of *Desperate Housewives* with you."

"Well, I have a reprieve for you. I'm on my way. All sanctioned. Come out to the corner. I'll be by for you."

"Perfect. Jeans okay?"

"Jeans and sneakers. Great. See you in five minutes."

"This is cleared with Captain Lorenzo—and the FBI?"

"Yeah, we're supposed to be heading to a music venue controlled by the gang. Top groups. Acting like normal people. Waiting like the rest of the folks around us, finding out if Kozak is going to make it. Gauging their reactions."

"Okay!" Jasmine rang off and shoved her phone into her cross-body handbag. She hurried out, carefully locking her apartment, all but running by the bathers out by the pool, aware of the bright sun and the waving palms.

A car pulled over to the curb; it wasn't a car she knew, but an impressive SUV. FBI issue for work down here?

Jorge rolled down the passenger-side window. "Hop in!" he said cheerfully.

"Where did you get the car?" she asked.

"City of Miami Beach," he said. He was smiling broadly, but she frowned. Something about him didn't seem quite right.

But while she and Jorge might never have discussed their personal lives, they were solid working partners. They always had one another's back. He would die for her...

It wasn't until she was next to the car that she realized Jorge wasn't alone in the car.

There was a man in the back, but Jasmine's focus went to the fact that he had the business edge of a serious knife against the throat of a woman he'd shoved down in the seat. The young woman was trying desperately hard not to snuffle or cry out, with that blade so close to her artery.

It was Helen Lee, the sweet and lovely young woman with whom she and Kari had shared the runway.

Helen was absolutely terrified.

The man with the knife smiled. She was not entirely surprised to see who it was.

"Welcome, Jasmine. Now, Jorge, drive. And no tricks, no running us off the road. You wouldn't want my hand to slip. You wouldn't want to see this blade slice right through Helen's throat, would you? Jorge—

drive. Now. Jasmine, smile. Please. It will keep my hand so much steadier."

Jasmine's gun was in her purse, but she couldn't reach for it then. So was her phone. She believed that the man would slit Helen's throat.

As she slid into the car, she kept her bag clutched tightly in her hands.

FROM THE OUTSIDE, it looked like any other house. It sat off 122nd Avenue and Southwest Eighth Street—the Tamiami Trail there and farther west—or Calle Ocho when you headed way back east toward downtown Miami.

Built in the 1970s, it was a ranch-style home like many of the others surrounding them. It had a large lot, but so did several other houses in the area. This house, however, had a little gazebo out front, covered with vines—a fine place for an agent to keep guard—and a large garage and a few storage sheds out back.

The living room was like any other living room. It had a sofa and some plush chairs and a stereo system and a large-screen TV. The windows were all barred—but then, so were many of the other houses in the area, a deterrent to would-be burglars.

Just like so many other houses, there were signs on the fence that warned Beware of Dogs, and the dogs were the kind for which people should be wary. Signs also warned about the house being protected by a local security company, one used by many of the other residents of the area.

There was a kitchen, usually well stocked. There was a well-appointed gym, but then again, other people had home gyms. A dining room sat between the living room and the kitchen. The house boasted four bedrooms.

One of those bedrooms had no bed.

It had a table and chairs, and it was where guests were often required to engage in conversation with those who had brought them here.

Kozak sat in one chair. Jacob sat in another. Also at the table was Dean Jenkins—the man Josef Smirnoff had first approached in fear for his life.

One other man had joined them, Carl Merrill, a prosecutor from the United States Office of the Attorney General.

"As I told Jacob—before I realized how determined my would-be murderer was—I have never killed anyone," Kozak said.

"Your actions have resulted in the deaths of many," Merrill said.

"I can give you so much," Kozak told him. "But I must have a deal. I must."

"What is that you think you can give me? We've got you, head of an organized crime gang, and enough evidence of your activities to prosecute," Merrill asked.

"Names. I can give you the names of men who look squeaky-clean, who are working with the cartels out of South America. There are bigger fish than me in Miami."

"Victor," Jacob said, "you can't even give us the name of the man who wants you dead, who wants to take over the Deco Gang. Let's see—he's been working for you. And we know he forced a lethal dose of cocaine into a young woman who was a model for you. And he's likely responsible for at least three corpses in oil drums in Broward County and three headless corpses in the Everglades."

Kozak spun on him. "I don't kill. And I don't order executions!" he said angrily. "If I knew, could a murderer have come so close, would I have been about to drink poison?"

"Deals have yet to be made, Victor. We need help now. Who locked the door to the balcony on the day that Josef Smirnoff was killed?" Jacob asked.

"Josef." Kozak sighed. "I can't go to a federal prison...not in the general population. We had reputations. There are too many men who might think me guilty of crimes I did not commit. A man in my position does not deny violent acts to others of his kind. A reputation is everything. I let mine grow as it would."

Jenkins leaned forward. "Victor, let's start here. Did you know that Smirnoff contacted me?"

"No, I did not."

"Had he been acting nervous in any way?"

Kozak appeared to think about that and slowly shook his head. His voice was husky when he spoke. "If he was afraid, he would not have shown it anyway."

"Do you believe he suspected you?" Jacob asked.

"If so, he shouldn't have."

"Was he sleeping with Natasha—were they a real couple?"

Kozak hesitated on that one. "Yes, she was...strong. And good."

"So, you inherited Natasha along with the leadership," Jacob said. "She had the key to the balcony yesterday."

"There is only one key. She had it because I would not be present."

"Do you think it is Natasha who might be trying to kill you? Would she be hard enough to have one of her girls killed—and to order the execution of those men?"

Kozak smiled. "Natasha, she is a woman. But in business...this business? Natasha serves," he said softly.

Jacob had to wonder at that.

But Kozak was convinced of the truth of his words. He shook his head. "I don't know, I really don't know. As they say, keep your friends close, but your enemies closer. I have kept my people close. I don't know how they can be hiring these killers, desperate people."

There was a knock at the door. The agent who was the house's "owner" stepped in. "Special Agent Wolff, a word."

"Now?"

"Yes, sir. Now."

Jacob politely excused himself. Outside the room, he realized the agent was anxious.

"It's a call from Captain Lorenzo, sir, MDPD. Our men on the beach were following a car out of the club, but they lost them on the causeway. I—"

He stopped talking and handed Jacob the phone.

The man on the line quickly, tersely, identified himself as Captain Mac Lorenzo.

"I don't know how she did it, but Jasmine managed to contact this number and leave her phone on. She's in a car—they're headed west somewhere. Jorge is driving, Jasmine is in the front. There's a man in back, and from what I can hear, he's taking them somewhere. It sounds as if they're headed for an execution. We've got men on it, but they keep losing them. I've already asked the Feds to hop on it as quickly as possible, but you were close to that group. I'm hoping you might know where they're being taken."

Jacob froze for a split second; he felt as if the life had been stripped out of him.

"I need the exact location those headless bodies were found," Jacob said. "Speak fast, I'm already moving. And keep the others back. If the killer feels cornered, he'll kill whoever he has close out of spite. Get me backup, but keep the backup back."

Lorenzo kept talking. Before he finished another sentence, Jacob was in a car and heading west down the Tamiami Trail.

"Not so slow that the police notice us. There's no need to risk another of the city's finest."

Hearing the voice of the man in the back, Jorge cast a quick glance toward Jasmine. His eyes were filled with agony. She knew how he felt.

A quick look in back assured her there was already a fine line of blood creating a jagged necklace along Helen Lee's throat.

Jasmine and Jorge would both fight, play for time, for the life of another, as long as they were both still breathing.

There was no way to let him know she'd gotten her

hand into her purse, and that she was pretty sure she'd hit the number one; a priority call that would hit the phone Lorenzo had just for communication with her.

But would Lorenzo know where they were going? How could he know when she didn't know?

West. They were headed west. Jorge was driving as slowly as he could reasonably manage without drawing the man's ire or suspicion. He was in no rush to bring them to their destination. They were off the beach now, across the causeway on a long, long drive that seemed to be taking them out to the Everglades.

It was a land a few of the hardiest knew well, where airboat rides could be found, where the Miccosukee kept a restaurant and reservation lands, where visitors could find out about their lives and their pasts.

A place where, no matter how many hearty souls worked and even lived, there were acres upon acres that was nothing but wetland, part of the great "river of grass," filled with water moccasins and alligators, even pythons and boas.

"To the Everglades," she said aloud, as they whipped past the Miccosukee casino.

She turned around and stared at Ivan Petrov.

"You want to kill Jorge and me. Why?"

He eyed her coldly and then smiled. "I don't believe that Kozak is dead. He's the one who brought Marensky in. You did something with his drink. Marensky called the ambulance, and now...now they do not report that Kozak is dead."

"Whatever your argument with me, why Helen?" she asked.

His smiled deepened. "She happened to be there," he said.

Ivan Petrov. They should have figured; they had looked at Kozak, at Natasha, at the goons... They would have gotten to Ivan. He was never off the list.

"I need some guarantee you're going to keep Helen alive," Jasmine said. "Then Jorge and I will do as you ask."

"You are with the government," Petrov said.

"I swear to you, I am not an FBI agent. Neither is Jorge."

"Then you are trying to take the lead, playing up to Kozak. Well, they have cold feet. The enterprise will never be what it should be under Kozak. He is a weakling—he doesn't know how to remove what festers among us. Drive, Jorge. And turn around, Miss Jasmine."

The casino was behind them. Minutes were counting down. They were coming up to Shark Valley when Petrov told Jorge to slow the car down.

He couldn't be going to Shark Valley! There were trails and bike paths, tourists and rangers all about. Unless he meant to kill anyone in his way.

They didn't turn into Shark Valley. They passed the entrance, and the Miccosukee restaurant to the right on the road.

Then suddenly, Kozak said, "Here."

Here? She knew of no road here...

"Now!" Petrov commanded.

Helen let out a scream as the knife pierced her flesh. Jorge turned.

JACOB WAS MET by Mickey Cypress of the Miccosukee Police. The man was in his early forties, lean, bronze and no-nonsense. He'd been waiting for Jacob right outside the entrance to Shark Valley.

"You don't want to go exactly where the bodies were found," he told Jacob. "The Everglades is literally a river, and the bodies were carried until they were snagged by the mangrove roots." He had a map out on his phone and he pointed to a spot that seemed to be just beyond a canal where they stood.

Jacob glanced at the map. Suddenly, two giant male alligators went into some kind of a battle in the canal.

"Leave them alone, completely alone," Cypress told him. "There's a marshy trail we can take through here, and a small hammock. That's where I think we'll find their killing grounds. There was no road there before, but some fairly solid ground. I think they created their own way."

Cars drove up next to them. Men in suits got out—the backup.

Cypress looked at him. They were probably good agents; they just didn't look ready for a trek into the water and marshy land.

"Special Agent Wolff!" one of them called.

Jacob looked at Cypress.

"I'm with you," Cypress said. "Um, if you're trying for stealth…"

Jacob nodded and headed back to the agent calling to him. He asked him to hold their position and keep a line of contact open. He walked back to Cypress.

The local cop told him, "Trust me, I know how to

get there. I was the first on call when the bodies were found. I've been on this."

"I trust you," Jacob assured him. "We need to hurry. I got after them right away, but they still had a head start."

"Then we move."

Cypress started over a small land bridge, just feet from the male alligators defending their turf. Water came cascading over them from a massive flip of a tail.

They kept walking.

IVAN PETROV HAD his knife—and a gun on his belt. He kept the knife at Helen's throat.

Jasmine clung to her purse.

"Drop it!" Petrov commanded. His knife moved ever so slightly.

Helen gulped out a cry. Tears were streaming down her face—silent tears. She tried not to sob and stared at Jasmine—any movement would cause a great chafe of the knife against her throat. Her eyes were both imploring and hopeless.

"Go!" Petrov commanded. Jorge walked ahead; Jasmine behind him. He sheathed the knife and drew his gun.

"I don't understand, Ivan. Who were the people in the oil drums?" Jasmine asked.

"Well, I will tell you," Petrov said. "The first, his name was Terry Meyers. He thought he should manage the club—and the women. That was long ago, when Smirnoff had barely begun to settle into South Florida. Smirnoff was, in fact, surprised when Meyers failed to arrive for a meeting. The second, well, he failed to show with a payment. He made me look bad. You can't deal with people who don't deliver on goods or who don't make their payments. It's bad for business if you don't follow through. Same deal for the third loser."

"The three who weren't in the drums," she said. "They were the ones who killed Josef."

"Yes, actually, they were very good. I was sorry to see them go. But you see, they couldn't live. If they had been apprehended, well… I did hire them personally."

"You admired them so much, you beheaded them," Jasmine murmured.

Jorge glanced back at her; she was doing the right thing, keeping him talking. There were two of them. They could survive this. They had to get Helen in a safe position, and then they could rush Petrov—he couldn't shoot them both at the same time.

But they had to get Helen away from him first.

Jorge suddenly stopped, letting out a shout.

"Move!" Petrov commanded.

"There's a gator ahead in the path," Jorge said, falling back by Jasmine.

"That's fine," Petrov said, dragging Helen around and waving his gun at the small gator on the trail. "We're almost there." He fired the gun toward the gator. The creature moved off into the surrounding bracken.

There was some kind of a structure there, a broken-down shack, a remnant, Jasmine thought, from the time when various Florida hunters had come out and kept little camps.

It was now or never—Petrov had just fired the gun,

he was looking away, he was holding Helen, but the gun wasn't directly at her throat.

Jasmine didn't let out a sound; she made a silent leap for the man.

She bore him down to the ground. Helen slipped free, screaming hysterically. She began to run back in the direction from which they had come, screaming all the while.

Petrov's gun hand was flailing; in a second, the barrel would be aiming at Jasmine's face.

But Jorge was there, stomping on the man's wrist, kicking at the gun. It went flying into a gator hole, filled high with water.

But Petrov wasn't going down easily. He caught Jasmine and flipped her down to the muddy earth.

Jorge kicked his head.

Petrov had the knife on his belt now; Jasmine went for it. Seizing it from Petrov, she sliced his hand. He cried out as blood gushed.

And then, a gunshot fired. They all went still.

The knife still tightly in her grip, Jasmine turned to the sound.

Standing casually now before the rotting wood of the old shack was Natasha. She shook her head.

"Men. They are worthless, eh? They continually think they are in charge, and they have no idea. Ivan! A silly girl and these two. You have a gun, you have a knife, and they best you. What would you have done without me, Ivan?"

She shook her head again at Ivan, but then smiled at Jasmine. "Yes, you are one who knows how to manipulate a man, eh? It's the only way, until you have seized the position of real power. And then they will bow down before you, and they will become your toys, and you will command them. It's a pity you must die. It will be hard for me… Oh, maybe not so hard, because now Ivan and I will have to crawl through this wretched swamp looking for that silly Helen. If she doesn't kill herself first. Maybe it will not be so hard. I will kill your friend first, so you can watch him die, and he will not have to watch you die? How is that?"

"I should have known you were the one with ice-cold blood running in your veins—right from the beginning," Jasmine said.

Natasha shrugged. "Me? I am not so much the killer. I like others to do the killing."

"And then you kill the killers."

Natasha smiled. "Ivan killed the killers. I simply cut off their hands and their heads…and fed them to the swamp. Enough talk." She took aim.

But Natasha couldn't have known what hit her.

He came from behind. His arm came down on hers and Natasha screamed with shock and pain as she lost her grip on the gun, as she was tackled to the ground.

Jasmine stared.

Jacob was there. Impossibly, Jacob was there. He'd slipped around silently from behind the hut, and he was now reading Natasha her rights and handcuffing her, heedless of the fact that he was on her back and pressing her face into the mud.

He looked at Jasmine, his recitation breaking. He nodded toward Petrov, who was trying to turn and escape.

Jasmine turned to Petrov, but another man—never before sensed nor seen—went sliding past her.

"Not to worry. I've got that one."

Jacob yanked Natasha to her feet. He spoke into his phone. Jasmine and Jorge were still just standing there, incredulous to be alive, when men—a little ridiculously dressed in fine blue suits and leather loafers—came running through the brush.

"Got her, sir," one of them said to Jacob, taking Natasha. He was young, younger than Jasmine. A brand-new agent, she thought, but ready to do whatever was asked of him, including running through a swampy, mucky river in his office attire.

He was gone; Natasha was dragged away. And then they heard shouts; Ivan had been apprehended, as well.

"Helen—Helen Lee is running through the swamp," Jasmine called out, her voice echoing through the mangroves and pines.

One of the agents came back. "No, ma'am, we've got her. She's fine. A little scratched up and still hysterical, but…we've got her. She's going to be okay."

"Hey, I'm coming with you," Jorge said. "She knows me. I'll get her calmed down."

And then, for a moment, Jasmine and Jacob were standing there alone. A large white crane swooped in and settled down near them, seeing a fish in the shallow gator holes that surrounded them on the small hammock.

Slowly, Jasmine smiled. "Your timing is impeccable."

He let out a long soft sigh, and then he grinned. "So I've been told."

She raced across the mud and the muck that separated them and threw herself into his arms. And they indulged in one long kiss, both shaking.

"You are kick-ass," he told her.

"But not even a kick-ass can work alone," she whispered. "You saved our lives."

"Only because you were doing a good enough job saving your own life," he assured her. "Lord, help me, this may be ridiculous, but I think I love you."

"This may be more ridiculous," she said.

"What?"

"I know I love you!" she told him.

"Special Agent Wolff? Detective?" They were being summoned.

Hand in hand, they started back along the path. "Paperwork," Jacob murmured.

"And then?" she asked.

He wiped a spot of mud off her face. "Showers," he said. "Definitely showers."

She smiled and he paused just one more minute, turning her to him.

"And then," he said, blue eyes dazzling down on her, "then figuring out our lives. If that's all right with you, of course."

She rose on her toes and lightly kissed his lips.

She could have done much, much more, but others were waiting—and there were some very large predators near them. The human ones might be down, but while she wasn't afraid of the creatures here, she wasn't stupid enough to get in their way either.

She broke the kiss and looked into his clear eyes. "It's all right with me."

Epilogue

The woman hurrying toward him along the long stone path over the castle's moat was truly one of the most stunning creatures Jacob Wolff had ever seen. His initial opinion of Jasmine had never changed.

Her skin was pure bronze, as sleek and as dazzling as the deepest sunray. When she smiled at him, he could see that her eyes were light. Green, he knew, an emerald green, and a sharp contrast to her skin. She had amazing hair, long and so shimmering that it was as close to pure black as it was possible to be; so dark it almost had a glint of violet. She was long-legged, lean and yet exquisitely shaped, even in jeans, sweater, boots and a parka.

She didn't pause when she met him. She threw her arms around him and leaped up so he had to catch her, and laughed as he spun with her in the rising sunlight that did little to dispel the chill of the damp day. No one saw them.

Donald McPherson Connor's "estate" had proved to be a castle. Small, admittedly, but *a bit of an historic home*, as Donald called it, and far out in the countryside of northern England.

"Best vacation ever!" she told him, sliding down to stand.

He looked behind her. They were no longer alone.

He'd headed out for a walk on the grounds right after morning coffee; Jasmine had stayed behind to wait for Mary and Jorge—the two had been in a lengthy discussion of just how cold it might get during the day, and throwing her hands up, Jasmine had indicated he should go ahead.

His hike had been serene. The countryside seemed to stretch endlessly, beautiful rolling land with horses and sheep and cattle.

He'd had vacation time built up—you couldn't just hop off to an amusement park or the mountains or the French Riviera in the middle of work when you were deep in an undercover operation. He felt this time off was well deserved, for himself and for Jasmine. It had been impossible for them to turn down Donald Connor's suggestion that they come to visit Mary.

They had a suite in the tiny castle. No windows facing a beach, but instead an arrow slit that looked out over a stretch of land that was misty and green. They had long nights together and days with amazing friends.

Jorge and Mary caught up with them. "Off to the theater, if you're sure you don't mind the walk," she said.

Mary was as gentle and sweet a woman as Jasmine had said, wide-eyed and kind, with blond hair as long as Jasmine's raven tresses. Mary had cried when she'd come to the airport to meet them; she'd been so sorry to have frightened Jasmine, to have put her in danger. But Donald had explained that he was just an ordinary citizen—he'd needed Mary to not say a word to anyone until she was safely out of the clutches of the Deco Gang. She'd been lucky to have an up-to-date passport.

Mary told them that Natasha had instructed her they had more escort work, and the intended client was a man she had seen come and go with different suitcases. She had suspected the man was part of their drug operation. And by then she knew that the girls weren't really models, that the so-called models were being prostituted, and that she just might not be able to do all of the things expected of her. And that if they suspected that she knew too much—or anything at all—she just might wind up dead.

Jasmine explained to her over and over again that it was all right—they'd put a stop to it all, and possibly saved many more lives.

Natasha had gone through people quickly. In her mind, so it seemed, people were as disposable as silverware or linens that were no longer needed.

There was, of course, a note of sadness to it all. They could do nothing for Donald's daughter; she was gone. But while he couldn't be happy, the man was grateful and satisfied. Her killers would find justice.

"A walk is great," Jacob assured her.

"Okay, so maybe these ugly shoes are good," Jorge said, slipping an arm around Mary's shoulders. The two of them moved slightly ahead. Mary began telling Jorge about the history of the area and how old the theater they were about to attend was.

Jasmine looked up at Jacob and smiled. "It's a children's play we're seeing, you know."

"Mary wrote it—I can't wait to see it. Donald will join us there?"

"Exactly," Jasmine said.

Mary suddenly stopped. She looked back, grinning. "Hey, I was talking to Donald this morning, earlier. He thinks you guys should have your wedding here."

Jasmine stopped dead. "Mary, we're visitors here. And we haven't—" she looked at Jacob, a flush rising to her cheeks "—we haven't even…"

Talked about marriage.

They had talked about everything else. A long-distance relationship seemed like half measures. But then, what to do? Jasmine loved the people with whom she worked, and she loved Miami. Jacob understood. They were looking into a transfer for him to the Miami office.

It had only been a few weeks since they'd survived the murder attempt in the Everglades; they'd been mulling over all possibilities in the meantime. And of course, finishing the endless paperwork, the United States Attorney General, the police, evidence, witnesses and everything else that went with the end of such a complicated case.

Kozak was going into witness protection; both Ivan and Natasha would be prosecuted for the murders they had committed. Victor Kozak had given the authorities all they needed to apprehend a number of the drug smugglers in Miami Beach, and information regarding them that might lead to solving many of the cold cases on file across Greater Miami.

Antonovich, Garibaldi and Suarez had worked for Kozak, and though they had faced stiff interrogations, they hadn't actually been proved guilty of any crimes. Jacob hoped that the three would find better employment.

Petrov still had a problem believing he was going down—he'd tried to throw everything on Natasha, but in turn, Natasha had tried to throw everything on him.

The man had been a fool, Jacob had told Jasmine, when they had been alone and curled together one night. He'd underestimated the power of a woman. And, smiling, he'd assured her, "That's something I never would do."

Now, Jacob grabbed her hand, forcing her to look at him. "I don't know—the wedding here. What do you think?"

"I…" Jasmine looked at him.

Jorge let out a sound of frustration. "Oh, come on! You know there's going to be a wedding. Seriously, who else could either of you live with forever and ever, huh?"

He was right. You were very, very lucky in life when you found that one person who complemented you in every way.

Jacob looked into her eyes, so strong, so gentle, so giving… Dazzling.

He figured he could answer for both of them. "I don't really care where we get married. As long as we do. And I do need to get you all to New York. I have a friend—I've worked with him and the love of his life, and her family owns an Irish pub on Broadway. Her brother is also an actor and can score all kinds of theater tickets, Mary."

the SUV, walked into the sparsely wooded landscape and disappeared.

"I have a bad feeling about this," Jake said. "Let's move."

Percy "Pitbull" Taylor leaned across the cab of the SUV and flung open the passenger door. "Get in."

Jake shook his head, his gaze scanning the area and coming back to the village where Ashiri had disappeared. He gripped his rifle in his fists. "I'll walk alongside until we're past the village. I don't trust Ashiri or Dubaku at this point." Then he spoke into his mic. "Diesel, keep a safe distance between the vehicles."

"Wilco." Dalton "Diesel" Landon waited until Pitbull pulled several vehicle lengths ahead.

Graham "Buck" Buckner climbed out of Diesel's vehicle and raised his M4A1 rifle at the ready.

Harm, already on the other side of Pitbull's vehicle, moved forward as the SUV inched along at a slow, steady pace.

Buck and Trace "T-Mac" McGuire brought up the rear of Diesel's SUV. Every SEAL on the ground had an M4A1 carbine rifle with the Special Operations Peculiar Modification (SOPMOD) upgrade. Pitbull and Diesel had their weapons in the SUVs, within easy reach.

At that moment, Jake wished he had an HK MP5 submachine gun with several fully loaded clips. That prickly feeling was getting worse by the minute. Jake didn't see the normal congregation of women and children outside the huts. In fact, since they'd arrived outside the village, those people who had been hanging around had all disappeared.

"Let's move a little faster," Jake urged. "The village appears to be a ghost town."

"Something's up," Harm agreed.

"I thought this was supposed to be a routine fact-finding mission," T-Mac said.

"'Don't engage,' they said." Buck mimicked the intel officer who'd briefed them in Djibouti. "Well, what if they engage us first?"

"That's when all bets are off." Jake's hold tightened on his rifle.

The lead vehicle had passed the village and was moving along the dirt road leading to the next village when an explosion ripped through the air.

"What the hell was that?" Diesel asked.

"We've got incoming!" Harm yelled. "Someone's got an RPG and they're targeting our vehicles."

Another rocket hit the ground fifty yards from where Jake stood. He dropped to a squat and waited for the dust to clear.

When it did, he counted half a dozen men in black garb and turbans rushing toward him, firing AK-47s.

"They fired first," Jake said, returning fire. "Six Tangos incoming from the west." He took out two and kept firing.

"I count five from the east," Harm said from the other side of the SUV. Sounds of gunfire filled the air.

"Got a truckload of them coming straight at us on the road," Pitbull said.

"I count at least half a dozen comin' at us from the rear," T-Mac reported.

"We're surrounded," Buck said. "Use the SUVs for cover."

The men rolled under the SUVs and fired from beneath.

"Guys, get out from under the lead vehicle!" Pitbull yelled. "They're going to ram us!"

Jake rolled out from under and kept rolling, staying as low to the ground as he could, firing every time he came back to the prone position. He slipped into a slight depression in the hard-packed dirt and fired at the black-garbed men coming at him.

A loud bang sounded along with the screech of metal slamming into metal.

Giving only the fleetest of glances, Jake's heart plummeted. The lead SUV had been knocked several feet back from where it had been standing. If Harm hadn't made it out in time, he would have been crushed by the ramming enemy truck.

"Pitbull?" Jake held his breath, awaiting his friend's response.

"I'm good," Pitbull said. "Shaken, not stirred. I shot the truck driver before he hit."

"Good. Everyone else," Jake said, "sound off."

In quick succession, the other four men reported in.

"Harm."

"T-Mac."

"Buck."

"Diesel."

A man leaped up from the ground and ran toward Jake.

The navy SEAL fired, cutting him down, only to have another man take his place and rush his position. He pulled the trigger. At the last minute, the attacker swerved right. The bullet nicked him, but didn't slow him down.

Jake pulled the trigger again, only nothing happened. He pushed the release button, and the magazine dropped at the same time as he reached for another. Slamming the full magazine into the weapon, Jake fired point-blank as the man flung himself at Jake.

The bullet sailed right through the man's chest, and he fell on top of Jake.

For a moment, Jake was crushed by the man's weight. He couldn't move and couldn't free his hands to fire his weapon.

Gunfire blasted all around. Dust choked the air and made locating the enemy difficult at best.

Jake pushed aside the dead man and glanced around.

"They fell back," Buck said. "But they're regrouping."

"Get in the rear SUV and get the hell out of here," Jake said. "I'll cover."

Buck and T-Mac jumped into the rear SUV. Diesel revved the engine and raced up to the destroyed one.

The doors were flung open. "Get in," Buck said.

Harm ran alongside the vehicle, refusing to get inside. Pitbull pulled himself into the front passenger seat.

The enemy soldiers raced to follow them.

Jake laid down suppressive fire, emptying a thirty-round magazine in seconds.

"We're not leaving without you!" Harm yelled.

Jake shook his head and kept firing. "Get in the damned vehicle. I'll remain on the ground and cover."

Harm complied and the SUV moved forward, using the crashed SUV for cover.

Jake popped out the expended magazine and slammed in one of the last two he had.

The enemy soldiers either hit the ground when they caught a bullet, or dived low to avoid getting hit. Either way, Jake's gunfire slowed their movement. But not for long. "Go!" he yelled, lurched to his feet and backed up to the enemy truck without letting up his suppressive fire against the oncoming threat. "You have to leave now. It's the only way any of us are getting out of this alive."

Jake flung open the door of the truck, dragged the dead driver out and climbed behind the steering wheel. He hung his rifle out the window and fired with his left hand. "I'll head for the hills, head south, get to safety and come back when you have sufficient backup." He started the engine and attempted to reverse. The front grill of the truck hung on the grill of the damaged SUV.

"I don't like it," Diesel said into Jake's earpiece.

"You don't have to," Jake said. "Just go before I run out of bullets."

Diesel pulled away in the SUV.

Jake fired again, laying down a barrage of bullets at the men advancing on his position. He ducked low as bullets hit the windshield and pinged off the metal frame of the truck. He shifted into Drive, hit the accelerator and slammed the SUV. Then he shoved the shift into Reverse and gunned the engine. The SUV dragged along with him for several feet until the front grill broke free.

Jake backed up fast and considered racing after the other SUV. But, already, another truck had appeared from the direction of the village. If he didn't take out the oncoming vehicle, the rest of his team would gain little lead time on the enemy.

Shifting into Drive, Jake revved the engine and shifted his foot off the brake. The truck shot forward, plowing through the line of attackers, knocking some down and scattering the rest.

Driving head-on toward the truck, Jake held true, daring the other driver to back down first but guessing he wouldn't.

At the last moment, Jake grabbed his rifle, flung open the door and threw himself out of the truck. He hit the ground hard, tucked and somersaulted, his weapon pressed close to his chest.

The truck he'd been driving plowed into the other with the clash of metal on metal. Both vehicles shook and then settled, smoke and steam rising from the engines.

Jake didn't wait around to see what the remaining jihadist would do. He jerked a smoke grenade from his vest, pulled the ring, tossed it behind him and then ran toward the only cover he had—the short, squat mud-and-stick huts of the village clustered against a bluff. He figured the enemy wouldn't start looking for him there.

He prayed he was right. From the intel briefing they'd received, the ISIS faction was alive and well in the Tillabéri region of southwestern Niger and was known for the extreme torture tactics they used against their foes. He refused to be one of their victims. He'd die fighting rather than be captured. Surrender wasn't an option.

REVEREND TOWNSEND BURST through the door of the makeshift schoolhouse, interrupting Alex's reading lesson. "Alex, get the children out of the building. Now!"

Alexandria Parker's heart leaped into her throat. "Why? What's wrong?"

The reverend's wrinkled face was tense, his hands shaking as he waved children toward the door. "Kamathi just came through the village and told everyone to get out. If I hadn't been there, I wouldn't have known."

Alex closed her reading book. "Why do we have to leave?"

"Al-Waseka is coming."

Fear rippled through Alex. One of the men in the village had been captured by al-Waseka, the most notorious Islamic State leader in all of Niger. He had been beaten, whipped and burned in many places on his body. The only reason he'd survived was because they'd thrown his body off the back of a truck, presuming he was dead. He'd crawled under a bush and waited until his captors had left the area. Then he'd used what little energy he had remaining to wait near the road for the next friendly vehicle to pass. Fortunately, it had been the good reverend's.

In his seventies, Reverend Townsend got around well for his age. He worked hard and never complained. The villagers loved him and treated the white-haired old man and his wife like family.

Standing in Alex's makeshift schoolroom, he appeared to have aged ten years. "By the time I left the village, every man, woman and child had gone. They ran into the hills. We have to get these children out of the orphanage as quickly as possible. Take them into the hills."

Alex waved to her assistant, Fariji, the tall young man who'd been more than happy to help her with her lessons and, in the process, was learning to read himself. "Help me get the children out."

"Yes, Miss Alex." He had the older kids hold hands with the younger ones and led them out the door.

Alex herded the rest of the children toward the door. "Leave your books," she said. "Older children, help the younger ones."

The children bottlenecked at the door, where the reverend hurried them through. Once they were all outside, he faced the children. "Follow Miss Alex and Fariji," he said. "Stay with them."

Alex turned to the reverend. "Where do I go in the hills?"

"Anywhere, just hide. Some of the older children play in the hills. Let them lead you." He turned to stare into the distance, where the road led into the village.

Alex didn't like that the reverend wasn't coming with them. "What about you and Mrs. Townsend?"

"Martha refused to leave the sick baby." He looked back at her. "Go. We are in God's hands."

Maybe so, but the ISIS terrorists didn't believe in the reverend's God. They believed in killing all foreigners and many of their own people in their efforts to control the entire region. "Reverend, let me help you bring Martha out of the village."

He shook his head. "She won't abandon the mother and child she has been helping for the past few days. They can't be moved."

"Have you considered the fact that you and your wife staying with them might give the terrorists more reason to not only kill you and your wife, but also the woman and her baby?"

He nodded and repeated, "We are in God's hands." He nodded at the children running toward the hills. "Go with them. They need someone to ensure their survival."

Torn between saving the children and saving her mentor, father figure and friend, Alex hesitated.

"You can't help everyone," the reverend said. "Martha and I have lived long, productive lives. No regrets. You and the children have not." He waved her toward the children. "Go. Live."

Alex hugged the reverend. "I'll go, but once the children are safe, I'm coming back for you and Martha."

He patted her back. "Only if it's safe."

An explosion rocked the ground and was followed by the sound of gunfire.

Her pulse hammering in her veins, Alex hurried after Fariji and the children running through the village streets toward the hills.

She counted heads, satisfied she had all of her little charges. Some of them clustered around her, while others ran ahead. One little girl tripped and fell.

Alex scooped her up and set her on her feet, barely slowing. She clutched the child's hand and kept moving.

More gunfire sounded behind her. She didn't look back. She had one goal: to get the children to safety. Only then would she think about what was going on in the village.

At the far end of the community, they neared the base of the bluffs rising high over their heads.

A shiver of fear rippled through Alex. She had never hiked in the hills because she was afraid she wouldn't find her way back out. Now she was purposely heading into unknown territory—with children. For a moment, she hesitated.

Then another explosion shook the earth beneath her feet. She glanced over her shoulder. A plume of dusty fire and smoke rose up into the air near the road leading into the village.

She didn't need any more motivation. Bullets were bad; bombs were even worse. "Hurry!" she yelled.

The youngest children had slowed, their little legs tired from running through the village.

Alex despaired. How could she get all of them up the steep slopes? And if they did make it, where would she hide them?

She'd heard from some of the elders that there were caves in the hills. In the past, when their village had been invaded, the people had fled to the hills and hidden in the caves until the attackers moved on.

Alex lifted one of the smallest girls and settled her on her back. She started up the hill, holding the hand of a little boy, small for his seven years. She tried not to think about what was happening down in the village.

If the threat was the ISIS faction, the reverend and his wife were in grave danger. Alex's heart squeezed tightly in her chest. The elderly couple were incredibly kind and selfless. They didn't deserve to be tortured or killed.

Ahead, Alex caught glimpses of other villagers, climbing the rugged path upward. She felt better knowing they were heading in the right direction. Hopefully, the men terrorizing the village wouldn't take the time or make the effort to climb into the hills to capture villagers and orphans. What would it buy them?

However, Alex, being an American and female, might be a more attractive bargaining chip. Or she'd make for better film footage on propaganda videos. She had to keep out of sight of the ISIS terrorists.

Once they could no longer see the village, Alex breathed a little more freely. Not that they were out of danger, but if they couldn't see the village, the attackers couldn't see them.

Ahead and to the north rose stony bluffs, shadowed by the angle of the sun hitting the ridge to the south.

Alex paused to catch her breath and study the bluff. Had she seen movement? She blinked and stared again at a dark patch in the rocky edifice.

A village woman slipped from the patch and climbed downward to where Alex stood with her little band of orphaned children.

Another woman followed the first, and then another. Soon five women were on their way down the steep slope to where Alex and Fariji stood. Each gathered a small child and headed up to what Alex realized was a cave entrance.

Alex, burdened with the girl on her back, started up the path, urging the other children to climb or crawl up the slippery slope. By the time she reached the entrance, she was breathing hard.

She slipped the girl from her back and eased her to the stone floor of the cave.

More than a dozen women and children emerged from deep in the shadows, their eyes wide and wary. They gathered around Alex, all talking at once.

"Where are the others?" Alex asked in French.

"Scattered among the caves." A woman called

Rashida stepped forward. "There are many caves. This is only the first one."

"They will find us here," a younger woman said. "We must go deeper into the hills."

"We can't," Rashida said. She tipped her head toward three older women sitting on the ground, their backs hunched, their eyes closed. "The old ones will not make it. It was all they could do to come this far."

Alex's heart went out to the old and young who couldn't move as fast or endure another climb up steep hills.

"None of us will last long without food and water," the other woman argued.

"We can't go back down to the village." An old woman called Mirembe glanced up from her position seated on the ground. "We would all be tortured or killed."

Alex didn't want to argue with the women when the reverend and his wife were down there with no one to help or hide them. With the children safe in the cave, Alex couldn't stop thinking about the elderly missionaries. She drew in a deep breath and made up her mind. "I need you women to care for these children."

Again, the women gathered around her.

"Where are you going?" Rashida asked.

"Don't leave us," another woman pleaded.

"If you go back, you'll be killed," Mirembe predicted.

"I have to go back. Reverend Townsend and his wife stayed behind."

Mirembe shook her head. "They are dead by now. They must be."

A sharp pain pierced Alex's heart. "I choose to think

they are still alive. And I'm going down to see if there is anything I can do to help." She glanced around at the women. "Will you care for these children?" she repeated with more force.

Rashida nodded. "We will look after them until your return."

A tiny hand tugged at her pant leg. "Miss Alex, please don't go."

Alex glanced down at Kamaria, the little girl she'd carried up the hill. She had tears in her big brown eyes as she stared up at Alex.

Her chest tight, Alex dropped to one knee and hugged Kamaria. "I'll be back," she promised. "Until I return, I need you to help take care of your brothers and sisters." She brushed a tear from the child's cheek. "Can you do that for me?"

Kamaria nodded, another tear slipping down her cheek.

Alex straightened. "I'll be back as soon as I can."

Fariji followed her to the cave entrance. "It is not safe for you to return to the village. I will go with you."

"No." Alex touched his arm. "Stay here and protect the women and children. They have no one else."

The gentle young man nodded, his brow dipping low. "I will do what I can to help."

And he always did. Fariji was one of the most loving, selfless men in the village.

Alex hugged him, and then she left the cave and slid down the gravelly slope to the base of the bluff. She figured returning to the village would be dangerous, but she couldn't abandon the missionaries. If she could help, she would, even if it meant risking her own safety.

Chapter Two

Going down from the hills alone went a lot faster than climbing, carrying a child on her back and herding half a dozen more. Within minutes, Alex reached the edge of the village.

She hid behind the first wall she came to, pushed the scarf she wore down around her neck and listened, her heart beating so loudly against her eardrums, she could barely hear anything.

The gunfire had ceased, but men shouted. A woman screamed and vehicle engines rumbled.

The reverend's wife had been in the home of a woman who'd given birth to a baby boy. The baby had been breech, complicating the birth. Both had survived, but were weak and unable to travel.

Mrs. Townsend had been caring for the two since the baby's birth.

Alex dared to peek around the side of the hut. The narrow street between the dirt-brown mud-and-stick buildings appeared empty. She sucked in a deep breath and ran to the next structure.

A man shouted nearby. Footsteps pounded in the dirt,

along with the rattle of metal against metal or plastic, like the rattle of a strap on a rifle.

Alex held her breath and waited.

Shouts grew closer. The sound of something smashing made Alex jump and nearly cry out.

She clapped a hand over her mouth and slipped farther back into the shadows.

Another man yelled, the noise coming from inside the building behind which Alex huddled.

Voices argued back and forth, and then...*bang*!

Knowing it was too late to change her mind about coming back to the village, Alex shrank into a dark corner and prayed the men in the hut didn't come out and discover her there.

The home the reverend's wife had been in was a couple huts over from where Alex hid. If she could get there without being seen, perhaps she could convince the missionaries to leave before the men found them.

Voices sounded again as the men exited the building and moved to the next.

Alex waited, fully expecting them to come around the corner and start shooting.

She froze and made herself as small as she could in the meager shadow.

A loud bang erupted nearby, as if someone had slammed a door.

The men in the street said something, and then more footsteps pounded against the dirt street, moving away from Alex's hiding place.

She let go of the breath she'd been holding. After another moment or two, she rose and eased to the corner. The street was clear.

Someone shouted from a couple houses over.

If she was going to move, she had to do it before the men returned.

Alex ran across the street, skirted another hut and checked around the next corner.

It, too, was clear.

She started across the street, heard a cry and nearly froze. Realizing she couldn't make it around the next home in time, she dived through a door and squatted inside, trying to control her breathing in order to hear the enemy's approach.

Footsteps clattered along the path outside the hut. Then they stopped.

For a long moment, Alex heard nothing. She waited a little longer and then eased toward the door.

Before she reached it, an arm wrapped around her middle and a hand clamped over her mouth, stifling a scream rising up her throat.

She struggled to free herself, but the arm holding her tightened, trapping her arms against her side and her back against a hard wall of a chest. "Shh," he whispered against her ear, his breath heated and minty. Not what Alex would have expected from an enemy rebel.

"Check in that building," someone said in French outside.

Alex froze. Though she was unsure of her captor, the men outside had been shooting. She'd make her escape from the man holding her after the other men passed in the street. Until then, she held still against the warm, hard surface of a hulking, big man with arms like steel vises. As she waited, she listened for the sound of movement outside the building.

Someone called out next to the door, "I have this one, you check the next."

The door jiggled.

The hand over her mouth dropped to her arm and she was shoved backward, behind the man.

If she wanted, she could escape him. But to what?

She couldn't go back out into the street and risk being captured by the rebels storming the village. She'd be better off taking her chances with her unknown captor in the dark interior of the hut.

The door swung inward.

Alex was shoved behind the opening door as a beam of sunlight slashed across the floor.

A man in black clothing stepped into the building, pushing the door wider with the rifle he held in his hands.

As the light beam fanned out, it chased away the darkness of the rest of the room. In the gray light out of the sunshine's wedge, Alex studied her captor.

He wore a desert-camouflage military uniform and a helmet, and carried a wicked-looking rifle of the type the Special Forces units carried. She searched for some indication of whose team he played for. Was he American, French or—God forbid—one of the paid mercenaries so often found in conflicts where they didn't belong? He wasn't from Niger. The skin she could see was too light. Granted, it appeared tanned, but not the rich darkness of the native Niger people.

The man who'd pushed open the door stepped inside the room, his weapon raised. Then he fired several bullets.

Alex flinched and shrank back into the corner. If

the shooter turned any farther in their direction, he'd hit her captor.

The rebel turned slowly.

Alex's captor leaped forward, slamming the butt of his weapon into the side of the shooter's head. The weapon dropped from his hands and fell to the floor. Before the man could react, the military guy pulled a knife and slit the shooter's throat. Her captor bent to retrieve the other man's weapon. With equally efficient movements, he removed the bolt, slid it into his pocket and laid the remainder of the rifle on the ground next to the dead man.

Then her captor turned to her and held out his hand. "We have to move."

She remained frozen in her position crouched on the floor of the hut, her heart beating so fast she could barely breathe to keep up with her need for oxygen.

His hand shot out, palm up. "Now!"

Alex stared at the big, calloused hand that had just dispatched a rebel fighter with such ease and efficiency of movement. Would he do the same to her?

Shouts outside the open door of the hut shook Alex out of her stunned silence.

Her captor dropped his arm, eased up to the door and glanced out. Without turning, he spoke softly, "If you want to live, come with me now."

"Who are you?" she asked.

"Introductions later. Run now!" He hooked her arm, jerked her up off the floor and rushed her to the doorway.

After a quick pause, he dragged her out into the street and back toward the hills.

They'd gone past several huts when Alex remembered why she'd returned to the village in the first place. She dug her heels into the dirt and ripped her arm out of his grasp.

He wheeled around, his gaze shooting in all directions. "Why are you stopping?"

"I came to help Reverend Townsend and his wife," she said.

His lips pressed into a thin line. "You can't help anyone if you're dead. We have to get out of the village, before they find that man's body."

"I didn't kill him," she pointed out. "You did."

"It was him or us." The man grabbed her arm and pulled her off the street and into the shadow of one of the huts. "Now isn't the time to argue. The terrorists outnumber us twenty to one. And they won't hesitate to shoot first. If they take prisoners, they won't be kind to them."

"Exactly my point. The reverend and his wife stayed behind with a new mother and her baby. I can't leave them to the terrorists."

"You will do them no good if these ISIS bad guys capture you, as well. The best we can do is get out of here, notify someone with more firepower than we have and let them launch a rescue mission."

"Why should I go with you? I don't even know if you're one of the good guys."

"If I was one of the bad guys, I would have left you behind for ISIS to find instead of wasting my time arguing with you." He peeked around the corner of the building. "Now, if you're done flapping your jaw, we need to move."

He had an American accent, and, despite his gruff demeanor, he had saved her from being filled with bullets. Or had he saved himself? Either way, she was still alive and he was the reason.

This time he didn't grab her and drag her; he glanced back and raised his eyebrows. "Ready?"

She nodded.

He held out his hand.

Alex laid hers in his. A jolt of awareness raced up her arm into her chest. His fingers curled around hers, strong, sure and rough. A fleeting thought ran through her mind. What would it feel like to have those hands run freely over her naked body?

Shocked at her thoughts, Alex shook herself and fell in step with the man who had her life in his hands. Once he got them out of the current situation, he could do anything he wanted with her.

A trickle of fear and something else slipped down her spine. Alex refused to think past getting out of the village to somewhere safe where they could hide. For all she knew, she was trading one bad set of cards for another.

JAKE HADN'T EXPECTED to find an American woman in the village. When she'd run into the hut where he'd been hiding, he knew he couldn't leave without taking her with him. The ISIS terrorists would either kill her, or rape and torture her until she wished she were dead. Leaving her behind wasn't an option. But taking her with him made them both more vulnerable. She slowed him down, and two people made a bigger target than just one person attempting to escape and evade capture.

With the sun starting its descent toward the horizon, their best bet would be to either make a dash for cover in the hills, or hunker down in one of the huts and wait until dark to make their move.

The crack of gunfire filled the air with the answer to Jake's question. They had to get out now rather than later. When the terrorists found the dead man, they'd be out for blood. He felt bad about leaving behind the reverend, his wife and the new mother, but he couldn't take on the entire ISIS force that had stormed the village. They were far outnumbered, and his ammo wouldn't last long enough to take out all of them.

He prayed his diversion had bought the rest of the SEAL team time enough to get away from the ISIS rebels. They would expect him to seek refuge and escape from the occupied village before attempting to reconnect with friendly forces.

Jake wondered what had happened to the drone that was supposed to be flying over while they were on their mission. Had the drone been in the vicinity of the village, they would have known the ISIS group was on its way and either been prepared for the attack or gotten the hell out of Dodge before they'd arrived.

Instead, they'd been outmaneuvered and outgunned. If Jake hadn't rammed the other truck, they would have been mowed down by the sheer number of bullets the terrorists could have unloaded into them.

Hut by hut, Jake led the way, making it to the edge of the village. He paused to assess the chances of strolling across a wide, barren expanse of land. By himself, he could low crawl or run in a zigzag line long enough to achieve the safety of cover behind some of the larger boulders at the base of the nearby hills. With the woman, he wasn't sure he could reach safety before they were discovered, and he didn't know her physical capabilities.

He ran his gaze over her length. "Can you run?"

The woman tilted her chin. "I was on the track team in high school."

"I didn't ask if you were on the track team." He drew in a deep breath, let it out and asked again, "Can you run now?"

She frowned. A nearby shout made her jump. "Yes. Yes, I can run." She inched closer to him.

"Then on the count of three, I want you to take off in front of me and run like the hounds of hell are on your heels. Keep as low as you can. I'll be right behind you. Don't slow down until you reach those boulders at the base of the hills." He touched her arm. "Can you do it?"

Her eyes round, she pulled her bottom lip between her teeth and nodded.

After one more glance around the vicinity, Jake whispered, "Go."

For a moment, the woman didn't move. Then she took off like a bullet shot from an M4A1 rifle. He'd never seen a woman run as fast as that woman ran from the Niger village.

He almost smiled, but he didn't have time to admire her resilience and strength. He took off after her, staying as close as possible to block the bullets someone might shoot their way. He had the bulletproof vest, but the woman had nothing.

Once they were over halfway there, he began to think they'd make it without being noticed. That was not the case. The sharp report of gunfire echoed off the hillsides.

Jake automatically ducked lower, and he was glad to see the woman in front of him doing the same.

With over two hundred yards between them and the village, they could potentially make it to the hills without being shot. Hitting a still target at two hundred yards was hard enough. Hitting one that was moving was even harder. He closed the distance between himself and his lady counterpart, keeping his back between her and that village. Fifty yards. All they needed was another fifty yards, and then they could duck behind the cover of the boulders.

Something slammed into his back, pushing him forward. He stumbled and plowed into the woman, sending her flying forward. She hit the ground on her hands and knees, but kept moving, crawling as fast as she could go.

Jake regained his footing, scooped up the woman, set her on her feet and hustled her toward the boulders.

Bullets kicked up dust at their feet as they rounded a man-size rock that had fallen from the bluffs above.

After a few deep breaths to refill his lungs, Jake stared at the woman who wasn't breathing any harder than he was. "By the way, I'm Jake."

"Alexandria Parker. Most folks call me Alex." She looked past his shoulder. "I can hear voices coming nearer. Let's go."

She stepped out with purpose, heading away from the village and up into the hills.

Jake followed. "You weren't kidding about running track."

"I run whenever I get a chance," she said without slowing to catch her breath. "Even over here in Niger."

When they came to a bend in the trail, Jake glanced back, his pulse picking up again. "Well, you're going to have to keep running. They're coming after us."

Alexandria picked up the pace, climbing higher and faster. Soon the village was completely out of view behind a hill. They couldn't keep up the pace, but, thankfully, neither could their pursuers, and they didn't have the benefit of ATVs to speed up the search.

"If you're up to it, we should keep moving until nightfall," Jake suggested.

"I'm good to go," she said, her breathing a little labored. But she didn't slow, didn't falter, just kept going.

Jake thanked his lucky stars this woman wasn't one to fall to pieces when the going got tough. A glance ahead at the rocky path provided a good indication that the going promised to get tougher. And they had no food or water to sustain them if they had to hide out for any longer than a day or two.

At the moment, though, their number-one need was a safe haven from gunfire.

The path into the hills forked. When Alexandria turned right instead of left, he didn't question her choice. It made sense to choose the path least traveled. The other appeared to be recently disturbed.

The crack of gunfire echoed off the hillsides. As they slipped over the top of a ridge, Jake glanced back.

Several men dressed in the black garb of the ISIS rebels were climbing the path they'd taken.

"Wait on the other side," Jake commanded.

Alexandria dropped below the ridge and did as told.

Hunkering low to the ground, Jake steadied his rifle and peered through the scope, focusing on the movement below.

His hands tightened on the rifle. "Damn."

"What?" Alexandria started to climb up beside him.

Jake held out a hand to stop her and replied, "They're following our path."

"Good," Alexandria whispered. "They found the candy wrapper I left."

Anger surged as Jake sank back behind the ridge and stared at the woman as if she'd lost her mind. He stopped short of grabbing her by the arms and shaking some sense into her. "Why the hell did you do that?"

Her lips firmed and she lifted her chin. "The other path led to where the orphans and villagers are hiding in the caves. I didn't want the militants to find them."

His ire abated as he stared into the eyes of a woman who had sacrificed her own safety for that of others. He couldn't fault her for that, not when he'd done the same for his team. "Okay. I get it. But that doesn't make it any easier on us. We can't stop moving until dark." He glanced one last time over the top of the ridge.

They'd lost some of their lead. They'd have to get a move on to gain ground. He'd counted six of the ISIS fighters. The predators outnumbered the prey, but they still had the lead. With only a few rounds remaining in his magazine, Jake couldn't risk a firefight. He had to get himself and Alexandria back to his team before they were caught or died in the arid landscape.

Chapter Three

Alex's calves and thighs were past sore and now bordered on numb, but she kept climbing. Dusk settled in around her and Jake, making it more difficult to judge distance. She slipped on the path and almost tumbled down the hill they were on.

Jake grabbed her arm just in time and jerked her backward, slamming her into his broad, muscular chest.

She clung to him, appreciating his strength for a brief moment. He didn't seem to be winded at all, whereas she was breathing hard and every muscle in her body quivered with overuse. Sure, she ran and kept in good shape, but she hadn't been climbing hills, which required the use of a different set of muscles.

"We need to find shelter for the night," Jake said, his voice so close to her ear it warmed the side of her neck.

She pushed against his chest and straightened. "I can keep going." It was a lie, but she refused to be the one to hold them back. If the rebels caught up to them because of her, she would be responsible for the outcome.

"You might be able to keep going, but I'm tired and I don't have any desire to fall off a cliff in the dark."

"Okay." She stared up at the bluffs surrounding them. "These hills are riddled with caves. Will a cave suffice?"

He nodded and glanced up. "Yes."

Alex's lips twisted. "We passed several in the last valley. But, of course, when you're looking for one you can't find one."

"We'll keep moving. Maybe there will be one over the next ridge."

Jake took the lead, picking his way through the brush and bramble. The trails had become nothing more than animal paths, crisscrossing the sides of hills and seeming to have no rhyme or reason to their course. He headed toward a pass between two hills, climbing up a steep slope to reach it. He didn't linger on the ridgeline, dropping to the other side quickly to keep from being silhouetted against the fading light.

Alex did the same. When she stood beside him on the other side of the ridge, she scanned the hillsides, cliffs and valley below.

"There." Jake pointed to several dark areas along the side of a bluff, across the narrow valley from where they stood.

Alex squinted. The dark shadows could be caves. The only way to know for certain was to get closer and check them out. With darkness settling in around them, they had to hurry or they'd be stumbling around in pitch black before the stars came out to shed a little light on their situation. And when the stars came out, that might allow for enough light that their pursuers could pick them out against the slopes and give away their hiding place before they even reached it.

Jake eased down the slippery slope one side step at a time.

Alex sucked in a deep, tired breath and hurried down the hillside, slipping and sliding on the loose gravel and stones. Her feet flew out from underneath her and she sat down hard, her momentum carrying her downward faster than she'd intended and bruising her backside as she went. She reached out, flailing for purchase, grabbing at the brush or anything that would slow her descent. The roots and brush she tried to hold on to ripped from the dry soil, barely slowing her fall.

"Watch out," she called out as her body picked up speed, heading straight for the man who'd saved her from the ISIS rebels. And she could do nothing to stop herself.

About the time Jake turned to see what was happening, she plowed into his shins, knocking him off his feet. He fell, landing on top of her.

Instead of slowing her fall, he slipped down the hillside with her, like an avalanche of human flesh, plummeting to the bottom.

When she finally came to a halt, Alex lay for a moment, trying to breathe.

Jake was still on top of her, his face dusty, his eyes wide. "Are you all right?" he asked.

She tried to say something, but she couldn't get enough air into her lungs to pass her vocal cords. "Can't..." she wheezed.

"Can't what?" he asked, untangling his legs from hers. Finally he pushed up on his arms, still leaning over her.

"Breathe," Alex said on a gasp. She filled her freed

lungs with precious air. "Though we needed to get down the hill fast, I believe there could have been a better way than using me as a human sled."

He chuckled and leaned over on one arm so that he could push the hair out of her eyes. "Sorry. I couldn't move out of your way fast enough."

"No, it was my fault. I should have taken better care coming down the side of the hill."

"How bad is your backside? After sliding down a rocky hill, it's bound to be bruised and cut. Roll over, and let me take a look."

Alex shook her head. "No time. We have to make it to those caves before we're spotted by the ISIS rebels. We might make it there before them, but if they see us, we might as well be sitting ducks." Though her back hurt and she was bruised and scratched, as he'd guessed, she couldn't give in to self-pity. They had to keep moving or risk capture.

A shiver shook her frame. She'd heard what the ISIS men did to women they captured, and she didn't plan on finding out just how bad it was.

Jake rose and held out his hand.

She took it in hers, let him pull her to her feet and straightened her torn shirt.

He turned her hand over in his and studied the cuts and scratches. "You're bleeding."

Alex tugged her hand free and wiped it on her jeans. "I'll live. We need to move."

For a moment, he remained standing in front of her. Then he nodded. "We'll take care of it when we get to the cave." He hooked her arm and set off through the brush and across the narrow valley. At the valley's center was a narrow stream with running water.

Jake squatted on his haunches and scooped water into his palm. He splashed it up into his face, washing away the dust. Then he scooped another handful and drank.

Alex dropped to her knees and slipped her sore hands into the cool stream, letting the water wash away the dirt and grit from the cuts and bruises. Then she scooped some and drank, praying she didn't get deathly ill from contaminated water.

"We don't know when we'll find water again, or how long it will be until my men come back for us," Jake said. "Drink up. But make it fast."

Not willing to give their pursuers time to catch up, Alex drank as much as she could in a few precious minutes and then pushed to her feet.

Having crossed the stream, Jake held out his hand to Alex and helped her to navigate the wet stones in the shallow water, guiding her over. Her foot slipped on the last rock.

Jake pulled her into his arms and held her long enough for her to get her feet beneath her. And long enough for Alex to appreciate the warmth and solid strength of his body against her.

Heat seared a path from where their chests met all the way to her core. When he set her back from him, she ducked her head, afraid he might see the awareness in her eyes. The man had a hard body, one most women would find hard to ignore and even harder to resist.

Thankfully, Alex wasn't most women. She couldn't be so easily influenced by a man with delicious muscles and narrow hips. And the way he wore his uniform trousers, fitting snug across his tight bottom, shouldn't affect her, either. Shouldn't…but it did. Having spent the last couple hours with the man, following him through thorny brush and bramble, she should be too tired to think about how sexy this stranger was. Perhaps *because* she was tired, she was thinking naughty thoughts when she should concentrate instead on survival.

Squaring her shoulders, she picked up the pace. Darkness and distance made it harder to see that tight butt, and she didn't want to lose him. Not out in the middle of the hills in Niger. She wasn't sure what wild animals they might encounter. They weren't far from one of the major national parks and wildlife preserves. For all she knew, they'd need those last few bullets to protect them from lions or other, more dangerous animals than the humans hunting them.

JAKE KEPT MOVING, determined to find a cave to hide from the men following them. Alex would need to rest before they continued on to find a way out of the hills and away from the ISIS terrorists that had taken control of the village.

Once they'd crossed the creek, he headed up the side of a hill, following an animal path to the dark, shadowy maw on the face of a bluff. By the time they reached the cave entrance, the path was nothing more than a thin trail, probably created by some surefooted sheep, goat or deer. He'd snagged Alex's hand and held on as they navigated the treacherous hillside.

If either one of them slipped, it would be a long, bumpy way down. He wasn't sure Alex could with-

stand another beating courtesy of a fall. Her hands were
scratched, as were her elbows. And if her torn shirt was
any indication, her back would be pretty messed up, too.

Jake had wet a bandanna while at the creek and
stuffed it into one of his cargo pockets on the side of his
pants. When they stopped, he'd attend to her wounds.
She couldn't afford to get an infection. Not when he
was unsure of when his team would send out a drone to
search for their whereabouts. The rescue mission could
take days to find him. If the ISIS terrorists continued
to hunt them, a drone might lead them straight to their
location before help could arrive to extract them.

At the cave entrance Jake took out a small flashlight
from his shirt pocket, aimed his weapon into the darkness and switched on the light, careful not to shine it for
too long in case the ISIS predators were close enough
to see the beam.

The cave didn't go back far enough for them to hide
in the depths. Anyone who climbed the hill and peered
inside would see the man and woman huddled against
a far wall.

"Too shallow," Jake muttered.

"There's another one farther along the bluff." Alexandria motioned toward the west.

They left the shallow cave and eased along the narrow path, lit only by the stars beginning to pop out one
by one in the indigo sky. Again Jake held Alexandria's
hand, helping her to keep her balance.

When they reached the second cave, he shined his
light into the darkness and couldn't see the back wall. He
stepped inside, his weapon pointed into the blackness.

"Aren't you afraid of animals?" Alex whispered.

"I'm more afraid of having to shoot one. If I fire a round, I give away our location."

"And if a lion comes at us?" Alex asked, her voice shaking.

"I'll do whatever it takes to keep us alive," he assured her. "Stay behind me in case something does jump out. Or better yet, wait here."

He entered the cave.

Alex followed. "If you don't mind, I'd rather face a lion than a militant."

"Suit yourself," he said, and continued his perusal of the interior of the cave.

"So, what are you? A Special Forces soldier or something like that?"

His lips quirked. "Something like that."

She stayed close enough behind him that he could almost feel the heat of her body, but not so close that she hampered his ability to use his weapon.

"Don't the Special Forces soldiers work in teams?"

"Yes."

"So?"

"So what?" He stalled, shifting the beam of his flashlight back and forth to cover every inch of the cave floor and the dark crevices that could contain wild animals. He even checked behind a large boulder near the back of the cave.

"So, where are the rest of your teammates?" she asked.

Completing his inspection, he turned to face her. "The cave is clear."

"And you haven't answered my question." She raised her brow.

"We were separated in battle." He took her hand and led her to the back of the cave and pointed to the cave floor. "You might as well bed down for the night back here. If someone does come into the cave, they won't see us immediately." He turned to leave.

She touched his arm. "Where are you going?" Her voice held a note of panic.

He covered her hand with his. "I'm going out to scout for a few minutes."

"Do you have to?" she asked, smoothing her hands over her skirt nervously.

"I like to know what other options we have if we need to beat a hasty retreat." He handed her a small penlight. "Here. Keep this. It's not much, but it will give you a little light to see by. I'll need my bigger flashlight out there."

Alex held up the flashlight that looked more like a ballpoint pen, and cocked an eyebrow. "Like that's going to do me any good against a lion."

"No, but this might." He pulled a handgun out of his belt and handed it over.

"I haven't fired a gun since my father showed me how when I was a teen." She smiled.

His lips turned upward on the corners. "I'm surprised you've fired one at all."

"Oh, my father was all about taking care of yourself." She weighed the handgun in her palm. "He wanted me to be able to defend myself. I think he wanted me to test for the concealed carry license. Only I didn't feel comfortable carrying a gun in my purse. Most of my friends only carried makeup, a credit card, driver's license and the keys to their cars. I was afraid someone would take the gun out of my purse and shoot himself accidentally. Thus, no gun in my purse."

"Do you know how to operate this, or do I need to show you?"

"I can figure it out," she said. "Especially if my life depends on it."

"Good. I'll be back shortly." He touched her hand holding the gun. "Promise not to shoot me?"

Her lips twisted. "I promise not to shoot you."

And he left to go down into the valley and back up over the pass to see if the men who'd been following them were still on their tail.

He paused just short of the top of the ridge. Inching just to the top, he peered over to the valley below. On the valley floor, he could see the warm glow of a campfire and shadowy figures gathered around the flames.

The ISIS rebels weren't far behind them, with only a ridge standing between them.

Jake returned to the creek, rewet the bandanna and hurried back to the cave. If the cuts and scratches on Alex's back were deep, they could become infected and cause her a whole lot more grief if left untreated for any length of time.

They could stay the night, but they'd have to leave early the next morning, while it was still dark, to be gone before the terrorists made it up over the ridge.

When he arrived back at the cave, he eased into the darkness, searching for the woman who'd escaped the village with him. Nothing stirred. No sounds of breathing or indication that anyone was there.

His pulse sped as he switched on his flashlight, using the red lens setting, making it harder for anyone outside the cave to see but illuminating the interior up to three feet in front of him.

Where was she? Had he entered the wrong cave? Or had some of the rebel forces found their way around him and made off with the pretty teacher?

He drew in a shaking breath and whispered, "It's me." Then he waited, his breath lodged in his chest.

Chapter Four

As soon as Alex heard those words, she launched herself out of her hiding place behind the giant boulders and flung her arms around Jake's neck. "Thank God," she said, burying her face in the front of his bulletproof vest.

He wrapped her in his embrace and held on.

In the back of Alex's mind, she wished he didn't have on the bulletproof vest. She would like to have felt all of his body against her, imagining its warmth pressed against her cave-chilled skin.

"Hey." He set her at arm's length and chuckled. "Did you think I wouldn't come back?"

Alex shrugged, her face cast down. She didn't want him to witness the fear in her eyes when she'd come to the conclusion he wasn't coming back. "The thought did cross my mind, as I fumbled around in the pitch dark. When you came into the cave, I didn't know if you were friend or foe." She snorted. "I'd never been so happy to hear the sound of someone's voice. You were gone for what felt like forever."

He smoothed a loose strand of hair out of her face, brushing her cheek with his calloused thumb. "Sorry. I backtracked to see whether we are still being followed."

She stiffened. "And?"

He drew in a deep breath and let it out. "They're on the other side of the ridge."

Alex's heart rate sped up. "We should leave. Now."

"They've stopped for the night. I think we'll be all right for now, but we need to head out before daylight to stay ahead of them."

Her brows knit. "Are you sure? I can keep going, if you can."

He smiled. "I know you can, but we're running on empty. At the very least, we could use some sleep." He nodded toward her. "And we need to take care of your cuts and scratches before they get infected."

Alex crossed her arms over her chest. "I'm fine. I can keep going."

"I have no doubt you can, but I need the rest and I want to see your backside. You can't ignore your injuries." He spun his finger. "About-face."

She hesitated. "Really—"

"I know. You're fine. But let me be the judge. You can't see what's on your back, but I can." He twirled his finger again. "Just do it. The sooner we take care of you, the sooner we sleep."

Swallowing hard, Alex turned her back to the man who was not much more than a stranger.

He lifted the tattered remains of her shirt.

Alex held on to the front to keep it from riding up high enough to expose her breasts in the lacy white bra she wore.

When he didn't say anything for a moment, Alex's pulse quickened. "How bad is it?" Sure, it stung and burned every time her ruined shirt rubbed against her scratches and cuts.

"It's not great, but the good news is that you'll survive, as long as the wounds don't get infected." He pulled a wet cloth from his pocket and patted her back with it. The cloth had been warmed by his thigh, and his touch was gentle. One hand held her side, steadying her, while the other removed dirt and debris from her wounds. When he was done, he released the tattered ends of her shirt and let them fall back down over her body. "The shirt has to go."

Heat seared a path through her, heading south to her core. "It'll have to do for now. I don't have another."

Jake stepped back. "You can have mine."

When Alex turned to face him, a protest on her lips, she stopped, her thoughts flying out of her head as Jake unclipped the fasteners on his vest and lowered it to the ground.

Her mouth went dry and her palms filled with sweat. "What are you doing?"

He smiled. "Giving you my shirt. Granted, it might be a little sweaty, but it will be better than what you have on."

He unbuttoned his uniform jacket and slipped out of it. Then he yanked his T-shirt up over his head in one fluid, ever-so-sexy move.

He stood in front of her wearing only his trousers and boots, his broad chest shining in the dim glow of the red-lensed flashlight. The man looked like a Roman gladiator, all hard muscles, strength and magnetism.

Alex lost her ability to form thoughts and words. Her

gaze swept over the massive amount of skin stretched tautly over his frame.

When he handed her his T-shirt, she gulped. Her fingers touched his and a shock of fire raced through her hand and up her arm. "Thank—" she squeaked, cleared her throat and tried again. "Thank you."

The man turned his back to her, allowing her the privacy to shed her shredded shirt and slip the T-shirt over her head. It smelled of male, that outdoorsy scent that made her insides quiver. The fabric slid over her breasts and torso and hung down to her knees.

"I'm decent," she said. "Thanks again."

He turned, a smile spreading across his face. "It's a little big."

"But better than nothing." She wadded the torn shirt into her fist.

"Let me have that." He reached out for the ruined shirt.

Again her hand touched his. This time he glanced up sharply, as if he too felt the electric shock. Just as quickly, he looked back down at the fabric in his grip. "I want to bind the wounds on your hands."

"They'll be okay," she said.

"You need some protection to prevent further injury to your palms if you slide down another hill." He ripped a piece off the front of her shirt. Then he took her hand and wrapped it gently over the cuts and scratches, tucking the end in to keep it from unraveling.

The whole time he held her fingers in his, she couldn't breathe; nor could she control her wildly racing pulse.

When he had finished both hands, he released her

and stepped back. "We need to get some rest. Morning will come all too soon."

"Shouldn't we stand watch?" she asked.

"Actually, I'd planned on staying awake and keeping an eye out for trouble."

"You need rest as much as I do." Alex lifted her chin. "I can take the first shift."

"I don't mind staying awake all night. I'm used to it. It's part of the job."

"I can stay awake half the night," Alex insisted. "I'd rather you get some sleep to keep sharp."

He studied her for a moment. "Keep an eye on the valley below. If you see any movement whatsoever, wake me immediately. Even if it's an animal scurrying out from under a rock. Wake me." His brows drew downward. "Understand?"

She popped a salute and smiled. "Yes, sir." Then she took up a position at the mouth of the cave and sat, leaning her back against the stone wall.

A glance at Jake proved he was taking her up on her offer to get some sleep. He lay on the hard floor of the cave, bunched her shirt beneath his head and crossed his arms over his chest. "Do you need the light?" he asked.

"No," she said. "The stars are enough light for me to see by."

There was a soft click, and the red glow from the flashlight blinked out.

Alex could just barely discern the outline of the man lying on the ground, but she didn't need to see him to know he'd be there for her if she needed him. The least she could do was let him sleep while she kept watch.

Staring out into the night, she scanned the valley

below again and again, going over all that had happened leading up to their escape. Some things still niggled at her.

"Are you army Special Forces or something else?"

"Something else," he replied.

"Delta Force?" she guessed.

He snorted. "Please."

Not army Special Forces or Delta Force...

"Mercenary?" she tried again.

"I don't get paid enough to be a mercenary," he replied.

"What does that leave?" She glanced over her shoulder. "Marine?"

"Navy," he replied.

"Don't you need a ship nearby to be in the navy? Or at least a body of water?"

He chuckled. "Not if you're a navy SEAL."

"You're a navy SEAL?" she asked, unable to keep the awe from her voice. "Aren't they the best of the best?"

"So we're told."

She glanced back at him. "What were you doing in the village?"

"Intel had it that ISIS was in the vicinity," he said. "We were on a recon mission."

"Recon?"

"We were only out seeking further intelligence. We weren't there to engage."

"But you did," she pointed out.

"Only because they surprised us. We thought they'd be several miles up the road. We were supposed to have some drone support."

"I take it you didn't get it?"

"No." His voice was hard.

"Did the rest of your team make it out?" she asked softly.

"I hope so." For a long moment, silence reigned in the cave.

"What brought you to Niger?" he asked.

Alex stared out at the night, thinking back over her reasons for leaving Virginia and her home. "I needed a new start, and I wanted to go somewhere I could make a difference with my teaching and my ability to speak French."

"Sounds like a breakup," Jake said.

She shrugged, though he wouldn't see the movement. "Yeah. It was something like that." She had broken up with her fiancé, realizing he wasn't the right man for her. They'd been together since their first year in college. He'd proposed after they'd been together for six years.

When they'd started planning the wedding, something had made her step back and rethink her decision to marry Paul. He'd been a good friend, and she liked his company, but there wasn't any spark and no fire in their kisses. Sex with Paul had been something she did because she knew it was expected, not because she couldn't wait to get naked and in bed with him.

Rather than go into the sad details of her less-than-exciting life, she asked, "What about you? Are you married? Do you have kids, a dog and the house with the white picket fence back in the States?"

He didn't answer for a while.

"You don't have to answer," Alex said. "It's none of my business."

"You're right," he said. "It's none of your business."

A flare of anger surged inside Alex, but she bit her tongue and refused to rise to his tart retort.

"I figured the life of a navy SEAL wasn't conducive to marriage or long-term relationships. So, no. No wife, no kids, no dog or white picket fence. Just me and my team. I keep it simple."

Alex told herself to leave the conversation there. But she couldn't help asking, "Did you ever want more?"

Again the silence stretched between them.

"Sorry, I shouldn't ask such personal questions," she whispered.

"The answer to your question is yes. There was a time when I was fairly new to the team that I thought I wanted it all. I thought I could have it all." He sighed. "I was wrong."

"I'm sorry," Alex said.

"For what?"

Her heart pinched. "That things didn't work out for you."

"I'm not. The relationship wasn't meant to be. Once a SEAL, always a SEAL. It takes a special person to put up with our lifestyle. I don't believe she exists for me. Now, let me sleep."

"Right. Zipping my lips here." She clamped her mouth shut and refused to ask a hundred more questions of the navy SEAL. He needed sleep, and it truly wasn't any of her business that he didn't think there was a woman who could love him and the life he'd chosen to lead.

Deep in Alex's heart, she knew the man was wrong.

But who was she to tell him that there was someone for everyone when she hadn't been completely convinced herself?

JAKE LAY FOR a long time with his eyes closed, willing himself to sleep. Normally he didn't have a problem dropping off into light sleep when he knew he needed the mental and physical recharge only rest could provide.

But sleep wasn't coming, and the more he lay there, the more he realized it was because of the woman sitting by the mouth of the cave. Since finding her in the village, he'd had a difficult time focusing on the mission at hand.

Alex's silky black hair, hanging down to her waist in straight lengths, made Jake want to reach out and run his fingers through the strands. And those ice-blue eyes made him look twice. He could swear he saw the vastness of the universe reflected in their depths. And her alabaster skin fairly glowed in the darkness.

She was beautiful, smart and physically capable of keeping up with the grueling trek through the hills and rocky terrain. She hadn't complained, even after sliding down the side of a hill, scraping the skin off her hands and backside. She was one tough lady, and she stirred up more feelings inside Jake than he cared to acknowledge.

The last time he'd felt this way he'd been too eager to make a relationship permanent, only to discover the woman he had fallen for wasn't willing to wait for him to return home from deployments.

Trish had left him after his very first deployment.

While he'd been gone, dreaming about her, she'd found a civil service employee on the navy base who would be home each night to see to her every want and need. With him, she would never have to worry that he'd return from work in a body bag or be deployed nine months out of the year to some godforsaken place he couldn't even discuss.

That was when Jake had sworn off meaningful relationships that lasted more than a date or two. He didn't have time for the games, and he didn't need the heartache. His team depended on him to have a level head and solid focus.

He opened his eyes and stared at the silhouette of the woman he'd rescued from the village overtaken by the ISIS terrorists. She wasn't someone who took the easy way out. She'd come to Africa to start over. And, boy, had she. Teaching orphans in a poor village had to be completely different from her life in the States, yet she'd done it. Not only had she taught them, she'd gotten her orphans out of the village when the terrorists stormed the streets. And she'd returned to help her missionary sponsors.

How many women had he known who would fearlessly head back into danger to help someone else?

Alex had gumption. She was the kind of woman who wouldn't settle for *safe* and *boring* in a relationship. But was she the kind of woman who could stand long separations from her significant other? What had been the reason for her breakup?

Jake found himself wanting to know more about Alex. But he needed to sleep so that he could be refreshed enough to continue the trek out of the hills and back to some measure of safety, away from the terrorists.

Thinking about Alex was pointless. Once he got her out of this situation, he probably wouldn't see her again. Why waste his time mooning over a beautiful woman? Hadn't he proved he wasn't cut out for anything more than a quick fling?

Alex didn't strike him as a quick-fling kind of woman.

With a sigh, he closed his eyes and willed himself to sleep. And he must have drifted off, because he woke with a start after what felt like only a few minutes.

"Jake," a soft, feminine voice called out to him.

He sat bolt upright, his gaze going to Alex. "What's wrong?"

"Nothing, but I'm nodding off. I can't keep watch through my eyelids." She wrapped her arms around herself and yawned. "And it's getting cold out here."

He glanced at his watch. "Four hours to sunrise. You should have woken me an hour ago."

"You were sleeping so peacefully I hated to disturb you."

He rose and crossed to where she sat with her back against the wall of the mouth of the cave.

Alex shivered and yawned at the same time. "I can't quit yawning," she said into her hand.

"Then lie down and catch some z's. I'll keep watch."

She didn't move. "If it's all the same to you, I'll just nap here, sitting up. I'm betting the floor of the cave is as cold and hard as it looks."

He nodded and stretched the kinks out of his back before sitting beside her. "It is." He held open his arms.

"I can offer you an alternative if you don't mind snuggling with a stranger."

"Right now—" she yawned again and laughed "—I'd snuggle with a bear just to get warm."

"I'm not a bear, but it might help to share body warmth." He slipped his hand behind her back and pulled her against his side. "I promise not to bite."

Her belly rumbled. "I make no such promises. And I'd appreciate it if you didn't mention biting, eating or food. I'd give my right kidney for a hamburger about now."

He wrapped his arms around her and held her close against his body. "Better?"

She was stiff at first, pressed against him but not letting her body relax.

He leaned back and stared down at the top of her head. "We haven't known each other long, but I'm not in the habit of taking advantage of women when I'm trying to escape and evade hostile enemy forces."

She tipped her head to stare into his eyes. "Did I say I was afraid of you?"

"No, but you won't get any sleep unless you relax."

"You're right." With a heavy sigh, she burrowed into him and rested her cheek against his chest. "Thank you for rescuing me from the village."

"You're welcome. Now hush and sleep."

"Yes, sir," she said smartly, the effect ruined by a huge yawn. "I am warmer. Didn't know they had bears in Niger," she mumbled.

"I didn't know they had beautiful black-haired, blue-eyed women in Niger," he whispered into her hair.

Her body relaxed against his, and her breathing became more regular and deep.

Alex slept, nestled in his arms.

Jake remained vigilant, afraid that if he fell asleep he wouldn't wake soon enough to get them out of the valley and over the next hill before the enemy found them.

The night stretched, long and cool. With Alex's body resting against his, he managed to stay warm enough.

She shivered several times, and, each time, he tightened his hold, trying to cover as much of her as he could with his arms.

His stomach rumbled, protesting the lack of food. They'd run short on energy as their bodies burned up the last of their fuel.

Jake knew he had to get them back on the road as soon as possible for his team to have even a ghost of a chance of finding them. And he needed to do it before he did something stupid, like fall for this courageous, beautiful woman.

Chapter Five

Just before dawn, Alex was nudged awake by a hand smoothing over her soft hair and a voice that whispered, "Time to go, sweetheart."

She cracked an eyelid and stared up at the man leaning over her. Had she imagined the endearment? "Are we leaving?" she asked, blinking open both eyes.

What a wonderful face to wake up to, and what a sturdy body to hold her through the night. She didn't want to wake and face the reality of their situation, not when she was wrapped in warm arms and feeling so incredibly safe.

"We are," he said. "The sun will be up within the next hour. We have to be over the next ridge before that happens."

Alex sat up and rubbed the sleep from her eyes. "But it's still dark out."

"True, but we don't want to wait until light. If we can see better, so can the enemy. We have to get out of this area before they enter it."

"I know, but I was having the best dream about eating eggs, bacon and hash browns. Could I go back to sleep long enough to finish my meal?"

"Sorry, but it's time to rise and shine." He rose to his feet, stretched and then held out a hand to her.

She grasped his hand in hers and let him pull her to an upright position. Stiff from all the climbing she'd done the day before, she stumbled and fell against Jake's broad chest.

The SEAL held Alex close until she could get her feet firmly beneath her. She couldn't tell him that part of her problem was how giddy and unsteady she felt around the handsome man. He'd likely laugh her all the way back to his buddies.

Then again, he'd been so kind and gentle the previous day, tending her wounds and holding her through the night. For such a big, rugged man, he was sweet and patient with her. Or was he just trying to keep her healthy so that she wouldn't slow them down on their mission to survive?

She straightened her shoulders and faced the task ahead. "Let's do this."

"Are you sure you're steady enough on your feet to make it down the slope?"

"You mean without sliding on my butt to the bottom?" Alex snorted. "I promise to be a little more graceful, if at all possible. I don't relish a repeat performance of yesterday." She held up her hands, which were still neatly bandaged with the remnants of her blouse. "I can't afford to tear any more clothing. All I have is what I'm wearing. I'd like to make it to civilization with at least your T-shirt on my back."

"That's the spirit. I'll go first. That way, if you fall, you'll bump into me."

"And I'll take you with me, as I slide all the way

down." She shook her head. "You'd do better staying far away. We can't afford for both of us to be injured."

"Nevertheless, I'm going first." He stepped over the lip of the cave's mouth and started down the hill. The gray light of dawn had only just begun to lighten the sky from pitch black to a dark battleship gray.

Jake picked his way down the hill, holding his hand out to steady Alex's descent while looking over the valley to make certain they weren't spotted or being followed.

She could have gotten down the slope on her own, but she appreciated that his strong hand provided stability and showed his concern for her safety. He probably only cared that she didn't break something and make his job of getting them out of there alive a lot harder.

Alex did her part and carefully placed every footstep. She refused to slide down another hill and risk taking Jake with her.

Once at the base of the hill, Jake snapped a branch off a leafy tree and handed it to her. "Drag this behind you to cover our tracks."

She did, careful to make sure the leaves stirred the prints left in the dust without looking like someone had dragged a branch over them.

Jake led her along the stream, urging her to keep to the shadows as much as possible. Every so often, she checked over her shoulder, expecting to see the ISIS fighters close on their heels. Thankfully, they weren't.

By the time the sun rose high enough to light the sky, Alex and Jake had reached the top of another ridge. Jake hurried her over the edge and paused long enough to check through his rifle scope.

Alex leaned close without raising her head above the ridgeline. "Do you see them?"

"Not yet." He shifted his concentration from the scope to viewing the entire valley with his naked eye. He stiffened. "No, wait. They just popped up over the other side of the valley." He watched a little longer. "One, two, three, four, five, six."

Jake ducked down beside her. "They don't seem to want to give up."

"What can we do?"

His jaw tightened. "Keep moving." He helped her to her feet and led the way through the hills, telling her they were heading southwest toward the city and hopefully they'd find a road that wasn't overrun by ISIS militants.

After two hours hiking in the hills, they found a dirt road and followed it for another mile. It wound around the side of a bluff and dipped down into a valley. When they came out of the vegetation to the other side of yet another hill, Alex gasped.

Jake snagged her arm and pulled her back into the brush. From there, they peered through the branches and observed the bustle of activity before them.

Where a hillside had once been now lay a giant, gaping hole with terraces spiraling down into a pit. People swarmed the pit, half-dressed, barefoot and covered in dirt. They carried buckets of mud on their heads or in their arms, or dragged them behind them as they climbed out of the pit like ants.

A backhoe dug deeper at the bottom of the pit, shoveling giant scoops of dirt into the backs of dump trucks. When the trucks were full, they rumbled up the narrow terraces to the top and emptied their contents in a huge pile.

"What's going on?" Alex asked.

"It appears to be a mining operation."

Alex frowned. "I didn't know there was one this close to the village. Most of the villagers would have known about any potential for jobs in the area."

"We've covered a considerable amount of ground since we left the village."

"Yes, but the villagers would have moved for the opportunity to work at a paying job. Those are hard to come by in rural Niger." She nodded toward a man standing on the edge of the pit, carrying a rifle and dressed like the ISIS militants. "Do you see what I see?" she whispered.

He nodded, pulled a camera out of his pocket and snapped several pictures.

"Why the pictures?"

"When we get back to civilization, I want to show the intel folks what we found." He tucked the camera back into his pocket and stood. "I don't think we want to announce our presence to these guys. Come on. We can move around the periphery and get the hell out of here."

Alex followed Jake on a circuitous route skirting the mining operation, giving it a wide berth.

As they neared the opposite end of the mine and nearby camp, Jake paused to snap more pictures, including some of the trucks hauling dirt out of the pit. They had some kind of logo on them.

"Look out," Jake whispered. "Our guys are entering the camp." He nodded toward the road where they'd been standing less than thirty minutes prior.

Six men dressed in black, their heads swathed in turbans, emerged from the brush and walked straight into the mining camp.

"That's our cue to leave," Jake said. He took Alex's hand and led her into the brush, following a course that paralleled the road leading into the camp. They stayed far enough away from the road to keep out of sight, but close enough that they wouldn't lose their way.

When they had gone a mile from the camp, Jake came to a halt and tilted his head to listen. "There's a truck coming." He glanced at Alex. "Stay here. I want to get a closer look at one of those vehicles."

Alex touched a hand to his arm. "But someone might see you."

"I'm good at blending into my surroundings. But I need to know you'll stay put and hide until I come back for you."

She chewed her lip, not liking that he was going to leave her to go near the road and risk the possibility of being captured. If he was, Alex wasn't at all sure what she was supposed to do.

He held up his hand. "I promise not to do anything dumb."

"Good. Because I don't want to have to fight my way into that camp to free you."

He chuckled. "You won't have to. I'm not going to get caught."

"Yeah," Alex muttered. "Famous last words."

He was going no matter what she said, so she kept her mouth shut, found a cluster of bushes and hid behind them. Through the leaves, she watched as Jake moved from the shadow of one tree to another. Before long, he disappeared, the shadows and leaves blending with his camouflage uniform.

A fly buzzed around Alex's head, and she was certain one was climbing up her leg, but she didn't dare move. Call her superstitious, but she was afraid if she took her gaze off the path Jake had taken, even for a second, he'd be lost to her.

Her heart hammering against her ribs, Alex lay in the bushes, counting the minutes until Jake's return. She prayed he'd come back for her. If he didn't, she would just have to go find him and bring him back herself.

JAKE CUT THROUGH the brush, angling toward the dirt road leading into and out of the copse of trees that had been their temporary sanctuary. He prayed Alex would stay hidden while he nosed around.

The rumble of a truck's engine alerted him to a vehicle approaching on the road.

Jake eased forward and dropped down behind a bush, getting as low to the ground as he could. He pulled the camera out of his pocket, aimed it at the road and waited for the truck to pass.

A modified SUV rolled by first. The top had been removed and a machine gun mounted in the center. A black-garbed soldier manned the weapon, turning left and right as they traversed the dirt road. The SUV kicked up dust behind it, temporarily clouding Jake's vision and the viewfinder of the camera.

A few moments later, a large truck came into view. The body of the truck was white, with a company logo painted in red lettering on the side.

He snapped a picture of the logo as the truck passed.

Snyder Mining Enterprises.

Another vehicle brought up the rear. This one was a pickup with another machine gun mounted in the bed and another black-garbed fighter perched behind the weapon, holding on as the truck bumped over the uneven surface.

As the vehicle neared Jake's position, the gunman in the rear banged a hand on the roof of the truck. The driver slowed to a stop.

Jake held his breath and sank lower into the brush and dirt.

The man in the back said something to those in the truck. Another man similarly dressed dropped down out of the passenger seat and climbed into the bed of the truck while the original gunman jumped out.

He walked toward the bushes where Jake lay hidden.

Jake braced himself for attack, slipped his knife from the scabbard on his ankle and waited for the man to get close enough to see him.

The ISIS gunman stopped short of the bush, lifted his shirt, unbuttoned his pants and relieved himself not two feet from where Jake lay.

Jake didn't move a single muscle, praying the man would move on as soon as he was finished.

Instead, he adjusted his clothing, frowned and stepped another foot closer to the bush.

A man shouted from the truck.

The gunman leaned close to the bush.

Jake gripped his knife, willing his heartbeat to a slow, steady pace, and prepared to launch himself at the soldier.

Another yell from the man in the truck caused the

one on the ground to spin and jog back to the vehicle. He climbed into the passenger seat and closed the door, and the truck jerked forward and sped after the others.

Jake lay for a moment, until the vehicles were completely out of sight. Then he crawled backward several yards before he dared to straighten and run back to find Alex.

When he reached the copse of trees and brush, he whispered, "Alex?" and held his breath.

"I'm here," she said, and climbed out into the open. "I heard the sound of engines. I was afraid they'd found you."

He shook his head. "They were close, but they didn't see me. Now that they're gone, we can continue to follow the road. Not on it, but parallel. Are you up for more hiking?"

She nodded. "I'm hungry, but still able to march."

"Do you want me to sneak into the camp and steal some food?"

She shook her head, her eyes wide. "No way. The people working in that mine need it more than we do."

"Agreed. Let's find our way back to my men. I'm sure they have a packet of MREs you're going to love."

"Meals ready to eat?" Alex smiled. "We get those at the orphanage sometimes. They beat starving any day."

Again Jake took the lead, with Alex following close behind. They traveled several miles just out of view of the road.

Eventually, they came to a point where the road ended in a T-junction.

"Which way?" Alex asked.

"West," he said, and turned right. "We came in from

the west. If the guys made it back to camp, they will be returning this way to find me soon. In the meantime, we need to get as far away from the mine as possible."

"Agreed." Alex shivered. "I have no desire to come face-to-face with the barrel of a rifle."

They continued along the road, walking and resting intermittently until the sun dipped low in the sky, heading for the horizon.

Night two settled in around them. This time, they didn't have the relative safety of a cave to hide in. They'd moved out of the hills onto the plains, broken up by stumpy trees and bushes. Occasionally, elephants trumpeted in the distance, and they would spot a herd of African buffalo or a couple of giraffes plucking leaves out of a tree. At one point, they spotted a pride of lions lazing in the sun.

Jake kept them moving, staying as far away from the lions as he could without getting too close to the road.

Whenever a vehicle lumbered down the road, he and Alex hunkered behind a bush until it passed.

With dusk settling in, Jake worried they wouldn't be safe sleeping on the ground. After passing the lions, he was determined to find a better alternative. Alas, they didn't have many choices, and Alex's energy reserve was fading fast.

Finally they came upon a village along the road. From a perch on a small rise in the terrain, Jake and Alex studied the layout.

Just outside the walls of the village was a well. Women and children gathered around, filling buckets and jugs.

Alex licked her lips. "I could use a drink of water," she whispered.

"Me, too. We have to stop for the night somewhere."

She frowned. "Are we stopping here? Is it safe?"

"No. But we can wait until dark and sneak over to the well, drink and then leave."

Alex nodded. "I like the idea. But is it safe?"

"I haven't seen a single ISIS militant since we stopped here."

"That doesn't mean they aren't hiding out behind the walls," Alex pointed out.

"True. But if we play our cards right, we can get that drink in the dark and be gone before they have any idea we're here."

Alex nodded. "I really would like a drink. And a hamburger. But I'll settle for water."

"Then water it is." Jake glanced at the sky. "We probably have an hour until dark. I don't think anyone will climb up here and find us, so we might as well rest."

"Good. We didn't get much sleep last night." Alex stretched, lay back on the ground, closed her eyes and laced her hands behind her neck.

Jake smiled down at the woman. She had to be hurting. No matter how much she worked out, the pace they'd kept through the hills had been grueling. Even *his* muscles were sore.

He looked down at the village once again. With no sign of ISIS militants and only women and children moving about, he decided he could afford to at least rest, if not sleep. He'd have to stay awake and keep vigilant. One truck full of ISIS soldiers could ruin everyone's day.

Still, he couldn't resist lying beside Alex. Dusty from a day and a half traveling cross-country on foot, she was still the most beautiful woman he'd seen in a long time, with curves in all the right places and a smile that made his knees weak every time she turned it in his direction.

"When we get back to my team, we can contact the American embassy in the capital city of Niamey," Jake said. "I'm sure they can help you get to the States safely."

She raised an eyebrow in challenge. "Who said I was going to the States?"

He turned on his side and propped himself up on his elbow. "I'd think that after what happened in that village, you'd want to go home."

"I don't want to go to the States. I have no one waiting for me there. Why would I want to go back?"

"You can't seriously consider returning to the village?"

She shook her head. "Only to help Reverend Townsend and his wife." Alex chewed on her bottom lip. "I hope they're okay."

"I'll check with headquarters when we rendezvous with my team. Maybe they'll authorize an extraction mission to free the reverend and his wife."

"That would be wonderful," Alex said.

"No guarantees, though," Jake amended.

Alex opened her eyes and stared up into his. "Don't you think they'll authorize a mission to free fellow Americans?"

If it were up to him, he'd conduct the mission himself. But he wasn't calling the shots. "I'll see what we can do. That's all I can promise." There might be even more dangerous and important missions than saving two missionaries from being overtaken by ISIS rebels. But he didn't say that to Alex. As far as she was concerned, the reverend and his wife were the number-one priority in her world. He couldn't blame her. He'd do his best to convince his commander that they needed to conduct the extraction as soon as possible. Which made it even more imperative for them to find their way back to his team.

The sooner he reunited with his teammates, the better chance they had of finding the missionaries alive. The longer it took to launch a rescue mission, the less chance they had of living through their captivity.

First, though, they had to get water in order to continue their journey. And they had to do it without being detected.

Chapter Six

"Alex, wake up." Jake's voice seemed to come to her in a dream.

Alex must have fallen asleep. When she opened her eyes, she thought for a moment she hadn't actually lifted her eyelids, it was so dark. Then she turned her head and saw a star twinkling in the heavens and realized it was night. She sat up straight and pushed her hair out of her face. "How long have I been asleep?" she asked.

"A couple of hours. It appears as if the people of the village have all gone to sleep. If we want to get water, now is the time to do it."

"I'm ready." She rolled to her feet, every muscle in her body reminding her that she'd abused it. She took a moment to stretch and turn, working out the stiffness.

Jake stood beside her, staring down at the village below and the well out in the open. "I think it would be best if you stayed here. I can fill my helmet and bring it back to you to drink."

She shook her head before he finished. "I'm going with you. You need someone watching your back. You'll be out in the open."

"I can manage. I don't want you exposed to some sniper's scope."

Alex tilted her head to the side and stared at Jake in the light from the stars. Damn, he was handsome when he was worrying about her safety. "Have you seen any evidence that this village is occupied by snipers?"

"I've seen young men," he said. "None of them were armed."

"Have you seen any of the ISIS rebels?"

He shook his head. "Not yet."

"Not yet isn't good enough." She lifted her chin, prepared to argue. "I'm going with you."

His lips quirked. "Are you always so determined?"

She nodded once, firmly. "I am, when I'm right."

"So be it." He started down the hill toward the village, circled the huts and paused beneath a tree.

Alex trailed behind and then stepped up beside Jake. Together they studied the open area around the well. As soon as they left the shadow of the tree, they'd be in the open, visible to anyone watching.

After five minutes, Jake drew in a deep breath and let it out slowly. "Well, let's do this."

"We're just a couple of travelers looking for a drink of water," Alex whispered, her mouth dry, parched. At that moment, she'd brave the ISIS terrorists for a single cup of water. She hooked her arm through Jake's.

"Just a couple of travelers, huh?" he chuckled. "One with a rifle and a bulletproof vest. Right." He shook his head and lowered his weapon to hang beside his leg, hopefully hiding it from the casual observer.

They stepped into the open, strolled to the well,

found a bucket on a rope and lowered it until it splashed in the water below.

Moments later, Jake had pulled up the bucket, filled with cool, clean water.

Alex practically fell into it, pouring it into her mouth, the refreshing liquid spilling over her chin and down the front of the borrowed T-shirt. Once she'd had her fill, she waited while Jake had his.

When he had slaked his thirst, he glanced around. "We should go."

The sound of footsteps rushing toward them made Alex spin to face the oncoming threat.

A woman with a shawl draped over her hair rushed out of one of the huts and ran straight for where Alex and Jake stood. She motioned for them to follow. "Hurry," she insisted.

"But where are we going?" Alex asked.

"Does it matter?" she asked in perfect English. "You must hide. Now."

"We don't want to bring danger to you or your people," Alex insisted. "We can hide in the trees."

"No, you don't have time." She took Jake's hand. "Come."

Jake shot a glance toward Alex. "Stay close."

She nodded, and three of them ran toward the mud-and-stick huts.

An older man held open the door as the woman led them through the outer walls into a narrow alley between huts. She navigated the twists and turns so quickly Alex was afraid they'd lose her.

But the woman had a tight hold on Jake's hand and refused to release him until they were somewhere she deemed safe. Through the maze of streets and alleys, they were led deeper into the village.

Alex was amazed at all the homes they passed as they moved farther away from the well and the road.

Behind her, the sound of vehicle engines roared into the village common area.

Alex picked up the pace, keeping close to Jake and the woman. Gunfire echoed off the hills, making her duck. More shots were fired, filling the night with a sense of terror.

Just when Alex thought they would never stop, their guide paused in front of a structure. "In here." She flung open the door and waved them inside.

Alex entered, appalled at how small the interior room was. How would they be hidden if ISIS searched each home one by one?

The woman entered behind them and then squeezed around Jake. She bent, swept aside a rug and pulled up a mat that hid a wooden door in the floor of the hut. She opened it and waved frantically. "Get in. They will be here soon."

Alex glanced down at a dirt cellar in the floor of the primitive hut.

"We need to get in. If the ISIS militants find us here, they will punish anyone who helped to hide us." Jake dropped down into what was nothing more than a hole in the ground. He held up his arms. "Now you."

Alex didn't like the idea of being in a small hole in the ground that could be plagued with spiders or snakes. A shiver rippled down her spine, but what choice did she have?

Shouts sounded outside.

Alex sat on the edge of the hole in the floor.

Jake reached up, grabbed her around the waist, and pulled her into the darkness and into his arms.

The woman closed the wooden trapdoor. The sound of the mat and the rug being slid into place was reassuring at the same time as it was frightening. What if the woman had tricked them into giving up their freedom? What if she had led them into her cellar to imprison them?

Alex's chest knotted. She stood in the cramped space, wrapped in the warmth of Jake's arms, counting the passing minutes, praying whoever was shaking up the village wouldn't continue their own brand of terror. She prayed for the woman who'd shared her home and hiding place to protect them from being captured and potentially tortured or killed by the militants.

Gunfire erupted outside the little hut.

Alex tensed, her fingers digging into the fabric of Jake's uniform jacket.

His arms tightened around her. "It'll be okay," he whispered into her ear, his warm breath making her heart beat faster for an entirely different reason. She couldn't get closer to him while he wore the bulletproof vest, but his arms around her were all him, all muscle, and made her feel protected, shielded from danger.

He'd already rescued her from one situation. Between the two of them and the generosity of the village woman, they'd get out of this one, as well.

Loud voices sounded outside the hut. The door slammed open, reverberating through the small building.

Alex kept perfectly still, her ears perked for sounds.

The woman who'd hidden them spoke softly to someone.

An angry male voice yelled, "Get out!"

The shuffle of footsteps was followed by heavier steps. Something crashed above, as if a box or chair had been overturned. Another crashing sound, and then a loud bang of a shot fired at close range.

Alex clung tighter to Jake, fully expecting the next round to pierce the wooden door over their heads. She tried to shield Jake's body with her own. If the gunman fired into the cellar, he'd get her first. And maybe the bullet would be slowed enough not to enter Jake, as well.

Those thoughts raced through Alex's head as the man above stomped through the small hut, destroying the woman's meager belongings. Then he stepped out, yelling to someone else outside.

Afraid to let go of the breath she'd been holding, Alex waited, listening.

After several long minutes, the voices grew faint and the gunfire ceased. The roar of vehicle engines sounded in the distance.

"Do you think they're gone?" Alex asked, her voice so soft she doubted even Jake could hear it.

"I think so, but we should remain here a little longer to be sure." He still held her in his arms, and she didn't fight to be free.

Jake raised a hand and cupped her face in the darkness. "Are you all right?"

She nodded. "Just a little scared."

He laughed softly. "Me, too."

A few minutes later, the sound of a grass mat sliding across wood was followed by the trapdoor being pulled up. The woman who'd hidden them stood on the dirt floor above, her face a blur in the dark. "They are gone. You can come out."

"You first," Jake said to Alex. He gripped her around her waist, but before he lifted her, he bent his head and brushed her lips with his. "You were brave."

Too shocked by the kiss, Alex didn't have time to respond before she was lifted to where she could sit on the side of the hole. She swung her legs around and pushed to her feet.

Jake handed her his rifle, and then dragged himself out of the hole to stand beside them in the dim glow from the stars shining through the open door of the hut. Even the little bit of light was better than the darkness of the tiny cellar.

Jake glanced around the single room. Every box, basket or container had been dumped over, the contents spilled onto the dirt. The pallet of rags in the corner that was probably the woman's bed had been torn and tossed.

Alex bent to right one of the baskets, but the woman touched her arm. "I will clean later. For now, I will take you to my brother. He will hide you until morning. But then you must leave our village. The Islamic State will return. They are searching for an American soldier and a woman with long black hair. They are searching for you."

Alex's heart dipped into her belly. The militants weren't going to give up until they found her and Jake. "We should leave now," Alex said.

"No," the woman said. "We have had troubles with

the lions at night. They have discovered a taste for human flesh."

A shiver rippled down Alex's spine.

"I have a gun," Jake said. "We can protect ourselves."

"And if ISIS hears your gun, they will find you, kill you and leave your bones for the lions." The woman shook her head. "The morning will be soon enough. My brother has a truck. He can take you to the nearest town. From there, you will be on your own."

Hope surged inside Alex. A ride to the nearest town would be heaven. As long as the truck made it past the militants without alerting them to the passengers inside.

Then again, Alex wasn't so sure a ride in a truck was such a good idea. However, she wasn't sure she could continue on foot, either. Even staying the night in the village held an element of danger.

She held out her hand to the woman. "What is your name?" Alex asked. "I want to remember the woman who saved us from ISIS capture."

"Sabra," she said. "My name is Sabra. My brother is Kirabo."

"Thank you, Sabra," Alex said, and hugged the woman.

"I learned to read and write from an American missionary," Sabra said. "We welcome those who come to help, and protect them from those who want to harm our people."

They were led through the village to a hut on the very edge, farthest away from the road and set back from the other huts. Jake held her hand through the narrow streets.

Alex took comfort in the gesture. She figured she could survive just about anything, as long as Jake held her hand.

JAKE KEPT ALEX close by his side as they maneuvered through the streets to the hut on the outer edge. A barefoot dark man, dressed in what appeared to be a long white shirt, emerged from the hut and hurried to greet them.

Sabra nodded to the man and turned to Jake. "This is Kirabo. He will help you to the next town."

Before Jake could thank Sabra, she disappeared back the way they'd come.

Kirabo flung open the door to his hut and waved them inside.

Jake entered after Alex and turned to face Kirabo. "We can leave tonight, if you prefer."

Their host shook his head. "You will only become food for the lions, or target practice for ISIS. You will remain here until morning when I drive to the market in Ouallam. From there you can contact your people."

Jake nodded. "Thank you for your help and hospitality. We are truly grateful."

Kirabo clasped his hands together. "I leave you now. If we are visited again by the men who came earlier, I will alert you."

"Will that give us time enough to leave?" Jake asked. "We don't want you or anyone else to suffer because you helped us."

A flash of white teeth was Kirabo's response. "We have guards standing watch all night. We knew when you approached our well. Sabra insisted on helping you. Otherwise, we would have left you to the lions. There is food in the basket. My sister made it today. Eat. You will need your strength tomorrow." With that, Kirabo left the hut, closing the door behind him.

Darkness surrounded them.

Jake found his flashlight, switched it on and, using the red lens, shined it around the room.

A pile of tattered blankets lay in one corner, and a basket sat on a small rickety table.

Alex crossed to the basket, removed the lid and raised a crusty round disc. "Ah, bread." She lifted it to her nose and inhaled, closing her eyes. Her stomach rumbled loudly and she laughed. Then her smile faded. "Do you realize how precious this loaf of bread is to these people?" She laid the loaf back in the basket and covered it. "I can't take their food."

Jake frowned. "You need to eat to keep up your strength."

She shook her head. "I can't. They need it more. Besides, we're heading back to civilization tomorrow."

Jake handed her the flashlight and removed the cover from the basket. "At least take a small piece." He tore off a chunk of the bread and handed it to her. "We don't know what will happen tomorrow, much less tonight."

Alex stared at the proffered piece of bread, and her belly rumbled again. "Promise me we will return the favor soon?" She shifted her gaze from the bread to Jake's eyes.

"I promise."

Alex sighed, took the bread and bit into it. She closed her eyes and moaned as she chewed.

Jake's groin tightened. To keep from focusing on the way Alex was enjoying the morsel, Jake took another hunk of the bread and replaced the remainder in the basket. The bread was hard and crusty, but after over twenty-four hours of being on the run, it was heaven.

He savored every bite, chewing slowly before swallowing. When he'd finished, he realized he could have eaten the entire loaf, but, like Alex, he couldn't deprive the people who'd sheltered them of food that was so hard to come by.

He crossed to the bundle of blankets on the ground. "It's not the Ritz, but it's better than sleeping with the lions." He shot a smile toward the woman who'd kept pace with him since they'd left the village the day before. "Alexandria, you can have the first shift of sleep. I'll stay awake."

"Alex." She brushed the crumbs from her fingers and rubbed her hands over her arms. "The only person who ever called me Alexandria was my grandmother. I'm just Alex." She crossed to stand next to him, staring down at the meager pallet of blankets.

Jake nodded. "Alex, you can sleep first. I'm too wired to nod off."

"After what just happened in Sabra's hut, I'm still wound up, too." She drew in a deep breath and let it out slowly. "But we need to rest."

"Right. Tomorrow might not be as simple as Kirabo transporting us to Ouallam."

"True," Alex said. "We might run into more ISIS fighters. In which case, we'll be on the run again." She shoved her hand through her hair and dropped to her knees on the blankets. "I'll give sleep a shot, though it would be a lot easier if I had something softer than the dirt floor to lay my head on."

"I can help you there." Jake shed his bulletproof vest, leaned his rifle against the wall and sat next to her, bracing his back against the mud-and-stick wall. "You can use me as your own personal pillow."

She eyed him. "I can't keep taking advantage of you like that."

His eyebrows hiked, and a smile tugged at the corners of his lips. "Why not? You seemed to sleep fine snuggled up to me last night in the cave."

Though he found it hard to tell in the dim light from the red-lensed flashlight, he could see that Alex's cheeks darkened with a blush.

"Maybe so, but I can't get used to it. You won't always be there for me to lean on."

His smile faded. The thought of leaving Alex didn't sit well with him. He'd gotten used to traversing the rugged Niger hills with her at his side, and he found her to be good company. She didn't complain, and, no matter how tired or dirty, she was still beautiful. What would it be like to spend time with her in a less stressful environment? Like a hotel room with a soft mattress and clean sheets?

His groin tightened again and he shifted to adjust his pants. He had no business thinking about bedding the beautiful teacher. She wasn't the one-night-stand kind of woman. Whatever man she chose to be with had to be there for the long haul. He'd have to want what she wanted: a home, family and children.

Though she hadn't told him that was what she wanted, he could tell by the kindness in her voice and her desire to help others. She'd been teaching orphans and had seen to their safety before going back to help her missionary friends. The woman had self-sacrifice written all over her.

As a navy SEAL, Jake wasn't the man for her. He would be away from his home base more than he was there. If he ever married, his wife would be alone more than she was with him. She'd have to raise their children by herself because he wouldn't be there to help. What woman would sign on for that kind of duty? Marriage should be a union of two people willing to share in the responsibility of taking care of a house and children. Navy SEALs, by the nature of their jobs, couldn't be 100 percent engaged in family. Their first responsibility was to their country. Family came second.

Alex sat beside Jake, leaning her back against the same wall. "I came to Africa for the adventure." She chuckled. "I got it and then some. What I didn't expect was to fall in love."

Jake stiffened, his heart skipping several beats before it raced on. All he could think was, Alex had fallen in love? With whom?

The pretty teacher leaned her head back against the wall and closed her eyes. "I fell in love with the children and the villagers who didn't ask to be caught up in the constant violence. I fell in love with their resilience and ability to smile and laugh even when things were at their worst. I fell in love with the way they made do with what little they had. They always had enough love for their children, and they cared enough to take responsibility for those children who'd lost their parents to violence or disease. I'm sure you've seen the same."

He nodded. "I've been in villages ravaged by war, where naked, starving children are crying for their parents and so hungry they can't remember the last time they ate."

"It breaks my heart." Alex turned to him. "I can always go back to the States, where I'm afforded the opportunity to work. I'll eat three meals a day and never have to worry about where my next meal comes from. I can escape the horror these people have to live each and every day. But they can't." She smiled a sad smile that touched Jake's heart. "I fell in love with their strength of mind and spirit. It made me realize how petty my own problems were and how fortunate I am to be an American. We take so much for granted." She leaned her head against his shoulder. "Thank you for preserving my way of life. I just wish I could do more. But what can one person do to change the minds and hearts of those who continue to ravage countries?"

"We all do the best we can," Jake said. "Each individual's efforts add up."

"Not fast enough to help these people now." She yawned. "Jake, you're amazing."

He laughed. "How so?"

"No matter what the situation, you make me feel safe." She yawned again. "Is it some navy SEAL mojo or something?"

"Or something," he said softly, and slipped his arm around her shoulders.

Alex pressed her face into his shirt and relaxed, her body molding to his. Soon her breathing became even and deep.

Jake eased her head down to his thigh and stroked

her hair, wishing he was in that hotel room with the clean white sheets. He wanted Alex to be more comfortable when he made love to her.

The second the thought came to him, he stiffened. His job was hard enough without wishing for things he couldn't—no, shouldn't—have.

The sooner he got Alex back to safety, the sooner they'd part. Making love to the pretty teacher wasn't in the game plan, he told himself.

As the hours stretched toward morning, with Alex asleep on his thigh, Jake could think of little else. Finally he eased her off his leg onto the pallet of blankets and stood, stretching the kinks out of his muscles. Morning light would come all too soon. He had to be ready to move. Getting Alex to a safe location was top priority. Then he would find his way back to his team and get on with his life.

Without Alex in it.

Chapter Seven

Alex woke and blinked her eyes open to darkness. When she rolled onto her back, she could see the pale light from the stars shining through the open door of the hut. Two figures were silhouetted outside, talking in low, urgent tones.

Immediately alert, she sat up, pushed the hair from her eyes and strained to hear their words.

When she couldn't make them out, she stood and hurried toward the door.

Jake stood with Kirabo in the darkness, speaking quietly enough not to wake the other villagers.

"What's going on?" Alex asked, and shivered in the cool air.

Jake slipped an arm around her and pulled her close. "We need to load into Kirabo's truck before daylight."

Alex snuggled closer, drawing on Jake's heat. "I'm ready whenever you are."

"Good." Jake nodded to Kirabo. "Let us know when."

"Sabra will lead you to my truck. I must go prepare." Kirabo left.

A moment later, Sabra appeared, carrying a plastic

jug of water. "You will need to drink. The day will be long and hot."

Alex took the heavy jug from her and carried it into the hut. Jake turned on his flashlight while Sabra found a bowl and a cup.

She poured the water into the cup and handed it to Jake. Then she sloshed water into the big bowl. "For you to wash."

Alex stared at the water for only a second before she pulled her hair back out of her face and secured it with an elastic band. The she scooped water in her palms and splashed it over her cheeks, eyes and forehead, washing away the dust and sweat from her trek through the hills. Once her face was clean, she scrubbed her arms and the back of her neck. If Sabra and Jake hadn't been in the hut with her, she would have stripped and washed the rest of her body with the meager bowl of water.

Finishing quickly, she stepped aside for Jake to have his turn at the makeshift bath.

"Thank you, Sabra," she said, feeling more human than she had a few minutes before. She'd feel even better if she had a toothbrush and a comb for her hair.

Jake washed his face and dunked his head into the water, scrubbing his hair clean.

Sabra handed him one of the blankets from the pallet on the floor to dry with when he was finished. He drank from the cup of water.

Alex downed an entire glass of the refreshingly cool well water that filled her empty belly for a short time. She hoped they reached Ouallam before the day was over and that they'd find food there. When they did, she'd make sure to send some back to Sabra with her brother.

When they were ready, they followed Sabra out of the hut and toward an old truck parked on the edge of the village.

The bed of the truck was loaded with crates and stacks of empty burlap bags.

"Where do you want us?" Jake asked.

Kirabo pointed to the back of the truck. "There is a gap between the crates. You and the woman will ride there. I will stack more crates around you. Hopefully, we will not be stopped, but if we are, you will be hidden."

Alex planted her foot on a tire and pulled herself up on the side rails.

Jake gave her a gentle shove to help her over the top and into the truck bed. Then he climbed in with her.

The space Kirabo had left for them was tight, barely enough room for two people to sit with their legs pulled up to their chins.

But Alex wasn't complaining. At least she wasn't walking all the way to Ouallam.

As soon as Jake and Alex were in place, Kirabo shoved heavy crates around them and piled a lighter one on top, closing them in.

Moments later, the engine rumbled to life and Kirabo drove the truck out of the village. Night eased into day with light finding its way through the cracks between the crates.

Traveling the rutted dirt road while sitting on the hard metal truck bed wasn't luxury transportation, but it beat hoofing it on foot.

Several miles passed in silence.

"Are you all right?" Jake asked.

Alex nodded and rested her chin on her knees. "I'm fine."

The roar of the engine made conversation hard, but there was no other way to pass time unless she slept. "Did you sleep at all last night?"

"Too wound up," Jake said. "I didn't want to be surprised by another visit from ISIS."

A wash of guilt rushed over Alex. "You should have let me take a shift so that you could get some rest."

He shrugged. "I can function on a lot less. I learned just how much less during BUD/S training."

Alex had seen videos about the navy SEAL training conducted in San Diego, California. It was some of the most mentally and physically demanding training someone could go through. That Jake had survived and completed the training made him one of the best of the best.

"Why did you choose to join the navy?" Alex asked.

He rested his elbows on his knees and stared at the boxes in front of him, as if seeing the past instead of the rough wooden slats. "I needed to get away from home. My father wanted me to go to college and become a banker like him." Jake shook his head. "I was a good student. I could have done it, but it wasn't me. I couldn't be what my father wanted me to be."

"You had to be who you are," Alex stated. "I was supposed to marry my fiancé a year ago, when I realized I couldn't do it. He was the perfect man for me." She gave a crooked smile. "Or so my parents said. He had a steady job and would have been a good provider for me and whatever family came along." She paused, sure he couldn't possibly be interested in her pathetic excuse for a love life. Not when he had real life-and-death issues to deal with on a daily basis.

"But?" Jake prompted.

"He wanted me to stay in the same town where I grew up. He liked that we lived close to both of our parents."

"And that's a bad thing?"

It was Alex's turn to shrug. "Ever since I was old enough to understand the world was round, I've wanted to travel and explore this wonderful planet. I didn't want to stay in Virginia for the rest of my life."

"So he didn't want to leave Virginia. You don't have to move away to visit other countries. You can live in one place and travel to others on short trips."

"He didn't even want to do that. He was perfectly satisfied to limit our exploring to the state and national parks within a day's driving distance."

Jake chuckled. "So he was a homebody. Is that a crime?"

"No, it's not. And I'm sure there's some wonderful woman out there who wants the same thing as he does." Alex snorted. "She can have him. I wanted more."

Jake's eyes rounded. "You stood him up at the altar?"

She shook her head. "No, I left him the week before the wedding. I know it was poor timing, but I couldn't marry someone who wanted a different direction for our life than I did." Alex sighed. "I found the job with the missionaries and I left the day of my wedding."

"Ouch. That's harsh."

"I know, but it would have been much worse had I married him. I would have been miserable and would have made him just as unhappy."

"What made you finally realize he wasn't right for you?"

She tipped her head toward Jake. "Dinner the night before I called it quits."

"Dinner?"

"He didn't like that my fork kept tapping my teeth. He was raised by his mother and she had certain ideas about how a lady should behave. She passed those ideas down to her son. Apparently, clinking a fork against one's teeth is a social disaster."

"Did he question your manners about the fork?"

Alex's lips pressed together. "Yes."

Jake shook his head. "Your fiancé doesn't sound like the sharpest tool in the shed. What did you do?"

"I canceled the church and hall rental, broke it to my parents and fiancé, and signed up for a mission trip to Africa."

"And did absence make your heart grow fonder?"

Alex's lips twisted into a wry smile. "Just the opposite. Being here made me realize just how much I didn't love Paul and why it would never have worked between us. And it also made me realize how small and insignificant my problems were compared to what so many other people in the world have to contend with." She smiled at Jake.

"You made the right decision," Jake concluded.

"I did." A particularly big bump made Alex's bottom bounce on the hard metal floor of the truck bed.

She shifted to relieve the soreness and ended up leaning more into Jake. He didn't seem to mind.

He slipped his arm around her shoulders to keep her from banging her back against the railing and continued their conversation. "Does that make marriage and family out of the question for you?" Jake asked.

"I don't know. I want to find someone who cares enough about me to look past my faults. If bumping my fork against my teeth is considered a huge liability... Well, you know. Why can't I find someone who likes to see different places, try different things, maybe even leave the States on occasion? Is that too much to ask?"

"Not at all." He laughed. "I'm sure there are plenty of guys who want to see the world and who aren't offended by the sound of a fork bumping your teeth."

She shot a sideways glance toward Jake. He was smiling. "When you say it, it sounds different."

"I've seen a lot of the world, but I haven't seen it all. There are so many more places I want to visit. Like Ireland. I've always wanted to go to Ireland. And Italy to see the Colosseum and Pompeii. And one of these days I'd like to visit Jordan and see Petra. I grew up watching Indiana Jones movies. Our world is more than just where we grew up."

"Exactly." She smiled. "My fiancé was content to stay in his own little corner of it. Well, I'm not."

Why couldn't she find someone who dared to be different? Someone who'd chosen his own path, not settling for the path that was expected of him?

All these thoughts roiled around in her head as she sat in the cramped space, next to a man who knew what he wanted out of life and had chased his own dreams to get it.

"So, you jumped at the chance to go to Africa." Jake's lips curved. "Were you aware of the unrest in many of the African nations?"

Alex nodded. "We were briefed on Niger and the factions functioning within its borders. I guess we were naive to think nothing would happen to us."

"Well, you weren't the only ones." Jake's lips twisted. "We were surprised that ISIS had made it as far west as your village."

Alex leaned into Jake's side, glad he had been at their village when ISIS came to call. "Thank you again for saving me from the ISIS militants."

"You're welcome. But maybe we shouldn't count our chickens until we get to Ouallam."

As if to prove his point, Kirabo slammed on his brakes, bringing the truck to a halt.

Jake's arm tightened around Alex, and he pressed a finger to his lips.

A male voice demanded Kirabo get down from the truck.

Alex huddled against Jake's side, her pulse beating so hard and fast against her eardrums she could barely hear.

Beyond their little cave of crates, someone was harassing their driver.

The truck bed leaned slightly toward the driver's side and someone grunted. From what Alex could deduce, a man had climbed up the side rails and dropped down on one of the crates. The cracking sound of wood splitting made Alex jump. She swallowed a gasp and held her breath.

The man on top of the crates was searching through them.

Alex captured Jake's gaze, her eyes wide.

He dipped his head and pressed a kiss to her forehead, followed by one to the tip of her nose.

His lips felt warm, soft and beautiful, distracting Alex from what was going on over their heads. She lifted her chin and met Jake's lips with her own. If ISIS killed them that day, at least she would have known the kiss of the navy SEAL.

She would have no regrets.

JAKE HADN'T MEANT to kiss Alex, but when she'd looked up at him with fear in her eyes, all he wanted to do was calm her and reassure her that they'd be all right. One kiss to her forehead led to one on her nose. When she lifted her face, he couldn't resist.

He kissed her lips, long and hard, pushing his tongue past her teeth to tangle with hers. She still tasted of the bread they'd eaten the evening before.

While someone crawled over the top of their hiding place, Jake kissed Alex. He clasped one hand behind her head, deepening the kiss, while the other hand reached for the knife in the scabbard on his leg. He'd be ready should the person searching Kirabo's load discover them hiding. In the meantime, he had the person he desired in his arms, and she was kissing him back.

A crate lid was slammed back in place, and footsteps moved from one wooden box to another. Finally the truck bed shifted as someone dropped to the ground.

The door to the cab opened and closed with a sharp bang. The engine started and the truck lurched forward, continuing along the road in the same direction. After they'd been rolling for several minutes, Kirabo stopped the truck, got out and climbed into the back. He shoved the overhead crate to the side and stared down at them. "Are you okay?"

Jake nodded. He was more than okay. He'd kissed Alex. They hadn't spoken since, but he could still feel the warmth of her lips on his. "Who stopped you?"

"Armed guards from a mining company that operates in this area. They wanted to make sure I wasn't stealing from them."

Jake's eyes narrowed. "Was it Snyder Mining Enterprises?"

Kirabo nodded. "The Niger government has granted them permission to search for potential mining sites in this area."

"Search?" Alex asked. "But they're—"

"Not too friendly, are they?" Jake finished Alex's sentence.

"No. They have approached our village several times. Many of our men have gone with them with their promise of jobs. They haven't returned for six months."

"You've had no word from them?"

Kirabo shook his head. "None. When we asked Snyder's representatives, they said our men ran away. They have no record of where they went."

"Have you brought this to the attention of your local government?" Alex asked.

"We have," Kirabo said. "Our government has too many other problems with ISIS stirring up trouble and refugees crossing our borders. They don't have the time or funds to come to our aid. But these are not your problems. We will be in Ouallam in twenty minutes, and you will want to hide your rifle while in the town. You can put it in this box." He pulled the lid off a smaller cardboard box packed with straw and melons.

Jake disassembled the rifle into two smaller halves and buried the parts beneath the straw and melons.

Once the box had been sealed shut and tucked among the others, Kirabo shoved the crate back over their heads and climbed down from the back of the truck.

Soon they were on their way, bumping along the dirt road, breathing in the dust kicked up by the wheels.

"Snyder isn't searching for mines," Alex said.

"They're actively mining," Jake finished. "And using conscripted labor to get the job done. Otherwise, why the armed guards?"

"They weren't necessarily keeping people out," Alex said, "as much as keeping them in."

Though Kirabo's statement was correct, and Niger's problems weren't necessarily Jake's and Alex's, Jake couldn't ignore what they'd seen. When he reunited with his team, he'd share the photo and its coordinates with his commander and let the folks higher up in the food chain decide what to do with the information.

In the meantime, the truck slowed.

By the sounds of other engines and shouts from passing people, Jake guessed they'd arrived in a town. Until they pulled to a complete stop, he wouldn't know what town. He hoped it was Ouallam and that he would soon find his brothers, his team.

Chapter Eight

When Kirabo stopped the truck and climbed up in the back to remove the crates, Alex could barely move. She'd been crammed into the tight position for so long her muscles seemed to have forgotten how to function properly.

Jake was up first, reaching back to extend a hand to her.

She took it gladly and let him pull her to her feet.

The bright sunlight blinded her momentarily, and she blinked until she could focus on where she was.

Jake jumped down from the truck bed and held his arms up for Alex.

She sat on the edge and leaned into Jake's outstretched arms. He lifted her by the waist and set her on her feet, engulfing her in his embrace.

She held on to him until her legs steadied and her muscles responded. Reluctant to move away, she turned in the curve of his arm and faced their driver.

Kirabo stood on the ground beside the truck where he'd parked it in front of an official-looking building. "This is the police building. They will help you to find your people." He set the cardboard box containing the melons and rifle on the ground at Jake's feet.

Jake shook hands with Kirabo, and Alex hugged the man, thanking him.

Kirabo left them standing in front of the building and drove away.

Alex prayed he'd be all right and that none of the ISIS folks or the people from Snyder Mining Enterprises had seen him drop off his human cargo. She didn't want him to suffer any repercussions for helping them escape. Unfortunately, he'd left in such a hurry, Alex hadn't had the opportunity to load his truck with food for his family.

Standing in the bustling town of Ouallam made the madness of the ISIS militants seem far away.

Jake lifted the box and tucked it beneath one arm. He took Alex's hand with his other and walked with her toward the building.

Before they stepped through the door, Alex pulled him to a halt. "We can't take this box in there."

With a frown, Jake nodded. "You're right. But I can't leave it out on the street. Someone could take it."

"I'll stay outside with the box."

Jake shook his head. "I can't leave you and the box outside on the street. We'll have to risk taking it inside. As long as they don't have metal detectors, we should be all right."

"Great. And if they do?"

"Then I'll stay outside while you go in and ask to use the phone." He winked. "I'm betting they don't have the funding for expensive metal detectors."

"Maybe not, but they might want to check what's inside the box."

"And all they will see is melons."

"Let's hope that's all they see," Alex said.

Jake carried the box through the door and into the police building, walking with a confident swagger.

Alex stood back as Jake set the box on the floor and asked to use a telephone to make a collect call.

Jake cooked up a story about being an American soldier assigned to train the Niger forces. It wasn't the truth, but the facts might stir up the locals. He explained that his team had been attacked by rebel forces and he'd been separated from his unit, which wasn't a lie.

No one questioned the box on the floor. The man behind the desk asked Jake a few questions and checked with his supervisor, who came out from a room in the rear of the building to run his gaze over Jake.

Finally they agreed to let Jake use the phone, and he was able to call back to his base in Djibouti. Within seconds he was on the phone with his commander, giving his location and asking about the rest of his team.

The visible relief on Jake's face let Alex know his team had made it out of the hot zone intact. The smile he turned toward Alex lit up the room.

He cared deeply about his brothers in arms, and he must have been worried about them the entire time he was working to get her back to a safe place.

When he ended the call, he pulled her into his arms and kissed her soundly on the lips.

She laughed. "What was that for?"

"My guys made it out." He grinned. "We're going to be okay."

She cupped his face and asked, "Were you in doubt? Because if you were, you never let on."

"You never know what's going to happen in a foreign country."

For a moment, Alex basked in Jake's joy at the news that his men were fine. "So, what's the plan?"

"The good news is that my team is in the capital city of Niamey. My commander has been in contact with them. They're arranging for our transport to Niamey as we speak. Someone should be here to pick us up within the next two hours."

"And in the meantime?"

"We find food." He led her out the door with the box tucked under his arm.

"Way to woo a girl," Alex said. "Nothing says you care like offering a woman food."

"Right. And nothing says a man cares like riding with a beautiful woman in the back of a truck, squished into a place only big enough for a child for two hours."

"After two days without a bath or shower?" Alex laughed. "You must be so hungry you're hallucinating."

"No." Jake took her hand and brought her to a stop. "I'm serious. You're an amazing woman. I don't know any other female who would have made that trek without crying every other step."

"You underestimate most women," Alex argued, though she was touched by his words.

"Not the ones I've known." He cupped her cheek. "You're special, Alexandria. Don't ever settle for less than what you want. You deserve more."

She stared into his eyes, her heart swelling at not only his words but the sincerity of them shining in his eyes. "Okay. I won't settle for less than what I want. And right now, I want food."

A smile curled the ends of his lips. "Then food you shall have. The man at the desk told me about a café around the corner with the best food in town."

"And you have something with which to pay for said food?" Alex tapped the pockets of her jeans. "I left all of my possessions back in the village overrun by ISIS. The only thing I have going for me is my passport." She pulled it out of her back pocket. "And only because I keep it on me at all times, a lesson learned from my mentor, Reverend Townsend." Her smile faded as she thought about the good reverend and his wife.

"You couldn't have helped them. The place was swarming with militants."

Alex nodded. "I know. I hope they made it out. When we get to Niamey, I want to see if we can get someone to help me find them and bring them to safety."

"I'll help you as much as I can," Jake said as he led her down the street and around the corner of a building.

"Thank you," Alex said. "You've already helped me so much. I don't think I can ever repay you for saving my life."

"No payment required. It's what I do. And this must be the place."

They stopped in front of a building with bistro tables set outside, umbrellas shading the seats from the sun.

As if they were tourists on vacation, Jake held Alex's chair until she took her seat. Then he rounded the table and sat beside her, his back to the wall of the building.

Alex stared out at the people passing in the street, a little on edge—understandably, she thought—after having the village she'd lived in peacefully for so many months taken over by dangerous rebels.

A man dressed in a white shirt and dark trousers stepped out of the building to take their order. He recited what was on the menu, as no menus were available. The fare was limited and Alex wasn't exactly sure what the items were, but at that moment, she'd eat shoe leather and be satisfied to have something in her empty belly.

She let the waiter choose for her and asked for bottled water to drink.

A few minutes later, the waiter returned with the water and two bowls full of some kind of soup or stew consisting of fish, vegetables, onions and spices.

Alex dug into the meal, amazed at how good it was. She and Jake didn't talk until they had finished every last bite. The waiter returned, cleared their bowls and set plates of some kind of kabob in front of them.

The succulent chunks of meat melted in Alex's mouth. By the time she'd eaten two of the kabobs, she couldn't swallow another bite.

When they'd finished their meal, Alex could only sit back in her seat and groan. "That had to be the most wonderful food I've ever eaten."

Jake patted his flat belly. "Agreed. Now we should be heading back to the police station. Our ride will be expecting to collect us there." Jake pulled a wad of local currency out of his pocket and laid some of it on the table.

"Where did you get that?" Alex asked.

"We always carry the currency of the area, in case we get stranded."

"Smart." With a full stomach, all Alex wanted to

do was take a nap. After two nights of little sleep, she wished she could crawl onto a flat spot on the ground and close her eyes.

When they returned to the police building, they were met by a large dark SUV.

Five men climbed out and engulfed Jake in bear hugs.

A tall man with black hair and brown eyes clapped him on the back. "Man, you're a sight for sore eyes."

Jake grinned. "You have no idea how good it is to see all of you."

"We thought for sure you were dead," said a slightly shorter man with a stalky build and a broad barrel of a chest.

An auburn-haired man with blue eyes stepped in and clasped Jake's forearm. "We've had a drone flying over the village, but couldn't spot you nearby."

"Because we headed straight into the hills." Jake turned to Alex. "I met Alex in the village right before we had to make a run for the hills. She and I have been hoofing it through some pretty rugged terrain, chased by the guys who ruined our day."

"No kidding?" A man with brown hair and blue eyes stuck out his hand. "I'm Buck. Nice to meet you, Alex."

Alex shook his hand and nodded politely, slightly overwhelmed by the group of muscle-bound men.

The auburn-haired guy reached out. "T-Mac."

She shook his hand and turned to the shorter man with the barrel chest.

He nodded and took her hand in a bone-crushing grip. "Pitbull."

"Nice to meet you," Alex said and turned to shake the next man's hand.

"Harm," said a man with black hair and brown eyes. "Not that I'd do you any harm, but that's what they call me."

"And I'm Diesel," said the man who'd first hugged Jake. He shook her hand and backhanded Jake with his free arm. "Roughing it in the mountains, huh?" His lips curled into a sly grin. "I'm sure it wasn't all that rough with Alex."

Jake's brows drew together. "Alexandria was a teacher in that village. She worked with a missionary couple. She'd like to find out what happened to them. Any word on the status of the village?"

"None. Our contact via the Special Forces say al-Waseka's militants have set up security around the village. No one is getting in."

"Or out?" Alex's heart squeezed tightly in her chest. "What about Reverend Townsend and his wife?"

Harm shook his head. "We haven't heard anything about the missionaries."

"No word from al-Waseka concerning any ransom?" Jake asked.

"None," T-Mac confirmed.

"We've made contact with the American embassy in Niamey." Harm held open the door to the SUV. "They're expecting you to debrief them on what happened. We should get moving."

Diesel, Buck and T-Mac climbed into the rear seat.

Jake handed Alex up into the middle seat next to the man who introduced himself as Pitbull and then climbed in next to her. "What's our mission?"

"We're to stand fast in Niamey until intel digests everything. But we're to be prepared to mobilize if we're needed. We have a helicopter on standby with the closest Special Forces team."

"Good." Jake took Alex's hand in his. "We can't leave the missionaries to al-Waseka's mercy."

Alex shot a glance toward Jake. She hadn't expected him to express an interest in rescuing the reverend and his wife. He'd been clear that he was on military time and took his orders from them. Her heart swelled with hope.

"We also found something interesting in the hills," Jake added.

"What's that?"

"A mining operation that isn't supposed to be mining yet."

"Interesting. How close was it to the village?"

"Close enough." Jake's jaw tightened. "And at the last place we stopped, we discovered men had been taken by a mining company and promised work, and they haven't been heard from since."

"Conscripting?" Harm asked from the driver's seat.

"Could be," Jake said.

Alex's pulse kicked up. "You think what happened in my village has anything to do with the mining operation we ran across?"

Jake shrugged. "It seemed a little too coincidental that the villages surrounding the mining operations have been targeted by ISIS." He turned in his seat to face T-Mac. "Can we get the drones to do some scouting over the hills?"

"As soon as we get back to Niamey, I'll contact the drone squadron and get them on it."

Alex sat back in her seat, hope building inside. When she'd left the village, she'd thought for certain the reverend and his wife would be casualties to ISIS. But since no one had reported seeing their bodies, as gruesome as it sounded, they could be prisoners in need of a sharp SEAL team to rescue them.

Her only concern was that she wanted to be with them if they did decide to go after the Townsends. And she'd bet her last dollar Jake wouldn't allow it.

JAKE HELD ALEX's hand all the way back to Niamey. Not long after they left Ouallam, she fell asleep against his shoulder and slept the entire hour and a half back to the capital city of Niger.

They didn't stop until they reached the gates of the embassy.

Jake woke Alex so that she could show her passport. Once the marine gate guard was satisfied by their identities and another had checked their vehicle for explosives, the gate was opened and they were allowed to enter.

Jake helped Alex out of the SUV and slipped an arm around her. "Just think, you're only a few steps away from a shower and a real bed."

"Almost heaven," she murmured.

"Just have to attend a debrief with the ambassador's staff, and we'll see about getting you some clothes and toiletries."

"Everything I brought with me to Africa is back in that village."

"I know. If the militants still have control, you won't be getting your things back anytime soon."

"And I need to call my parents and let them know I'm safe." Alex smiled. "Hopefully, they haven't heard anything about the village being overrun. Not much news from Africa makes it back to Virginia on the television stations. But my father reads online news and worldwide news sites. He might be worried."

"The embassy staff will help you with your phone call," Harm said. "All of that will have to wait. The ambassador wanted to conduct your debrief as soon as you two arrived."

Harm led them into the embassy building where staff members took Alex and Jake to a conference room. An army lieutenant colonel and a marine major were present, along with the state department staff. One staff member offered apologies for the ambassador, who was in a meeting with representatives from the African Union.

Alex gave her statement about what had occurred from the moment Reverend Townsend had entered her schoolroom and told her to evacuate the children to the point where she returned to the village to try to find the reverend and his wife.

Jake gave a brief description of how he and his team had been overrun by militants and how he'd rammed their truck to buy time for his team to escape. He continued the tale of finding Alex and their race through the hills to stay ahead of the fighters following them.

He stopped short of telling the group about the people who'd helped them in the town along the way or about the mining they'd run across in the hills. He didn't know why, but something inside made him keep that information to himself and his team.

Alex shot a questioning glance his way.

He gave a slight shake of his head.

Apparently, she got the message and didn't say anything to the gathering about the ride they'd received, the people in the last village or the mining operation.

Jake answered a few questions until he'd had enough.

Beside him, Alex sat straight, holding herself together, but he could tell by the dark circles beneath her eyes that she was exhausted and needed sleep.

Pushing to his feet, Jake announced to the room, "We'll be here for at least a day, and we've had very little sleep the past two nights. After we've rested, we'd be happy to answer any more questions. But, for now, let Alex and I take showers and find a couple of beds to sleep in."

The embassy staff excused themselves. On his way out, one man stopped beside Jake and Alex. "The ambassador would like to have a word with you tomorrow, after you're rested. Let me know when you're ready and I'll make the arrangements for you to see him. And so that you know, there is a reception tonight in the embassy ballroom. You and Miss Parker are welcome to attend, along with the other members of your team."

"Thank you," Jake said. "We'll let you know about the reception." He'd had it in mind to sleep through to the next morning, but if he could speak with the ambassador that evening at the reception, he might ask him about mining activities and the American companies involved in Niger.

How many people in Niger knew what was going

on with the mining interests? Surely the American embassy had a finger on the pulse of all American corporations doing business in Niger, in which case the ambassador might know what Snyder Mining Enterprises was up to.

First, though, Jake needed to brief his teammates on what he expected to get out of the reception that evening. Until he knew more about what was going on in Niger with the mining and the ISIS attacks, Jake didn't want to share with the embassy staff all of the knowledge he and Alex had gained on their trek through the hills.

Knowledge could be power. It could also make him and Alex targets for someone who didn't want anyone else to know what was going on in the hills.

Chapter Nine

Alex was assigned a room next to the one Jake had been given. With no connecting door between them, she couldn't get to him without venturing out into the hallway.

After spending the past couple days with him in life-and-death situations, she felt bereft and exposed.

She told herself it was ridiculous, but she couldn't stop that feeling. They were in an American embassy, surrounded by Americans who'd sworn to uphold the constitution and protect people from their own country.

Then why didn't she feel safe? In the two days she'd known Jake, had she become dependent on the man? Now that she was away from him, all she could think about was when she'd see him again. Two days wasn't long enough for her to fall for a guy, was it? She'd spent six years getting to know Paul before she'd agreed to marry him.

Yet she'd taken only a couple of minutes to realize what a mistake that was and ended her engagement.

Falling for someone she'd known for two days was silly.

She gathered the bathrobe and travel-size toiletries

and entered the bathroom. For the next fifteen minutes, she stood under the shower's spray, washing away the dirt and grime of the past forty-eight hours. No matter how long she stood there in the warm water, she couldn't shake a feeling of unrest.

Then she stepped out, toweled off and blew her hair dry, smoothing it with the brush that had been provided. She felt almost human.

One of the ladies on the embassy staff had given her a dress and open-toe sandals to wear, which helped with the guesswork of shoe size. She'd also given her a scarf to wrap over her head in deference to the culture of the area.

She could have put on the nightgown and gone straight to bed. After the debriefing and Jake's withholding of key information, she wanted to talk to him, to ask him why. An embassy staff member had escorted them to their individual rooms, giving them no time to discuss anything in private.

Now that she was bathed, dressed and feeling more human than before, she wanted to talk to Jake. The man was on the other side of the wall. So close, but so far.

Alex edged the door open and stepped into the hallway. She had raised her hand to knock when Jake's door opened.

She stood still, staring into his eyes. Her own stung, embarrassingly close to shedding tears. Why was she so emotional? They'd only been apart for a few minutes, not days or weeks.

Jake grabbed her arms and dragged her into his room. Once she was over the threshold, he kicked the door closed and backed her against it, his mouth crashing down on hers.

Shocked by his desperate kiss, Alex opened her mouth on a gasp.

Jake dived in, caressing her tongue with his in a long, sensuous kiss.

She clung to him like a life preserver in a stormy sea.

When at last he raised his head and inhaled deeply, he pressed his cheek to the top of her hair. "I don't know why, but it felt like the past fifteen minutes was the longest stretch of the entire time I've known you."

Alex chuckled and rested her forehead against his chest. "I felt the same."

Jake smoothed a hand over her hair. "I wanted to tell you why I didn't say anything about the mining camp we ran into."

"Good." She smiled up at him. "Because I wanted to ask you why you didn't mention it in the debriefing."

"Harm came by my room. I told him not to mention the mining camp until we could find out a little more by doing some of our own sleuthing. T-Mac is a master at the computer. He can find out anything you never wanted revealed."

"What exactly are you looking for?" Alex asked.

"I want to know who is in charge of the Snyder Mining Enterprises activities here in Niger. Who owns it? Who does the owner have in his pocket to slide by the fact that they were supposed to be simply looking for places to mine, not start the mining operations?"

Alex nodded. "All valid questions. Still, why didn't you bring the embassy staff into your confidence?"

"I want to know these things before I talk to them.

What if they know what's going on and are turning a blind eye to it? They might attempt to cover up the problem rather than admit there is one."

Alex frowned. "What makes you think the embassy personnel aren't loyal, law-abiding citizens?"

"Nothing but a hunch."

"Will you at least clue in the ambassador?" Alex asked.

"Not yet." He stared down at her, holding her at arm's length. "If you're going to a reception tonight, you will need a cocktail dress."

"A cocktail dress in Africa?"

"You'd be surprised by the level of decorum the leaders strive for. I want you at the reception to listen for anything that might have to do with the mining and circumventing the Niger government rules and regulations. We also need to listen for anything concerning the ISIS uprising."

"Okay, I'll buy a new dress." She glanced down at the one she was wearing. "At least I won't have to shop in my underclothes."

Jake's eyes flared. "Now that gives an interesting mental image." He tipped her chin and stared down into her eyes.

For a moment, Alex thought Jake would kiss her again.

Instead, he sighed and offered her his arm. "Shall we go?"

Alex felt a flash of disappointment, followed by a warm feeling of being close to Jake.

In the lobby of the embassy, they met up with four other members of the SEAL team.

"Where's T-Mac?"

"He's on a borrowed computer, working his magic," Diesel said.

Harm leaned close to Jake and Alex. "He wanted to get all the information he could before the reception tonight. One of the staff members here showed us the guest list and told us who's who of the invitees. You'll want to be there. Hell, we'll all want to be there."

"Who's coming?"

"Mohamed Rafini, Niger's president."

"Nice. And they're letting us in?" Jake smirked.

"That's not all," Buck said. "Several National Assembly members will be here, along with some bigwigs from prominent corporations doing business in Niger."

"Anyone from Snyder Mining Enterprises?"

Harm crossed his arms over his chest. "As a matter of fact, yes. Quinten Philburn, CEO of Snyder Mining Enterprises. He's had an office in Niamey for over a year, negotiating mining speculation projects with the Niger trade commission."

"He might be the one causing all the unrest in the area," Jake said. "If he's conscripting men to do his mining, he's a problem."

"True." Harm's brows formed a V over his nose. "But is he *our* problem?"

Jake knew what Harm was saying. But with Alex standing at his side, the voice of reason and empathy, he had to measure each word carefully. "If the ISIS attack has anything to do with the mining operations, yes. We were attacked. The missionaries, who are American citizens, were attacked. We have an obligation to our countrymen to help them when they're in trouble. So, yes, he is our problem."

"The CO will have to agree on that." Diesel lifted his chin and stared at his teammates through narrowed eyes. "We can't conduct unauthorized missions in a foreign country without stirring up a hornet's nest with our higher-ups."

Jake's lips pressed into a thin line. "Since when has that stopped us from doing whatever it takes to make things right?"

"He's right," Pitbull said. "When Marley was in trouble, we didn't hesitate to help even though we weren't authorized to."

"And when the All Things Wild Resort in Kenya was targeted, we didn't back away. We engaged…without permission."

With a chuckle, Jake nodded. "That's right. We just have to be smart about it."

"And by 'smart,' you mean get permission from the CO?" Diesel prompted.

"Sure," Jake said. "Even if it's after the fact."

"That's not permission," Harm said. "That's forgiveness."

"Right now, we have to get outfitted for a formal party." Jake glanced around at his buddies. "How many of you have worn a suit in the past half century?"

"I wore one when I was seven to my great-aunt's funeral," Harm admitted.

Jake snorted. "Like I thought. We all need some threads to blend into the crowd tonight. We can't look like something the cat dragged in. Right, Pitbull?"

"Hey." Pitbull leveled a lethal stare at Jake. "No cat

is going to drag this dog anywhere. And what do I need with a suit?"

Alex swallowed a chuckle at the look on Pitbull's face.

Jake went on to say, "Think of it as practice for when you boneheads marry your ladies."

Pitbull's eyes lit up. "Now you're talking. Though I think Marley would wear her flight suit to the wedding instead of a dress. And she's damned sexy in that flight suit. I think that's the first thing I noticed about her."

"No way. The first thing you noticed about Marley was her plane and how it made you all jittery inside." Harm clapped a hand to Pitbull's back. "Come on, even Marley would appreciate a tailored suit on her man."

The men laughed and headed for the embassy exit and the borrowed SUV.

Alex enjoyed how they poked and prodded one another. She could sense the tight bond between these men who lived, played and fought as a team. Never having had friends as close as the men were to each other, she envied their camaraderie.

Any woman who married into the group would have to understand their relationship was number one; their loyalty to country would come first, family second. But she had no doubt anyone these men loved would be loved fiercely, like everything else they did in life.

As she slid into the SUV beside Jake, Alex studied the man who had never married. Perhaps he took his duty to country so seriously he would never choose a woman over the navy. Many men in the military found a way to have both. And many ended up divorced. The secret to the successful unions was the ability to adapt.

Both partners in the relationship had to come in strong and stay strong throughout. They had to trust that each would be there for the other if the going got tough. *When* the going got tough.

Alex didn't have any long-term expectations of Jake. Yes, he'd kissed her, but he hadn't declared an undying love for her, and she wouldn't expect it so soon after they'd met. But the girl inside her that always read the books with the happy endings wanted to see Jake have his happy ending. And she wanted one of her own.

THREE HOURS LATER, Jake, Alex and the men returned to the embassy, having found appropriate clothing for the reception that evening.

Alex disappeared as soon as they returned, claiming she wanted to get a nap in before the party. He suspected she was excited by the dress she'd found. That she hadn't shown it to him indicated she wanted it to be a surprise for him.

Warmth spread through Jake's chest and heart. He'd offered to escort her to the ball, and she'd accepted with a brilliant smile.

"Where's T-Mac working?" Jake asked.

"In another wing," Buck said. "He and I are sharing quarters."

"Let's find out what we've been missing," Jake said.

Buck led the way to the wing of the embassy where he and T-Mac had been sharing a room. When he threw open the door, T-Mac barely glanced up from his computer. "Hey," he said.

Jake entered the room and held the door for the others to come in before he closed it behind them. "What have you found?"

"Some interesting connections," T-Mac replied.

"Really?" Jake leaned over the back of T-Mac's chair. "Like what?"

"I looked up Snyder Mining Enterprises and traced it back to its mothership, the Transunion Mining Corporation. At least, it was a part of Transunion until a year ago, when its assets were sold to a corporation out of Colorado. I'm having a hard time tracing the Colorado corporation. Its base is somehow buried in the Cayman Islands. It might take me longer to sift through the data there."

"Interesting." Jake tapped the side of his cheek.

"I did some checking on our man Quinten Philburn, the CEO of Snyder Mining Enterprises here in Niger," T-Mac added. "He's got a pretty checkered past. He was fired from his job as chief operations officer at Rocky Point Mine in Alaska when the company was sued by indigenous people for polluting the nearby lake and river. Before the lawsuit, Philburn had a record of the most profits for any mining company in the area. After the lawsuit, the company folded and filed for bankruptcy."

Jake snorted. "Fired for taking advantage of the resources in America, yet he's working here in Africa, pretty much unregulated. We saw some of the men working that mine. The conditions were unenviable."

"Sounds like Philburn is squeezing as much of the profits as he can out of the operation." Harm spun away from the computer and paced across the room and back.

"But, again, it's not our job to police the actions of civilians, even if they are from the US."

"No," Jake said. "It's not our job, but US citizens are in danger. We've been on missions to rescue Americans held hostage in foreign countries. It happens."

"It happens when the orders come from higher up," Harm reminded him.

"One other thing I found…" T-Mac turned in his chair. "Ambassador Brightbill had shares in Transunion Mining Corporation back before he joined the State Department."

"Does he still?" Jake asked.

T-Mac shook his head. "I couldn't find a current connection." He raised his hands. "That's all I have so far. But I'll keep digging."

"Thanks." Jake straightened. "I need to get ready for the reception. If all the players are there, I want to get a feel for who we're up against."

"Assuming we're up against anyone," Diesel cautioned. "We don't have clearance to go after the missionaries."

"If we don't get the clearance, I'm going without it," Jake said. "The sooner we go, the better chance we have of getting them out alive."

"I'm with Jake," Pitbull said. "They're American citizens. If they were my grandparents, I'd want someone like us to get them out of there."

"That's right," Jake said. "Think of them as your grandparents. Would you leave your elderly grandmother and grandfather in the clutches of terrorists?"

Harm crossed his arms over his chest and glared at Jake. "You play dirty, don't you?"

Jake spread his arms wide. "I do what it takes."

Harm nodded. "You do." Then he clapped his hands together. "Let's go hunting. For information."

"And I'll stay behind and go through more data." T-Mac returned his attention to his computer screen. "Maybe there will be more connections that lead us to the primary source of issues."

"At least we have a good start on who to keep an eye on." Jake headed for the door.

Harm followed. "This evening's reception should be good."

"Counting on it." Jake opened the door and stepped out into the hallway. "I promised Alex we'd do something about her missionary friends. And I don't like to go back on my promises."

Chapter Ten

Alex couldn't wait to step out of her room wearing the beautiful ice-blue dress that matched her eyes and contrasted perfectly with her dark hair. The strappy silver sandals made her feel delicate and feminine after she'd spent the past few days hiking in the hills, smelling like a locker room and wondering when or where her next meal would come from.

Luckily the blisters she'd earned on the hike didn't hit any of the sandal's straps. She could stand in the shoes for a couple hours while she and Jake mingled with the guests, hopefully learning more about Niger and the location of the reverend and his wife.

If all else failed, Alex would go back to the village and ask the people there where the militants had taken the missionaries. For all she knew, the ISIS leaders might have taken pity on the Townsends and left them alone to care for the new mother and her child.

Alex snorted softly. "Fat chance." From what she'd heard, the ISIS group wasn't into charity or leniency. If the Townsends were still alive—her heart clenched at the other possibility—they were being held captive somewhere.

Smoothing a hand over her hair, she pulled the feathery-light, pale blue scarf up over her head, liking the way it made her appear even more delicate. Not that she was weak or terribly girly, but she relished the idea of others underestimating her. She saved her tough side for when she really needed it.

After one last glance in the mirror, she flung open the door and stared into the broad chest of a man standing there with his hand raised. She nearly had a heart attack until she realized it was Jake. When she got a look at him in a dark suit, his chin shaved and his hair slicked back, her heart palpitated a billion beats a minute.

The man positively took her breath away.

When she finally remembered to breathe, she looked up into his gray eyes. "Wow."

"I should say the same, but it would be completely inadequate to describe you." He took her hand and raised it to his lips. "You're stunning."

"You're not hard on the eyes, yourself." Heat pooled at her core. She knew she looked good in the dress, but damn. She'd rather strip out of it, take Jake back into her room and make love to him.

Her blood raced, hot and fluid through her veins at the thought of getting naked with Jake. Two days? She felt as if they'd been together for much longer than two days. With all they'd gone through, it felt more like a lifetime.

She tore her gaze away from his and looked around his big body. "Where are your teammates?"

"The guys will meet us in the ballroom." He tugged on her fingers, pulling her enough that she had to take a step forward.

Alex laid her free hand against his chest, not to push him away but to balance herself when she was feeling so very off-kilter. The man made her experience so many different emotions, it caused her head to spin.

"Ready?" he whispered.

Oh, baby, was she. Alex nodded.

When he drew her arm though his and started for the stairs, she blinked several times and fell in step beside him, chastising herself for the idiot she was. Ready for what? To take him to her bed and make wild love with him? Was she out of her mind? They were strangers. He was a navy SEAL; she was a teacher. He'd never spoken of anything between them that would last beyond when they went their separate ways. No commitment, no words of love.

Her breath caught in her throat and she nearly stumbled going down the stairs. They would eventually part, and the thought made her sad.

Jake tightened the arm holding hers, and he stopped long enough for her to regain her balance. "Okay?"

She nodded, heat rushing into her cheeks. Thank goodness he couldn't read minds. She'd be mortified if he knew her deepest, most sensual thoughts. What if he didn't think of her in the way she thought of him?

Naked.

She walked alongside him, proud to be with the gorgeous man, but conflicted on where they were going from there.

For now, anyway, to the reception.

Already the stately ballroom was filled with people dressed in their best clothing. Alex and Jake glanced toward the ambassador as they entered.

Alex had never been to such a grand event, and she was glad for the dress she'd purchased on Jake's credit card. She'd make certain she paid him back for the costly dress as soon as she could access her savings account back in Virginia. At least she fit in with the wives and female dignitaries. And the navy SEAL team did their country proud. Each man had shaved his beard and dressed in a suit and tie. They were handsome men who filled out the shoulders of their jackets like no other men in the room.

Jake, the tallest of his team, stood with his shoulders back, appearing like a Greek god lording it over his underlings.

Alex's chest swelled with pride when she had no reason to be prideful. He didn't belong to her. But he *was* her date for the night. She might as well enjoy it.

Jake met with his team. "We need to spread out, mingle with the guests and find the men we talked about earlier."

The others nodded and split up, blending in with the guests as much as handsome men could blend.

"What men did you discuss?" Alex asked.

"T-Mac had a list of people of interest. Like Quinten Philburn, CEO of Snyder Mining Enterprises. We also need to meet Ambassador Brightbill."

Alex frowned. "Is he a person of interest? Our ambassador?"

Jake shrugged. "There's a connection between him and the mining company. It's old, but it's a connection."

Alex nodded. "Okay. Philburn and Brightbill." She glanced around the room, studying the people. "The ambassador is still greeting people as they enter the ballroom. We won't get a chance to speak with him or even to shake his hand in the reception line. We'll have to wait until all of the guests have arrived."

"In the meantime, would you care for a drink?" Jake tilted his head in her direction, like an attentive date.

"I'd love one," she said, and laughed. "Two days in the hills with little water made me appreciate every drop I drink."

"What if there's alcohol?" Jake asked.

Alex shook her head. "I want water. Pure and cold. I think it'll be days before I feel any differently."

"Same here." He left her standing by a palm tree to walk toward the refreshments table.

Alex's gaze followed him all the way. Holy smokes, he was hot.

"I don't recall seeing you at any of the functions," a deep, male voice said close to Alex's ear.

She jerked around to face a man in a charcoal-gray suit with salt-and-pepper hair and blue eyes. "Excuse me?"

He held out his hand. "Let me introduce myself. I'm Thomas Whitley."

"Alexandria Parker." She took the man's hand and gave it a perfunctory shake.

"As I was saying, I don't recall seeing you at any of the embassy functions."

"That would be because I arrived today." She smiled. "Do you come to all of the events?"

He laughed. "Most of them. I'm the ambassador's executive officer. His right-hand man."

"Then you would be at most of the functions. I would think you'd be in the reception line."

"Normally, I would be at the ambassador's side," he said, staring at the line of dignitaries greeting each guest as he or she entered the ballroom. "I arrived back from a trip an hour ago, and barely had time to shower and change."

"At least you made it in time to enjoy the party," Alex said. "Do you know most of the people in attendance, Mr. Whitley?"

"Please, call me Thomas." He glanced around the room, his gaze pausing briefly on each individual, as if tallying the faces he knew. "Yes, you could say I know most of the people in attendance. Until I spotted you and the young man heading our way with refreshments."

Jake arrived with two glasses of sparkling water and handed one to her, freeing his hand to shake Whitley's.

"Jake Schuler," Alex said, "this is Thomas Whitley, Ambassador Brightbill's right-hand man, his executive officer."

"Call me Thomas." He shook Jake's hand.

"Thomas was telling me he knows just about everyone in the room," Alex said.

"That's impressive." Jake sipped from his glass and then nodded toward the room in general.

A man walked up to Whitley and started to talk about weather and growing seasons. When he paused in his diatribe, Thomas introduced him to Alex and Jake.

Since his wasn't a name mentioned earlier, Alex nodded politely, but didn't engage in conversation. Soon the man moved on to others in the room.

"Thomas." A man with dark hair and brown eyes, dressed in a black suit with a crisp white shirt, approached Whitley with a distinct and unwarranted swagger.

Alex imagined the man thought highly of himself, but she kept her feelings from being revealed on her face.

The man clasped Whitley's hand in both of his. "Glad I caught you."

"Quinten, what brings you to this neck of the woods?" Whitley asked, and pulled his hand free.

"We ran short on supplies on our mining expedition. I had to drive all the way in to Niamey to get what we needed."

Alex had to assume the man Thomas had called Quinten was Quinten Philburn, the CEO of Snyder Mining Enterprises. He was younger than Alex had expected. Probably in his midforties.

Whitley turned toward Alex and Jake. "Quinten Philburn, meet Alexandria Parker and Jake Schuler. They just arrived at the embassy today."

Quinten extended a hand to Alex first.

His grasp was strong, a little too strong, to the point it hurt Alex's hand.

She fought to keep from wincing. When he released it, she hid it behind her back to shake blood back into her fingers.

Then he turned to Jake and shook his hand.

The two men gripped hands for longer than the usual handshake. Jake's knuckles turned white before they finally let go.

"Where did you say you came from?" Quinten asked.

"We didn't," Jake answered, and turned to Whitley. "So, you work for the ambassador?"

"I do," Thomas said.

"How did that come about?" Alex asked. "Did he inherit you when he came to Niger to run the embassy?"

Thomas's lips twisted. "Not quite. We've been together for seventeen years. We go all the way back to when we both worked in the corporate world, prior to the ambassador's decision to join the State Department."

Alex raised her eyebrows. "And you both decided to work for the State Department?"

"After the dog-eat-dog world of corporate America, we were glad to dedicate our time to promoting our great country to others in the world." Thomas spread his hands wide. "And here we are, in the capital city of Niger, hopefully helping to make a difference."

"How altruistic." Alex softened the comment with a smile.

"And you, Mr. Philburn?" Alex gave him her most innocent, questioning look. "What brought you to Niger?"

For a short moment, Philburn hesitated, his gaze boring into Alex's.

She felt a shiver of apprehension, but held her polite and—she hoped—questioning gaze.

"I came for the potential of profit." He glanced across the room. "Niger is a country with vast resources, much of which have yet to be tapped. That's why I'm here. To find those resources."

"And when you do?" Alex prompted.

Philburn captured Alex's gaze with a steady one of his own that seemed to look right through her to her innermost thoughts. "The Niger government will decide how they want to go about mining those minerals." He held her stare for a moment longer and then turned to Thomas. "I understand Niger's President Rafini is here tonight?"

Thomas nodded. "He is. And he will be in the capital city throughout the week."

"About time. I've been trying to meet with him for a month. He travels a great deal."

"Patience is the key when dealing with anyone in the government. The president is a very busy man."

"As are most people," Philburn snapped.

Thomas's eyes narrowed. "President Rafini isn't most people. As a representative of our great nation, I urge you to be cautious in your dealings with President Rafini."

Philburn snorted.

"You need to get with his people to schedule a meeting with the man," Whitley said.

"I will." Philburn nodded to Alex, ignored Jake and walked away.

"Ah, the reception line is breaking up." The ambassador's executive officer hooked Alex's arm. "Let me introduce you to my boss."

Whitley insisted on taking Jake and Alex over to where the ambassador was speaking with several people from the reception line.

As they approached, the ambassador glanced up and smiled.

"Thomas, who do you have with you? I'm certain I did not have the pleasure of meeting this lovely lady." The ambassador held out his hand. "And you are?"

Alex introduced herself to the charming ambassador, who was old enough to be her father and had a kind face. "Alexandria Parker. It's a pleasure to meet you, Ambassador Brightbill."

"Ah, Miss Parker. Thomas mentioned we had guests from the States staying in the embassy. I also understand you're here with a team of navy SEALS."

She nodded and turned to Jake. "This is one member of that team."

"Chief Petty Officer Jake Schuler." Jake held out his hand.

The ambassador reached out to shake it. "I'm told you and Miss Parker were involved in an unfortunate raid on a village east of here in the Tillabéri region."

Alex nodded. "We were, but Chief Petty Officer Schuler rescued me and brought me to Niamey."

"We are privileged to have heroes among us tonight," Ambassador Brightbill said.

Jake nodded without commenting.

"We have had difficulties with a certain ISIS faction in the Tillabéri region. Our US Special Forces are training the Niger army to defend itself against such attacks."

"But the people of the village were defenseless," Alex said. "There was no one there to protect them when the militants stormed their homes."

The ambassador's lips pressed together. "President Rafini is aware of the problem and is doing his best to build his army and their skills, with our assistance."

Alex bit down hard on her lip, wanting to tell the ambassador that what they were doing wasn't enough. But she realized the US ambassador couldn't always influence policy in Niger. That had to come from within.

In the meantime, her friends the missionaries were either being held hostage or dead.

When the ambassador, his executive officer and the CEO of Snyder Mining moved on to greet others, Alex drew in a deep breath and let it out slowly. "What am I doing here?"

Jake slipped an arm around her waist. "What do you mean?"

"I need to go back to the village and help the reverend and his wife. I'm wasting my time here in Niamey."

"You can't help them alone." Jake turned her to face him and held her hands in his. "I'll work with my commander. He'll chase it up the chain of command. We'll get a mission launched to rescue your friends."

"When?" Alex demanded. "After ISIS has used them as an example, tortured or killed them?" She shook her head. "Bringing it up through the proper channels will take too long. It will be too late by then, if it isn't already."

She lifted the skirt of her beautiful dress and spun on her fancy heels. The spacious ballroom seemed to close in around her. "I need air."

"Let me walk you to the garden."

"That won't be necessary. I'm going back to my room. I don't need you to escort me." She tugged to release her hand from his grip, but he didn't let go.

"Promise me you won't do anything tonight," he said.

She gritted her teeth without answering.

Jake squeezed her hand. "Promise."

Alex sighed. "Fine. I won't do anything tonight. But by morning, I'll find a car, a truck, whatever I can and head back to the village. I can't leave them to their fate. It's not right." She jerked her hands free of his grasp and spun on her heels, heading for the staircase leading up to their rooms.

JAKE WATCHED ALEX LEAVE. He hesitated for only a moment and then strode across the floor after her.

Buck stopped him with a hand on his arm. "Hey, buddy, where ya going?"

"Alex is going back to the village," he stated in a flat tone.

Buck's eyes widened. "Tonight?"

"I think I talked her into waiting until morning," Jake said. "But I don't know if she'll actually stay."

"Damn." Buck frowned. "You might not be able to stop her if she gets it in her mind to go."

"That's what I'm afraid of." He looked past his teammate as Alex disappeared at the top of the staircase. "However, I can go with her and try to make sure she doesn't get herself killed."

Buck touched his arm. "Dude, you can't go running around the Niger countryside. It's not safe."

"And I'm supposed to let Alex go off by herself?" Jake shook his head. "No way."

"You don't have clearance to leave. We aren't on vacation in here. The CO will count you as AWOL." Buck looped an arm over Jake's shoulders. "You need a better plan than taking off without guns, ammo or backup."

"Then come up with a plan while I make sure Alex doesn't go off half-cocked." He ducked out from under his friend's arm and hurried after Alex, praying he got to her before she left the embassy without him.

As he weaved through the throng of people there for the reception, he passed Quinten Philburn, Thomas

Whitley and Ambassador Brightbill. Their gazes followed him.

He hadn't solved anything by being at the reception that night, other than putting faces to the names of the persons of interest T-Mac had come up with. At least now he knew who was behind the illicit mining operations. Philburn didn't strike him as a man he could trust any further than he could throw him.

One additional piece of information he had gleaned that night was that Whitley and the ambassador had been together since they'd worked in the corporate world. He'd have T-Mac research Whitley along with the others.

What he still didn't know was whether the ISIS militants were roughing up villages on their own steam or if they were somehow connected with the illegal mining.

Jake didn't know, but he was sure T-Mac could find out given enough time. Only he wasn't certain he had time. His number-one priority for the night was to stop Alex from leaving to save her missionary friends. Once he made sure she was safe, he'd work on helping her to rescue the reverend and his wife.

Chapter Eleven

Alex hurried down the hallway and turned right at the corridor she thought led to her room. When she reached the end of the hall and hadn't found her room number, she sighed in frustration.

"Miss Parker," a voice called out.

She stopped and turned to find Quinten Philburn heading in her direction. Alex stiffened. The last thing she wanted was a confrontation with a man she was sure was conducting illegal mining operations with conscripted workers. After she found and freed the Townsends, she'd go after Philburn and Snyder Mining Enterprises.

Alex lifted her chin and started back the way she'd come, forced to face the man. "Mr. Philburn," she said as she moved to pass him.

He reached out, snagged her arm and pulled her to a halt. "I'd like to have a word with you, Miss Parker."

"And you couldn't do that back in the ballroom?" She stared down at his hand on her arm and back up to his face. "Please, let go of my arm."

Instead of letting go, he squeezed tighter. "I don't know what you and your pet SEAL are up to, but don't be stupid and step into something you have no business meddling in."

Alex raised her eyebrows. "Whatever are you talking about?"

His eyes narrowed to slits. "You know damn well."

She tilted her chin in a challenge. "Perhaps you'd better spell it out for me."

The hand on her arm bit into her flesh, sending pain up her arm. When she tried to shake his hand free, he tightened his hold.

"I'll spell it out, all right." He jerked her around and pulled her back against his chest.

"Hey!" a voice shouted from down the hall.

Alex turned her head, relief rushing through her when she recognized Jake's stormy countenance.

Philburn released her arm and stepped away. "Things are different here in Niger. Just remember that." He stepped past her and strode toward the stairwell at the end of the hallway.

By the time Jake reached Alex, Philburn had disappeared through the doorway.

Jake wrapped his arms around Alex, lifted her chin and stared into her eyes. "Are you all right?"

She nodded, glad he was there, but not willing to let him know just how frightened she'd been.

Jake dropped his arms and turned in the direction Philburn had gone.

Alex grabbed his arm, her hand shaking. "Where are you going?"

He shot a glance back at her, his jaw tight, his eyes narrowed. "I'm going after him."

"Don't go."

He hesitated, one foot planted in the direction Philburn had gone, the other next to Alex. His fists clenched and unclenched while a nerve ticked in his jaw.

Then the muscles in his shoulders relaxed, and he slipped his arm around Alex. "I'll stay, but I'm staying with you tonight. I'll sleep on your floor, whatever, but I'm not leaving you alone." He pulled her into his embrace and crushed her to his body.

Alex melted into him, wrapping her arms around his waist. She rested her cheek against his chest, the sound of his heartbeat thundering in her ear. "Lately, I get the feeling trouble follows me."

"If you're referring to me, you're right. I'm following you until whatever's going on is resolved. You can count on that."

"But you have a job to do." She tilted her head up to stare into his eyes. "You can't babysit me against *potential* threats forever."

Jake's jaw tightened. "No, but I can protect you now. Where's your key?"

She pulled the key out of her pocket and held it up.

Instead of taking it from her, he scooped her off her feet and carried her back down the hallway and stopped in front of her room.

Alex's heart raced as she leaned over to unlock the door.

Jake kicked it open with his foot, strode in and let her legs slide down his body. Still he held her against him, slow to release her. "Tomorrow, we'll do something about finding the Townsends. I promise."

"Thank you," she whispered, and leaned up on her

toes to press her lips to his. "And thank you for being there when Philburn…"

Jake's lips thinned into a grim line. "Did he hurt you?"

"Not really," she said. There would be bruises on her arm by morning, but they would fade.

"What did he want?"

"I'm not sure. He more or less told me to mind my own business."

"About what?" Jake asked.

"He didn't say." Alex frowned. "Do you think he knows we've seen his operation?"

"It's possible." Jake smoothed back her hair from her face and then bent to kiss her forehead.

His lips were warm, soft and firm, making Alex tingle all over and long for so much more than a kiss on the forehead.

When he bent again to touch his lips to her forehead, she tilted her chin just enough to capture his mouth with hers.

Their lips touched, setting off an explosion of sensations throughout Alex's body.

He cupped the back of her head and held her closer, deepening the kiss.

She opened to him, sliding her tongue over his, reveling in his warmth and strength. After being with him every minute of the past few days, she'd missed him when they'd been apart for only a handful of minutes.

To Alex, the kiss became more of a frantic need to be close, to dive into him, to become a part of Jake. When he lifted his head, she dragged in air, her body pressing against his, fueling her desire, pushing her to the next level. "I want you, Jake Schuler."

"And I want you." He brushed his lips lightly across hers. "But I don't want to take advantage of you when you're most vulnerable."

"Oh, Jake. You don't make me feel vulnerable." She threaded her hands into his hair and brought his face down to kiss his lips softly. "You empower me." She slid her fingers along his neck to the tie knotted at the base of his throat. With deft fingers, she slipped the knot free and tossed the tie across a chair.

Jake chuckled. "Empowered?" He growled low in his chest. "I like the way that sounds." His hands skimmed up from her waist to her shoulders, located the zipper on her blue dress and dragged it halfway down her back.

Alex shivered in anticipation.

Jake halted before reaching the bottom of the track. "Say the word and I stop here."

"Good Lord, don't stop now." She reached behind her, covered his hand with hers and guided the zipper all the way down to the base of her spine. Then she hooked her thumbs into the lapels of his jacket and slid it over his broad shoulders and down his arms.

What happened next was a frantic effort to remove the remainder of the clothing between them.

Alex's pretty dress slipped off her body and over her hips, then dropped to pool around her ankles.

Jake bent to unbuckle the straps of her silver sandals and removed them with one hand on the shoe, the other on the back of her calf.

Heat built at her core, spreading outward to the tips of her fingers. Sure, she'd only known him for a couple days, but her body knew him as if they had been together for much longer. She couldn't stop the wave of longing, nor did she want to. Alex let it consume and push her to do things she would never have conceived of before she'd met him.

When Jake straightened, he rose slowly, dragging his fingers up her calf, along the inside of her thigh to cup her sex over the lace of her panties.

Her hands shaking, Alex worked the buttons of his shirt, loosening them one at a time. When she reached the waistband of his trousers, he pushed her hands aside.

He had his shirt off in seconds, then toed off his shoes and stripped away his trousers.

When Jake stood in front of her wearing nothing but the smile on his face, Alex swallowed hard, her gaze roving his length, stopping on the jutting evidence of his desire for her.

Empowered, hell yes! She'd made him that hot, stirred him to such a proud erection. He wanted her as much as she wanted him.

Once again, he scooped her up, his arms cradling her nakedness against his. He laid her on the bed and parted her thighs. Inch by inch, he kissed a path from her ankle, up her calf, over the sensitive inside of her knee and along her inner thigh until he reached her center.

There, he parted her folds with his thumbs and blew a warm stream of air over her heated flesh.

Alex found it difficult to breathe. Her chest was tight and her gut clenched. She dug her fingers into the comforter and raised her knees higher, then let them fall to the side, giving Jake full access to the most sensitive part of her body.

He thumbed her there, tweaking the nubbin with the tip of his finger. Then he dipped the finger into her channel, swirled it around in her juices and touched her nubbin again, stroking her until she dug her heels into the mattress and raised her hips for more.

Jake laughed softly and bent to take her with his tongue. He licked, nipped and teased that tiny bundle of nerves while pressing a finger, then two, then three into her channel.

The coil of her core tightened, pushing her up, up, up. When she reached the peak, she dug her heels into the mattress and rose with the surge that shot her over the edge. Alex cried out, "Jake! Oh, dear sweet heaven."

Jake continued with his sweet torture, holding her at that peak for longer than Alex thought imaginable.

When at last she fell back to earth, he climbed up her body and settled between her legs, his erection nudging her entrance. Then he jerked upright. "Wait."

"Wait?" she wailed. "How can I when I want you inside me now?" How could the man tease her when she was on the very edge of the most profound lovemaking she'd ever experienced?

He laughed as he dived sideways, rescued his trousers from the floor and pulled a foil packet from the pocket.

When Jake righted himself on the bed, Alex took the packet from his fingers, tore it open and rolled the protection down over him. Without pausing, she gripped his hips and guided him to her aching, dripping channel.

Jake took over from there, easing into her, letting her adjust to his girth before taking it all the way. He sucked in a deep breath and held steady, buried deep inside her. Then he pulled back out and slid in again, settling into a smooth rhythm that grew faster with each thrust.

His body tensed as he slammed into her once more and remained deep inside. His shaft shook in spasms as he spent his seed.

Alex lay against the mattress, her mind blown, her body deliciously sated and her heart already grieving the loss. Because when they went their separate ways, she'd never see this amazing man again.

JAKE DROPPED DOWN on top of Alex, gathered her in his arms and rolled onto his side, taking her with him. He maintained their intimate connection, reluctant to leave her body when he felt so right inside her.

She'd been every bit as passionate as he had, taking charge when she wanted more and giving him her all. Not only was she gutsy, she was beautiful and amazing in bed and out. How could he walk away from her when their mission in Niger ended?

He lay beside her, stroking her hip, her arm, her hair, memorizing how she felt beneath his fingertips. When they parted, all he'd have left were the memories of making love to her and hiking through the hills of Niger with her at his side.

"I'll miss you when this is all over," Alex said and yawned, her eyes drifting closed.

Jake smoothed a strand of hair off her cheek. "We can see each other again. This doesn't have to be the end."

Without opening her eyes, she gave him a sad smile. "I'll be somewhere in Africa, teaching. You'll go on to your next mission…"

He didn't want to think they would never see each other again. Now that he'd found Alex, he didn't want to let go. "You'll eventually come back to the States, won't you?"

"Probably, but I don't know when or where I'll land. You can't wait for me." She rolled into his side and pressed her lips into his chest.

"What if I want to?" he whispered.

She didn't answer. Slowly Alex's breathing became more regular and her pulse slowed as she fell asleep snuggled into his side, her cheek against his heart, her arm over his chest.

For a long time, Jake lay awake, wondering what the next day held in store for him and his SEAL team. Mostly he wondered where it would lead with Alex. He couldn't let her go back to the village.

He and his team could launch an extraction mission to recover the missionaries, but they'd need additional ammunition and support from the rest of the unit back in Djibouti. That would take time. He wasn't sure Alex would be okay with waiting for that support to arrive.

Somehow, he had to convince her it was the right thing to do. If not, he might have to go it alone. He wouldn't want to risk the lives of the small contingent of SEALs there in Niamey on a promise he'd made.

The more he thought about it, the more he convinced himself going in alone would be the answer. At the very least, he'd be able to assess the situation. If he could get the couple out without the assistance of his team, all the better. The trick would be to keep Alex from coming with him.

To do that, he had to put one of his buddies on her

to hold her back. As he lay with Alex in his arms, a plan formed.

Well before sunrise, Jake pressed a gentle kiss to Alex's lips without waking her and then rose from the bed. He took the time to slip into his pants and padded barefoot around the room gathering the rest of his clothing. Jake exited the room, pulling the door closed as quietly as he could. He hurried to his room, shucked the suit pants and climbed into his freshly laundered uniform, impressed by how quickly the embassy staff had cleaned and returned the items. Dressed and ready before sunrise, Jake made his way to T-Mac's room.

His teammate answered the door quickly. Jake knew the man wouldn't have gone to sleep with so many questions still up in the air.

T-Mac shoved a hand through his hair and yawned. "What are you doing up so early?"

"I couldn't sleep." Jake stepped past T-Mac and his friend closed the door behind him. "I need you to do me a favor."

"Name it." T-Mac strode barefoot back to the desk where he'd set up the borrowed laptop.

"I need you to run interference with Alex and the rest of the team."

T-Mac frowned. "What do you mean?"

"I'm going back to that village to see if I can locate the missionaries. If I'm able to get in and get them out, I'll bring them back with me. If not, I'll return for assistance. But I at least want to put eyes on the target."

Before he'd finished speaking, T-Mac was already shaking his head. "No way. You can't go there alone."

"I can, and it makes sense." Jake paced the short

length of the room and turned. "If I go alone, I can get in and out without being detected. If I'm caught, I'll say I went AWOL and tell them the rest of the team knew nothing about my reconnaissance mission back to the village. You will all be in the clear."

"Thanks, but I'm not as worried about what the higher-ups will think as I am worried that you will be caught and used as an example of what happens when US military gets involved in Niger affairs."

"It's a chance I have to take. I can't drag everyone else into this, and I can't sit around and wait until Alex takes matters into her own hands and attempts a rescue on her own."

"Are you going to do this whether or not I agree with it?" T-Mac asked.

Jake nodded. "I am."

"Then get going. I'll see what I can do to sit on Miss Parker."

"And keep the team from coming after me, will ya?" Jake added. "This is my issue. None of you need to be involved."

"Uh, yeah." T-Mac turned away. "I can't make that promise."

Jake knew he was asking a lot of T-Mac. "Please. Don't let Alex follow me. And at least wait until I'm gone before you clue the rest of the team in on where I'm going. And if things go south, let them know... Well, you know."

T-Mac locked forearms with Jake and pulled him into a bear hug. "Don't stick your neck out too far. ISIS won't cut you any slack."

Jake didn't expect a promise not to do anything from

his teammate; in fact, he anticipated T-Mac would notify his team before he had a chance to collect his weapon at the gate and find transportation back to the village. If he were in T-Mac's shoes, he'd do the same. He just prayed he wasn't leading them all into one hot mess of a confrontation with the ISIS militants. Without the supporting artillery and additional SEALs, they didn't stand any more of a chance than they had during the first altercation.

But, this time, he had the element of surprise on his side. Who would expect a lone SEAL to infiltrate a stronghold? The SEAL would have to be crazy.

Or crazy in love.

Chapter Twelve

Alex woke to the sun creeping in around the edges of
the blackout hotel curtains.

She stretched languorously and smiled. That was
what incredibly great sex did for someone. It made her
wake up feeling rested and deliciously satisfied.

The pillow beside her was empty, but that didn't
alarm her. She figured Jake was either in the bathroom
or had gone next door to dress for the day, leaving her
to sleep off the effects of two days in the hills.

She rose and took her time in the shower, letting
the warm water wash over her skin. Her nerve endings
were strangely sensitized to anything that touched her,
reminding her of every inch Jake had kissed.

Once she'd dried her hair and dressed in her laundered jeans and the shirt she'd purchased along with the
dress the day before, Alex left her room and knocked
on Jake's door.

When she received no response, she knocked again,
a niggle of irritation pulling her brow lower. She told
herself it was okay. He'd probably gone to check status
with his team or to find something to eat.

Alex went in search of the other men on the SEAL

team. When she came to the corridor the other five men were staying on, she could hear voices behind T-Mac's door. With her heart soaring in anticipation of seeing Jake again, Alex knocked on the door.

The voices grew silent.

A moment later, T-Mac opened the door. "Alex, please come in."

She entered and smiled at the five men standing in the room that seemed far too small to hold their broad shoulders. Her smile faded. "Where's Jake?"

Four of the five men looked toward one. T-Mac.

The SEAL ran a hand through his hair. "Alex…" T-Mac started, cleared his throat and ran his hand through his hair again.

Her heart seized in her chest and she couldn't find her next breath.

Harm stepped forward. "We were just discussing Jake, trying to decide what to do."

"We can't just go balls-to-the-walls after him," T-Mac said. "We have to think through this issue and come up with a game plan—"

Alex sliced her hand through the air, cutting off T-Mac's words. "What issue and where's Jake?" She crossed her arms over her chest and stared at each SEAL one at a time, her eyes narrowing until they were no more than slits.

T-Mac sighed. "He left this morning."

"Left? For where?" Alex demanded.

"He's going to find your missionaries," Pitbull said. "He didn't want you to go off all half-cocked, so he did."

"Damned crazy if you ask me," Diesel said. "If he

doesn't get himself killed, we're gonna kill him for being a jerk."

Her pulse pumped so hard against her eardrums she couldn't hear herself think. "Let me get this straight… Jake went back to the village to find the Townsends?"

T-Mac nodded. "For the record, he didn't want you to go after him." The SEAL looked at the rest of his team. "He didn't want any of us to go after him."

Pitbull slammed his fist into his palm. "Well, that's bullshit. What kind of team lets one of its own go solo?"

"Not this team," Buck said.

"Damn right," Harm agreed.

"The question is, what are we going to do about it?" T-Mac asked. "He's got at least a two-hour lead on us."

"Five or six of us are not going to win a frontal attack on them. We have to launch a subversive attack, sneak up on them and surprise them."

Diesel nodded. "Yeah. We can't let them know we're coming. It gives them time to set up defense and repel our aggression. We have to hit them when they least expect it and run like hell to get away."

"I'm going with you," Alex said.

The room went deadly silent.

T-Mac held up his hands. "Jake wanted you to stay where it's safe. I more or less promised to make sure you stayed."

"Well, you'll just have to break your promise. Because if you don't take me, I'll find my own way back to the village—with or without your help."

"Alex, we can't bring you along. Having you there will be a distraction that could get one of us or Jake killed."

He had a point. But Alex wasn't going to stay back in

Niamey twiddling her thumbs while Jake and his team marched into the village and demanded the release of Reverend and Mrs. Townsend. Waiting for news would kill her. "I know which hut they were supposed to be in. If ISIS left them alone, they might still be in that hut. At the very least, if they left the mother and her baby there, she might know where they took the Townsends."

"Then tell us where to look," Harm said. "But we'll be the ones to go into the village."

Alex shook her head. "The villagers might not talk to strangers. They will be frightened of repercussions from ISIS. If I can get in there… They know me, they'll talk to me."

"The answer is still no," T-Mac said. "Jake wanted me to make sure you stayed away from the village. He put me in charge of securing you."

Alex stared at T-Mac over her crossed arms. "And you think you can keep me from doing whatever the hell I want?"

T-Mac cast a glance at Harm. "You tell her," he said, and turned away.

"If you go after Jake, you put him and the rest of the team in danger. We'll be too busy making certain your life is not at risk to protect our own." Harm took her hand. "Think about it. If Jake discovers you there in the village, he'll lose focus and potentially get himself killed. Do you want to be responsible for Jake's death?"

Alex's mouth set in a grim line. "If Jake dies, it's his own damned fault for running off without getting proper backup." She lifted her chin. "Go ahead, plan your own operation. I have plans of my own." She walked to the door, turned and glared at the SEALs.

"Whatever you do, get Jake out of there alive. That's all I ask."

She'd launch her own operation and fly solo.

Alex hurried back to her room, grabbed her passport and left again. She had some work to do to access her bank accounts and rent a vehicle. The embassy staff should be able to help her with the details. That was one of the reasons they were there. To help American citizens in trouble.

And if all else failed, Alex would steal a damned vehicle. She was going after Jake, come hell or high water.

JAKE WAS ABLE to borrow a vehicle from the embassy motor pool, promising to return it the next day. What he didn't tell them was why he needed it and that there was a strong possibility that he wouldn't return the SUV—or live to explain why. No one else needed to know that he was headed out on a potentially suicidal mission armed with a rifle, one magazine of ammunition and his trusty Ka-Bar knife.

He should be able to enter the village under the cover of night, find the missionaries and get them out without raising too much of a ruckus.

And pigs can fly.

All he could hope for was a miracle. He just couldn't wait around for Alex to make the same move he was attempting. She'd be in a much worse position as a single female targeted by ISIS. With him, he could fight back and they'd probably just shoot him and drag his body around for show. With Alex, they'd do a lot worse than kill her.

Jake got an early start, setting out before the sun rose

in the east. He covered quite a few miles before the big orange globe arose from the horizon. For the next couple of hours, he squinted at the bright sun as he drove along the rutted road toward the very village he'd escaped from days ago.

Several times he was slowed by herds of goats or cattle crossing the road in front of him. He slowed and inched his way through. When he came within five miles of the village where the ISIS militants had ambushed them and where he'd subsequently met Alex, he pulled over a hundred yards off the road. In a copse of trees and bushes, he hid the SUV, piling branches and brush around it to hide it from anyone passing by. He would need to bring the missionaries back this way and have a vehicle to transport them away from their captors.

If he found them, if they were still alive and if he was able to sneak them out of the village.

If, if, if.

At a little past noon, he walked away from the SUV, moving through the trees and brush toward his goal. He wouldn't attempt to enter the village until nightfall, but he could scout out the sentries guarding the perimeter.

By now Alex would be awake. The guys would have told her he'd left, and she'd be in a lather to follow. He prayed T-Mac and the rest of the team were successful in keeping her from climbing into a vehicle and setting out on her own.

He couldn't think about Alex now. Finding the Townsends was his major concern, and he focused all of his attention on getting close to the village without being spotted.

When he spied the first hut on the edge of the small village, he squatted between the branches of a bush, brought his rifle to his shoulder and peered through the scope.

A few women moved about the village, herding children or cooking and preparing food. On the surface, everything appeared to be normal.

Then he spotted a man in black garb shoving an elderly villager in front of him. The gray-haired old man fell to his knees. His tormentor kicked him in the side and yelled at him.

The old man staggered to his feet and kept moving toward one of the larger huts in the center of the village.

ISIS was still in charge, and the villagers were under their command. So much for hoping they'd only hit the village and moved on. Apparently, they were there to stay, and the Niger government wasn't doing anything to change the status quo.

Jake couldn't make his move until dark settled over the village, but he could look at the situation from all sides.

Over the course of the next six hours, he made a wide circle around the outskirts of the village, counting eight guards positioned at intervals all around it. Most carried AK-47 model rifles. They leaned against trees or squatted on the ground with their rifles lying beside them in the dirt. Evidently, they weren't expecting much action.

Throughout the day, Jake looked for signs of the missionaries. So far, he hadn't seen them. But the good news was he hadn't seen any bodies, either. If the ISIS fighters had killed the elderly couple, they wouldn't have done them the honor of burying them. That wasn't their way. If anything, they would have found a way to parade them before the others as a deterrent against subversive behavior.

As the sun dipped low on the horizon, Jake settled into his position and memorized what lay between him and the village. He'd sneak in from the direction of the hills, the same way he'd gotten out with Alex.

As he waited in the shadow of a tree, surrounded by underbrush, a herd of goats ambled toward him, followed by a child of ten or eleven years old.

The herd paused to nibble on the bushes concealing Jake.

As much as he wanted to shoo them away, Jake remained still, hoping the goats and the child would eventually move on without noticing the SEAL with the gun hiding in the brush.

That was not to be the case. A particularly frisky goat kid bounced around the bush in front of Jake, nibbled on the leaves and poked his head through the branches, coming face-to-face with Jake.

Jake blew a stream of air into the kid's face, hoping to scare off the little pest.

The child followed the kid, reached in to pull the baby goat out of the brush and froze when he spotted Jake.

"It's okay." Jake spoke in his broken French and held up his hand. "I'm not here to hurt you."

The boy looked from Jake back toward the village where an ISIS sentry sat, sleeping against a tree. When he turned back to Jake, he eased away from the brush, pulling the kid with him.

"Do you know Miss Parker?" he asked.

The boy backed up another step.

What did they call Alex here in the village? Why hadn't he thought to ask her? If Jake didn't capture the boy's trust and attention in the next second, the child would take off toward the village and alert the ISIS militants of the man in the bushes. He'd have the entire group of ISIS fighters swarming over him in less time than it took for him to say *I come in peace*.

"Miss Alex sent me," Jake said. "The teacher who worked with Reverend Townsend and his wife. She sent me to help."

The boy stopped his backward progression and narrowed his eyes. "You know Miss Alex?" The boy spoke in English.

"Yes," Jake said. "I was with her this morning. What's your name?"

"I am Jolani. Miss Alex was teaching me to read and speak English. We love Miss Alex. Is she all right? Is she safe?"

Jake nodded. "She's in Niamey. She sent me to find Reverend and Mrs. Townsend."

Jolani glanced over his shoulder toward the sentry, who'd just woken from his brief nap in the heat of the afternoon. "You must go. If they find you here, they will kill you. Tell Miss Alex to stay away. It is not safe here."

"I'll tell her. But first, can you tell me if the reverend and his wife are still alive?"

The boy nodded, his eyes rounding. "He's coming," the boy said.

The sentry who had been asleep a moment before

rose from the ground and started toward the boy and Jake's spot.

"I must go," the boy said.

"Please. Are the reverend and his wife alive?"

Jolani nodded and whispered, "They are being held prisoner in the biggest hut in the village. They are guarded by many ISIS men. You will not be able to help them. Go back. Tell Miss Alex not to come. She cannot help them."

"I'll tell her," Jake said.

But the boy had already moved away from the bush, herding the goats toward the man dressed all in black, blocking him from advancing toward Jake's hiding place.

Jake wished he could protect Jolani instead of the boy protecting him by diverting the militant fighter.

Hope swelled in Jake's chest. The Townsends were still alive. The next hurdle he faced was getting them through the gauntlet of ISIS soldiers to safety.

Chapter Thirteen

No matter how hard she tried to convince the embassy motor pool staff to loan her a vehicle, they refused, claiming they had to keep a number of the vehicles on hand for staff needs. They'd already loaned out two to various navy men.

Alex's fists clenched. "When did the men leave?"

"One before daylight. The others are just now loading up." The attendant called out after Alex's quickly departing figure, "They were in a hurry. They might already be gone."

Then Alex would run after them and chase them down. She'd be damned if they left her behind. That was her village and her friends being held captive. If she could help in any way, she would.

As she rounded the corner of the building, an SUV pulled out of the motor pool parking lot.

Diesel was behind the wheel, and Harm sat in the passenger seat. The others were seated in the rear.

Without thinking beyond her immediate needs, Alex leaped in front of the moving vehicle.

Diesel slammed on the brakes, bringing the big SUV to a screeching halt, but not before bumping Alex.

The impact wasn't hard enough to hurt her, but she fell to the ground, forcing them to stop and check on her.

Diesel shoved the gearshift into Park and jumped out. "Alex, are you all right?"

All five of the navy SEALs were out of the vehicle, surrounding her.

Alex lay for a moment with her eyes closed, letting them think the worst. Served them right for excluding her from Jake's rescue mission.

When Buck bent down, rolled her onto her back and felt for a pulse, Alex grabbed his wrist and opened her eyes. "I'm fine, but you're taking me with you."

Buck glanced up at T-Mac. "She's all yours."

T-Mac shook his head. "Alex, Jake needed to know you wouldn't follow him. I promised I'd make sure that didn't happen." He bent down and reached for her hand. "Come on, Alex."

"I'm going with you guys." She took his hand to allow him to help her up.

T-Mac jerked her to her feet, doubled over and shoved his shoulder into her midsection.

Alex hadn't expected the move and flopped over onto T-Mac's back as he lifted her in a fireman's carry. "What the hell, T-Mac. Put me in the SUV. I'm going with you."

"Can't take you, Alex. A promise is a promise." T-Mac waved at the others as they climbed into the SUV. "Take care of Jake and let me know if I can do anything back here to help. As soon as you're out of communication, I'll place the call to the CO and see if he wants to contribute more assets to this mission."

"Thanks, T-Mac, for taking one for the team," Harm said as he climbed into the passenger seat.

"What did he just say?" Alex kicked and squirmed against the iron arm clamped around her legs. "Let me down."

"Not until the others are gone."

"I'll just find another way to get to the village. You can't hold me captive forever. The embassy staff will arrest you."

"Nope. I don't think so." T-Mac carried her in through a side door of the embassy and climbed the stairwell to the second floor. Every time she tried to scream, T-Mac bounced her hard, knocking the air from her diaphragm.

They were in his room before she could draw attention to her plight, and, sadly, the others were long gone.

When T-Mac finally set her on her feet, she crumpled to the floor and gave in to the tears burning the backs of her eyelids. "I only wanted to help."

"You'll help best by staying out of it. Jake and the others need to focus on the job at hand. If you're out there, they'll be distracted from the mission." T-Mac booted up his computer. "You can help me convince my commander that the team needs additional support. He might take it better from you since you know the missionaries personally."

"Anything to help Jake and the others." She wiped the tears from her cheeks and rose from the floor. "Call him."

"I'll do better than that. I'll bring him up on video." T-Mac worked his magic with the laptop and a few minutes later, a man with short-cropped hair, wearing a navy camouflage uniform, popped up on the screen.

"T-Mac, give a current sitrep. I've got the State Department breathing down my neck about the ISIS attack in the Tillabéri region. What more have you learned?"

"Sir, the good news is Big Jake was able to recover the teacher colocated with the American missionaries in the village where we were attacked. The bad news is the reverend and his wife are still missing."

"The State Department wants us to back down. They had a call from our ambassador in Niger. He's concerned our meddling will undermine the Niger forces and national government. We're to stand down and let their military handle the situation."

Alex's heart slid into the pit of her belly. Jake and his team weren't going to get any help.

"Uh, sir," T-Mac said. "I'm afraid it's too late."

The commander's scowl filled the screen. "What do you mean it's too late?"

"Big Jake and the others are on their way now to the village in an effort to extract the missionaries."

The CO cursed and pounded the desk in front of him. "Who the hell authorized the mission?"

"No one, sir."

"Sir, if I may interrupt." Alex stepped into the screen view.

"Who the hell are you? T-Mac, what's a civilian doing in a classified briefing?"

"Sir, this is Alexandria Parker, the American Big Jake helped to escape the village."

"Sir, Jake and the others are going after Reverend Townsend and his wife because time is of the essence.

If we had waited for permission, they might not be alive to rescue. And if T-Mac and the others hadn't imprisoned me, I'd be with them now."

"Ma'am," the commander said, "I understand your concern, but what those men do is a reflection on the American military. The Niger president doesn't want us mucking around in his country. We have to respect his wishes. Otherwise, we might start an international incident."

"The reverend and his wife are American citizens," Alex argued. "We can't leave them to the mercy of ISIS. They're kind, gentle people who came to help the poor and sick."

"I understand. But they had to know the risks involved in coming to an African country," the commander said.

"Sir," T-Mac interrupted, "no matter what they want us to do, our men are going in and we don't have communication equipment to call them off. What can we do to make sure we don't have to collect them in body bags?"

Alex stared at the man on the screen. "Those are good men. Please tell me you're going to help them."

The commander sighed. "This better be the last time I have to bail out my men when they take matters into their own hands. I have a mind to redeploy you six back stateside. You're more trouble than you're worth at this point." He ran his hand over his face. "Here's what I'm going to do. It might be a little too late."

Alex released a sigh and listened to the plan. Then, while T-Mac took notes, she slipped out of the room, quietly shutting the door behind her. As soon as she was out of T-Mac's sight, she ran down the hallway to the emergency exit. She was outside the embassy and hurrying toward a taxi stand when a vehicle rolled up beside her. She moved out of the way, but the driver swerved closer. As the long dark body of an SUV slid to a stop, the door swung open.

Alex didn't have time to jump back.

A man reached forward, grabbed her from behind and covered her mouth with a cloth.

She fought, but the sweet scent covering her nose made her so sleepy she couldn't keep her eyes open. Alex was lifted and deposited onto the floorboard of the vehicle, and it sped away into a dark abyss.

Chapter Fourteen

Out of habit, Jake placed his headset in his ear. The team didn't go into any mission without the proper communication equipment. They depended on the ability to talk to one another and share what they were seeing from different angles.

For this mission, Jake was on his own. He wouldn't have backup. His team wasn't there to cover for him. Teamwork was what made the navy SEALs such an incredible force to reckon with. They'd learned in BUD/S training to rely on each other to get through the hard times.

Then why had he insisted on coming alone?

With no time to second-guess his decision, Jake waited for the darkness to cloak the village and make the sentries lazy and sleepy.

As soon as all sunlight had leached from the sky and the stars came out to light his way, Jake made his move. Ducking low, he ran from bush to tree to bush, keeping to the darker shadows and staying out of the open areas as much as possible. Within a few minutes, he was past the sentry he'd been watching and inside the perimeter, and had come to the first mud-and-stick hut.

Moving with the reflexes and stealth of a cat, he crept through the village streets, angling toward the big hut at the center. What he wouldn't give to have some of his buddies providing cover while he moved forward. Their method of leapfrogging forward had saved them on numerous occasions when they'd been surprised by a sniper perched on top of a building.

He'd reached the corner of a smaller hut across from his target when his headset crackled and a voice came over.

"Big Jake, you out there?" a familiar voice asked.

"Harm? That you, buddy?" he whispered.

"Roger," Harm responded. "The gang's all here, minus T-Mac."

Jake tensed. "Alex?"

"T-Mac's pulling guard duty back at the capital."

Jake let go of the breath he'd been holding. He owed T-Mac big-time.

"Where are you?" Harm asked.

"South side of the biggest hut in the village, about to make my move."

"Good. I've got your back. Buck just eliminated one of the guards on the back side of the big hut."

"There are two Tangos at the front door," Jake noted. "I'll take the guy on the right."

"I've got Lefty," Harm said. "On three?"

"On three," Jake agreed.

"One…two…three," Harm counted.

Jake looked both ways, slipped out of his hiding place, sneaked up on the right side of the hut's front and grabbed the man on the right half-dozing against the wall of the building.

At the same time, a shadowy figure came out of seemingly nowhere and snagged the guy on the left. Neither of the sentries had time to cry out before they were dispatched.

Jake eased open the door to the hut. In the limited light from the stars outside, Jake could see a short corridor stretched to the opposite end of the structure. There were doors on each side of the hallway and one at the end.

The doors on the sides had handles but no locks on the exterior. The entry at the other end of the corridor had a latch and a lock securing it on the outside. Jake figured they'd found the missionaries. Who else would they keep locked up? The rest of the villagers seemed to be going about their normal business, maybe short some of their able-bodied men.

Now that they'd found them, getting the missionaries out wouldn't be as quiet as Jake had hoped. But he'd brought along something to help in what he did best—explosives.

He pressed a small wad of C-4 against the hasp, set the detonator into it and backed up to the other doors on the side where Harm waited, his knife drawn.

The two men covered their ears and hunkered down as Jake pressed the button.

A soft version of an explosion sent dust flying, and the lock dropped to the ground.

That was when the fun began.

Men ran out of the two side doors.

Jake and Harm were ready, taking down the first men out on both sides easily. The next ones put up a fight, but were quickly subdued. Their jobs weren't done until they cleared the rooms and checked for any other fighters.

Jake stood to the side of the open door, inhaled deeply and dived through, then rolled across the ground and came up in front of a surprised ISIS rebel holding a rifle.

Jake had moved so quickly, the rebel was still aiming chest-high at the door. As he rose to his feet, Jake caught the weapon and pushed the muzzle toward the ceiling. The rifle went off.

"Shouldn't have done that," Jake said as he jerked the weapon from the man's hands and bashed the butt against the man's face, breaking his nose.

The man went down, and Jake dispatched him with his knife.

"I hope you two are done playing around in there," Diesel's voice came across the headset. "You're going to have company soon. Get out while the going's good. We've cleared a path to the south toward the hills. But you have to move now."

An old man and woman crouched on the floor in the corner of the room, holding each other in their arms.

"Reverend Townsend?" Jake held out a hand.

The old man laid his hand in Jake's. "Yes. That's me."

"Alex sent us. But we have to get you two out of here. Are you able to move on your own?"

"My wife may need a little help, but I can."

"Then let's get out of here." Jake hooked an arm around Mrs. Townsend and half carried her to the door leading out of the hut, stepping over the ISIS fighters they'd taken out of the running.

"We need cover," Harm said into his headset.

"Gotcha covered," Diesel said. "Go!"

Jake and Harm guided the older couple out of the hut and through the streets of the village.

Gunfire filled the night as Diesel, Buck and Pitbull made it sound as though an entire brigade had descended on the ISIS fighters. They had to move quickly since their supply of ammunition was low and they had a long hike to the SUV.

When Jake and Harm had their charges out of the village and well on their way to the hidden vehicles, Jake let the others know they could abandon the village and make their way to their predetermined rendezvous.

"Get out before they fire up their trucks and flood us with headlights," Jake said into his mic.

A chuckle came over his headset. "Got that covered," Buck's voice chimed in. "Diesel cut their battery cables. They won't be flooding anything but their engines trying to start their vehicles."

Jake loved his team. They thought of everything, and they'd come to back him up on his fool's errand. He couldn't have succeeded without their assistance.

But they weren't out of trouble yet. The reverend and his wife were slow, their old bodies no match for the younger rebels running through the night.

When Buck, Diesel and Pitbull caught up, Pitbull covered their tail while Buck and Diesel wrapped the old man's arms over their shoulders and ran with him.

Mrs. Townsend complained that her arms hurt from being carried in such a manner.

Jake and Harm stopped to regroup.

"I've got this," Jake said. "Sorry, ma'am, but we need

to move faster." He tossed the woman over his shoulder and ran toward his SUV.

Darkness was their friend, allowing them to get away without providing clearly visible targets for the rebels. But the rebels were closing in on them. Soon they would be within firing range.

The group split, heading in the direction of their hidden vehicles.

Harm stayed with Jake, offering to carry Mrs. Townsend.

Jake refused the offer, knowing they were only seconds away from trouble. They couldn't afford to stop again. His lungs burned and his muscles strained against the added weight. But he didn't quit. These people were Americans.

Shots rang out behind them.

Harm turned and fired into the darkness.

And then they were at the SUV.

Harm opened the back door.

Jake dumped Mrs. Townsend onto the seat, and Harm ran around to the driver's side.

By the time Jake slipped into the passenger seat, Harm already had the vehicle in Drive. He blasted through the brush and raced across the bumpy ground, navigating by starlight. He didn't hit the brakes once, knowing the brake and taillights would give the ISIS rebels targets to aim for.

Headlights flared behind them.

"What the hell?" Jake muttered, looking back at two vehicles following them.

"Damn, I must have missed a couple," Diesel said

into Jake's headset. "We're closing in on you. You've got the missus?"

Jake glanced back at Mrs. Townsend, who was still trying to buckle her seat belt. Thankfully, she was all right. "We've got Mrs. Townsend. How's the reverend?"

"A trooper," Diesel responded. "Now, if we could only shake this tail."

Harm drove the SUV out onto the dirt road leading back to Niamey. Another vehicle burst from the brush onto the road in front of them. Since it was running without lights, Jake knew it was the one carrying the rest of his team and the reverend.

They sped along the road, picking up speed, but they were at a disadvantage without lights. Several times, the vehicle in front of them skidded sideways to negotiate a turn.

Just when Jake thought they might actually lose the vehicles behind them, brake lights glowed bright red in front of them.

"Why are you slowing down?" Jake asked.

"Watch out. There's a herd of African buffalo lying on the road."

Jake muttered a curse and spun in his seat to watch as the rebel vehicles grew closer. "Honk! Bump them, do something. It's getting hot back here."

"Does no good for us to hit them. They'd put the vehicle out of commission."

The sound of a horn honking ahead might help with the cattle situation, but the oncoming ISIS vehicles weren't slowing one bit and Jake's vehicle was at a complete standstill.

"Pick me up on the other side of the herd," he said and jumped out of the vehicle.

"What the hell?" Harm said as Jake slammed the door.

Diesel was only halfway through the herd and making such slow progress they'd never get through before the ISIS militants closed on them.

Jake ran through the creatures, waving his hands and yelling at the top of his lungs.

One by one, the animals rose to their feet and ambled along the road.

Jake kept running to the other end of the herd and started on his way back, waving, shouting and sometimes shoving the animals out of the way.

The rebel headlights were less than a mile away and closing fast.

Slowly the buffalo woke and started to move a little faster.

Diesel's vehicle cleared the herd and sped away.

Harm pulled up next to Jake.

Jake jumped in, and Harm drove past the rest of the buffalo and picked up speed. But they'd lost a lot of their lead and the buffalo had, for the most part, cleared the road by the time the trailing vehicles reached them.

"Mrs. Townsend, lie low in the seat," Jake said. "We'll likely take some bullets."

She ducked out of the shoulder strap and lay across the seat, her eyes wide.

Within seconds, bullets peppered the back of the SUV, cracking the rear windshield. The bumpy road shook the glass so hard that shards broke loose. Soon the rear window was nothing more than a jagged hole.

Jake climbed over the console and Mrs. Townsend to the rear of the vehicle. He knocked out the glass and, staying below the tailgate, he aimed his rifle at a position just above the right headlight. With the SUV rocking over every rut, he knew his aim would veer off course. He pulled the trigger, firing several rounds.

The lead rebel vehicle swerved sharply to the right, flipped and rolled.

Jake pumped a fist and then braced himself as they hit another deep rut.

The second rebel vehicle slowed only slightly and then raced forward, leaving the other crashed vehicle on the side of the road.

Sitting cross-legged, Jake took aim again. The vehicle was closer. A man hung out of the passenger side firing rounds from a machine gun.

Focusing all of his attention just above the right headlight, Jake fired once, twice, three times.

The vehicle slowed and then jerked to the side. The man hanging out the window pitched forward and fell to the ground. The truck raced to the side and smashed into a tree.

Jake drew in a deep breath and let it out.

"Good job," Harm said. "Now, let's get these good people to Niamey." Harm turned on the lights. Ahead of them, Diesel did, as well.

Jake crawled back into the passenger seat, his heartbeat returning to normal. "That wasn't so bad," he said.

Harm chuckled. "You're just damned lucky we showed up when we did."

"Yeah, yeah. I could have handled it."

Diesel snorted into Jake's ear. "Yeah, right."

Jake knew his team had saved his butt, as well as the Townsends. And they knew he knew. "Thanks, guys."

Fifteen minutes later, they came across another vehicle headed their way, headlights glaring.

When Diesel swerved to the right, the other vehicle swerved in front of him.

Diesel and Harm slammed on their brakes.

Jake jumped out, weapon drawn.

Ahead of him, Buck and Pitbull had done the same, aiming their weapons at the vehicle blocking their way.

The driver in the other vehicle climbed out, his hands in the air. "Hey, it's me, T-Mac. Don't shoot!"

Jake ran toward the other man, his pulse kicking up. "What's wrong? Why are you here? Where's Alex?"

"We have a problem," T-Mac said. "Alex got away. I was hoping she'd found her way to you."

A lead weight settled in Jake's gut. "No, she's not with us. I thought you could handle her."

T-Mac shook his head. "I had a call from the CO. While I was online with him, she snuck out of my room. By the time I realized it, she was gone."

Jake's heart squeezed so hard in his chest he thought it would burst. "Where the hell is she?"

"I went to her room, hoping to find her there."

"And?" Jake snapped.

T-Mac shook his head. "Nothing but a cell phone in the middle of the bed." He dug the device out of his pocket and handed it to Jake.

Jake took it in his hand. It appeared to be a burner phone. He touched the keypad and it lit up.

No Service.

"Damn," Jake cursed. "She didn't have a cell phone on her. Are you sure the maid didn't leave it there?"

"The maid didn't leave it. Someone else did." T-Mac pointed to the phone. "There's a text message."

He pushed the button for the messages, and words appeared on the screen.

Jake's heart sank.

If you want to see the girl, follow the instructions.

He pressed several keys, but no more messages came up on the display. "What damned instructions?"

"We have to assume they'll be coming," T-Mac said.

He'd be waiting. Alex might be gone, but Jake wouldn't give up on her. She wouldn't give up on anyone she cared about.

Neither would Jake. And he really cared about the feisty female he'd met only a few days ago. He cared more than he'd ever cared about a woman before. If he had to go AWOL, he'd keep searching for her until he found her.

Chapter Fifteen

Alex blinked her eyes wide open. Where was she? The seat beside her wasn't part of an elaborate living room set. It was a car seat, and she wasn't on it. She was wedged between it and the backs of more car seats. Based on the bumps and vibrations, she was lying on the floorboard of a moving vehicle.

The windows were dark, indicating it was nighttime. How long had she been unconscious? Was it the same day Jake had left her, or had she slept through to the next night?

Where was she? What happened? Why were her wrists bound with zip ties?

A thousand thoughts raced through her fuzzy head as she shifted to relieve the pressure on her hip. The vehicle she was being transported in hit bumps too often for the road to be one of the Niamey city streets. Dust seeped in through the vents, settling on her skin and every surface.

They were on a dirt road, but where were they going? Did it even matter whether she knew? No one would find her. No one had seen her being taken in the night.

A face appeared between the two front seats—a familiar one. "Ah, Miss Parker, so good of you to join us."

"Philburn," she said, and winced at the pain slicing through her head. She felt like she had a hell of a hangover, but she pushed past the discomfort and the drowsiness threatening to reclaim her, desperate to know what was happening to her. "Where are we?"

"We're out in the godforsaken hills of Niger. You will likely recognize some of the landmarks along the way, as you and your navy SEAL boyfriend traveled this route recently."

"You're taking me to the mine?" she asked, attempting to pull herself up onto the seat and failing with each successive bump.

"I'm taking you to the test site. We aren't mining yet. That would be presumptuous of us when we haven't received government clearance to mine yet."

"In other words, you jumped the legal gun and started without government approval," she stated, wishing her head didn't hurt so badly and that she could push up to a sitting position. Every bump jolted her back and made the muscles in her body tense up.

"Only a formality," Philburn said.

"In the meantime, you're mining materials you aren't reporting to the Niger government."

"Not mining. Testing," he corrected.

"I see. And anyone who says differently will be silenced?" she asked, knowing the answer. A shiver shook her frame, but she refused to let him see that she was afraid.

Philburn's lip curled. "You're smarter than I gave you credit for."

"And the ISIS raid on my village?"

"Takes the heat off my operation and provides me with fresh workers." He smirked. "A killer combination."

"I'm surprised the Niger government hasn't caught on to you yet. Surely word gets around."

He snorted. "Only if you let it."

Based on the angle of the vehicle and the strain on the engine, they were climbing.

Whatever Philburn had drugged her with still pulled at her, making her drowsy. She drifted in and out of consciousness. Each time she came to, her mind was a little clearer and her throat more parched, dust filling her nostrils.

After what seemed like an eternity, the driver pulled the vehicle to a stop and switched off the engine.

Alex opened her eyes and noted the sky out the window had lightened into the dull gray of predawn.

Seconds later, another engine roared to life and wheels rumbled over the gravel near where they were parked.

Philburn exited the SUV and slammed the door. The driver climbed out and opened the rear door. "What do you want me to do with her?" he asked over the top of the roof.

"Take her to my office and secure her there," Philburn said.

His driver grabbed Alex beneath her shoulders, hauled her out of the vehicle, stood her on her feet and bent to toss her over his shoulder.

Alex brought her knee up hard, smashing it into the man's nose.

He fell to his knees, pressing his hand to his face.

Alex swiveled around in a sidekick, catching him in the temple. He went down and lay still.

With no plan in mind, only a loose-baked idea, Alex ran back down the hill they'd just climbed in the SUV.

Shouts sounded behind her, but she kept running, her hands bound at her back. If she could make it into the brush, she might have a chance of losing her pursuers.

Footsteps pounded in the gravel, closing in on her.

Drawing on her years of racing on the high school track team, she pushed harder, ran faster and ducked into the brush.

She'd run hurdles higher than the bramble and limbs she cleared, but she didn't have her arms free to balance her landings. On her first leap, she made it over the bush, landed, stumbled and righted herself. Alex charged forward, trying her hardest to put distance between her and the guards following her.

Just when she thought she might have a chance, she flew over the top of a bush and landed on the other side in a small rut. Small by the road's standards, but deep enough to twist her ankle. She went down hard. When she tried to stand, pain shot up her leg.

Alex rolled into the bush and lay still, praying the guards would run right past her without seeing her lying on the ground.

She focused on controlling her heavy breathing, wiggled herself into the dried leaves and brush, and willed herself to become the smallest, most easily ignored lump of human being she could be.

The first guard ran past her. The second one slowed

and walked by. The third stopped directly in front of the bush where she lay.

"Do you see her?" shouted the first guard.

"No. She was here a moment ago," the second one answered.

"Maybe she's hiding," the third guard said, and glanced down at his feet.

Why couldn't he have asked that question *after* he'd passed her? Alex didn't dare to breathe or move even an eyelash.

The three guards stopped running and glanced around the area, pushing branches aside, kicking at clumps of grass.

The one in front of her used his foot to push aside a low-hanging branch. The toe of his boot brushed against Alex's side.

She swallowed the gasp rising up her throat, her muscles tensing.

"She's here!" the guard shouted, and lunged for her.

Alex pushed to her knees and threw herself forward, half running, half limping, but not moving fast enough to get away.

The three guards surrounded her.

She glared at them. "What you are doing is illegal. You will go to jail when you're caught. Let me go and I'll see to it you are free."

None of them were deterred by her threat.

One darted forward.

Alex swung her injured foot out, caught the man in the chest and shoved him backward. Pain reverberated through her ankle, calf and thigh.

The other two pounced, grabbed her beneath her arms and legs, and lifted her off the ground.

She fought and kicked like a wild animal, but they were stronger and managed to carry her back up the hill to the mining compound.

Quinten Philburn waited with his arms crossed over his chest. "Do that again, and I'll authorize them to kill you." He jerked his head to the side. "Put her in my office, bind her and don't let her escape again, or I'll have you shot."

That was when Alex realized there would be no reasoning with the guards at the camp. They worked for Philburn. And if they didn't do what he said, he'd have them killed. Nice management philosophy, and, based on the number of guards and the number of men working the mine, it worked for him.

Her chances of escaping the compound looked pretty slim. Still, she wasn't giving up yet.

As the guards carried her into a small portable office made from a metal shipping container, she studied her surroundings, searching for something she could use to cut the zip ties they'd applied to her wrists and the one they secured around her ankles. If she could free her hands and feet, she might have another chance of escaping. She'd have to wait until dark and sneak out of the camp. Running in daylight gave her pursuers all the advantages. And this time, they wouldn't run after her. They'd just shoot.

She waited until the men left the building before she put her plan into place. All the while she worked at her bindings, she wondered if Jake had found the Townsends. And if he had, had he been able to get them away from their ISIS captors? Mostly, she wanted to know if he had survived.

Her heart squeezed hard in her chest. She prayed he was okay and that she would see him again soon. His kisses were heaven, and making love to him… Well, he was the kind of man dreams were made of. If she got a second chance, she'd tell him how she felt, even if it seemed silly after only a short time. And if he didn't reciprocate those feelings—oh, well. By putting herself and her feelings out there, she would have at least tried.

"CAN YOU GO any faster?" Jake demanded.

"I've got my foot to the floor and we barely made the last curve in the road without flipping this vehicle." Harm held his white-knuckle grip on the steering wheel as he maneuvered around another sharp curve in the road. "What more do you want?"

"I want to get to some place with cell phone reception." He shook the hand holding the burner phone in the air. "We have no other way to find Alex. This damned phone and the ability to receive messages could mean life or death for her."

The sun had yet to rise, and the predawn sky barely gave enough light to avoid obstructions in the road until they were practically on them. Twice Harm had to slam on the breaks to avoid hitting a large animal. After the buffalo herd, they'd come across a giraffe standing in the middle of the lane, munching on the leaves of a tree hanging over the road. At another spot, they'd almost run over a pack of hyenas fighting over a carcass. They were almost all the way back to Niamey before they regained cell phone reception.

The phone in Jake's hand buzzed with an incoming text message. He nearly dropped the device in his hurry to read the message.

While Harm kept driving toward the embassy, Jake read aloud: Jake Schuler, if you want the girl meet me at these coordinates at midnight alone, or she dies.

The coordinates were listed after the words.

"You can't go alone," Harm said.

Jake shook his head. "I can't risk taking anyone with me."

"We'll make a plan." Harm shot a glance toward him. "Hell, he's giving you all day to come up with something."

Jake frowned, staring at the text as if he might glean more information than was written on the screen. "Why did he set the meeting at midnight?"

"He's hiding," Harm said.

Jake clutched the phone in his fist, his heart racing, his desire to act making him edgy. "I say we go now."

"No way. If you go now, you'll be seen from miles away. We need to look at the map, see where exactly he's taking you." Harm sped through the streets of Niamey and pulled up to the gate at the embassy. "We need to let T-Mac do his computer thing and see if he can determine who sent that text. That might give us more of a clue who we're up against."

Harm spoke with the gate guard and waited for the guard to call for clearance to allow them to bring Reverend and Mrs. Townsend into the complex.

While the guards checked both vehicles for explosive devices, Jake tapped his fingers on the armrest, counting the seconds until they could get to their rooms and devise a plan.

Finally they were cleared to enter.

Harm shifted into Drive and continued their conversation as if it hadn't been interrupted for ten minutes. "While T-Mac's doing the computer work, we can get online with the CO and see if we can get some support for this operation." He glanced in the rearview mirror and smiled. "Good morning, Mrs. Townsend." Harm glanced over to Jake. "We couldn't have left immediately, anyway. We had passengers who needed to be delivered to safety."

Jake knew Harm was right on all counts, but it didn't make him feel any better. Every fiber of his being physically ached to be on the road to the coordinates listed in the text. He couldn't imagine what horrors Alex might be experiencing at that moment. But he knew Harm was right. His most recent solo experience had taught him a valuable lesson. He needed the support of his team. The more support he had, the better chance he had of rescuing Alex.

The SUVs were met at the front of the complex. An ambulance was on standby to transport the Townsends to the nearest hospital for medical care and evaluation.

Ambassador Brightbill insisted on a debriefing immediately and attended with the missionaries and the SEAL team.

Jake and his teammates filed into the conference room following the Townsends. The Townsends gave their statement and were cleared to leave in the waiting ambulance.

When they'd left the room, Ambassador Brightbill addressed the SEALs, his brow furrowed. "You realize you conducted an unsanctioned operation in this country, and I will have to answer to the repercussions, don't you?"

Jake stood tall and proud, refusing to take any kind of flak from some desk jockey of a politician. "Yes, sir."

The ambassador narrowed his eyes and stared at each SEAL one at a time. Then his frown lifted. "Thank you. I doubt I could have gotten as quick a response had I gone through the proper channels to get help. If you need anything, just ask me. Thomas, my executive officer, had a family emergency come up and had to leave Niger to return to the States on short notice, or he would have been at this debrief with me." He stood and shook hands with each of the men. "Thank you for all you do for our country and our people."

Shocked by the show of support, Jake shook the man's hand. "If you'll excuse us, we'd like to get cleaned up," he lied. To protect the ambassador as much as to protect Alex, Jake didn't enlighten Brightbill on the next nonsanctioned operation they would be conducting that night.

He found it better to ask for forgiveness than permission. Ambassador Brightbill would understand.

The team hurried to T-Mac's room. He brought up the borrowed laptop, keyed in the coordinates and zoomed in on the map.

Buck leaned over T-Mac's chair. "That's out in the middle of nowhere."

"The story of our tour in Africa," Diesel muttered. "At least it's not on the Congo River with gorillas and crocodiles."

"Yeah, but there could be hungry lions, or angry rhinoceroses," Pitbull said.

"Just so you know," T-Mac said. "While you all were out playing heroes and bad guys getting the Townsends out of that village, I made a deal with the devil."

"You called the commander." Hope swelled inside Jake. "And?"

"He thought things were hot enough around here to send reinforcements. Two more helicopters from the 160th Night Stalkers should be landing at the Special Forces location near us within the hour, where the previous helicopter is still waiting. The two additional choppers are coming complete with another twelve of our closest friends."

Jake grabbed T-Mac's shoulders from behind. "I could kiss you."

T-Mac held up his hands. "Save it for someone who wants it, dude. I'm not your type. But there's more."

"More?" Jake stared at T-Mac's reflection in the computer screen. "As if reinforcements weren't enough?"

T-Mac grinned. "He also sent the drone to conduct recon missions and provide additional firepower, should we need it. Give me a minute and I'll find out the status of both and convey the coordinates for a high flyover reconnaissance mission by the drone."

"As long as it doesn't alert the kidnapper that we're on to them."

"Got it." T-Mac bent to the computer and placed a video call to their commander back in Djibouti.

The CO responded in seconds. "You better be calling to say you found our AWOL SEAL."

Jake leaned down to get his face in view of the camera. "Sir, I'm here."

"Any casualties?" the commander barked.

"Not on our end, sir," Jake responded.

"If not on our end, then whose end?" their boss asked.

"Let's just say some of the ISIS folks who crashed our party a couple days ago won't be bothering us again."

"Good." The commander's eyes narrowed. "So, am I correct in assuming I can send a C-17 aircraft to pick up my choppers and drone and expect you six trouble-makers back in Djibouti with them?"

Jake ran a hand through his hair. "Well, sir, about that."

His commander's lips thinned and his jaw tightened until there was a tick twitching on one side of his face. "What now?"

"You remember that teacher I helped escape the ISIS attack on that village?" Jake asked.

"The one who insisted you go after the reverend and his wife?" The CO nodded. "What about her?"

"She was kidnapped last night."

The commander scrubbed a hand over his face and then stared at him from the screen. "I guess it doesn't make a difference if I tell you it's not your problem."

"Sir, no sir. It is my problem. If I don't agree to meet with them, they'll kill her."

"And how do you know they want *you* to meet with them, and not someone else?"

Jake sighed. "The text message had my name on it."

The commander nodded, his lips twisting. "Which makes it your problem."

"Yes, sir."

The CO scrubbed a hand over his face again. "You know I can't authorize you to go in alone."

Jake straightened, his fists clenched at his sides. "No disrespect, sir, but I'm going."

His commander waved a hand. "That's a given. I'm sure if I told you that you couldn't, you'd go AWOL again."

As a man who valued his career as a navy SEAL, Jake knew what that could mean. But it didn't matter. Alex was out there, being threatened and possibly tortured. "Yes, sir. I'd go anyway."

The CO tapped a pen against his desk for a moment and then glanced up. "Okay, then, but you'll do it my way, or I withdraw my birds. Got it?"

Jake scowled. "But sir, I have to go in alone, or he'll kill her."

"Did I say you weren't going in alone?" The older SEAL cocked an eyebrow.

"No, sir," Jake said.

"Then listen up." The CO looked past Jake. "And that goes for the rest of your team. Are they there? Can they hear me?"

"Yes, sir!" All six men gathered around the computer while their commander told them the game plan and how the helicopters and drone would play a part. When he was done talking, he signed off and the men put his plan into action.

Jake prayed they were in time, and that whoever was holding Alex wouldn't get nervous and kill her anyway.

He figured it was time to go to work, doing what SEALs do best.

Chapter Sixteen

With what little light came through the small window of the cargo container office, Alex searched for anything rough enough to help her break her bonds.

When she couldn't find a coarse edge, she made one by smashing the leg off a wooden chair and using the jagged, splintered end to scrape the plastic tie across. She held the broken wooden stake between her fingers and ran the plastic over the broken leg again and again.

A couple times she scraped the skin on her wrists, causing them to bleed. Ignoring the pain, she worked harder, determined to get herself out of the mess she was in.

No matter how hard she scraped, the zip tie didn't break. With her wrists bound behind her back and ankles locked together, she couldn't get very far.

After several hours' work at her bindings, the heat in the office bore down on her. Sweat dripped into her eyes, making them burn. Despair threatened to take hold and suck her under.

Each time she got the feeling all was lost, she'd remember how wonderful it had felt to make love with Jake. The images conjured up made her all the more determined to get free and see the man again, even if only for a minute, an hour or a day. She didn't try to think beyond that because he was a SEAL and she was a teacher. It wasn't as if they could have a future together. Heck, they barely knew each other. He probably didn't want the burden of a relationship anyway.

But she wouldn't know if she didn't try. And she'd never wanted to try more than she did at that moment. Jake was worth the effort.

When the broken chair leg didn't make much of a dent in the hard plastic bindings, Alex looked around the room for anything else.

In one corner of the office lay a metal ammunition box. If she could get it open, the edge of the box might be strong enough that she could rub the plastic tie over it until it broke.

Alex inched across the floor, turned her back to the box and fumbled with the latch. After a few attempts, she managed to open the ammo box, unhooking and then flipping up the metal clamp.

Inside the box were rifle magazines and bullets. She ignored the contents and rubbed the zip tie along the side edges of the container.

The metal was just coarse enough to impact the integrity of the plastic. When she was well through the density of the plastic and on her way to breaking the tie, the door to the shipping container office jerked open. Bright sunlight blinded Alex for a moment. Fresh warm air wafted into her prison, along with a haze of dust.

Alex sat up straight, pushing the ammo box behind her, out of sight. She blinked up as Quinten Philburn entered the office and smirked down at her.

The man laughed. "Not so cocky now, are you?"

Remembering her father's words that the best defense was a good offense, Alex faced Philburn. "I don't know what you're trying to accomplish, but you're doing it with the wrong person."

He laughed. "I'd say I caught a valuable little prize in you."

"I don't know what you're talking about," she said. "I'm just a teacher. I don't have rich parents. I'm not worth anything to you or anyone else. So why keep me?"

"Oh, but you are worth more than you think. You're going to buy me time."

"Time?"

"Time to clean up and clear out." Philburn waved a hand to the side. "All I have to do is collect a few of the loose ends you and your boyfriend created."

Alex frowned. "I don't understand."

"You will, soon enough." He glanced around the small space. "Any last requests before I leave you?"

"I'd say a steak dinner with a baked potato and a salad, but right now, water would be nice," she said, her voice gravelly, her throat parched in the heat.

Philburn snorted. "I can spare a little water to keep my prize alive a little longer." He gave her one last look and then left the building, closing the door sharply behind him.

Anger burned low in Alex's belly. If she got free, she'd take Philburn down any way she could. The man was the devil.

A moment later, the door burst open again. This time, a guard dressed in a dusty olive-green uniform stood in the door frame, his rifle pointing in at Alex. His glanced around the interior of the office and then stepped back.

A man Alex barely recognized entered, carrying a bucket of water and a dipper. His dark hair, skin and clothing covered in dust, he walked with a limp, and appeared to be much older than she knew him to be.

"Fariji," she gasped. This man, her classroom assistant, was one of the sweetest, kindest men in her village. Alex's heart broke when she spied what appeared to be whip marks across the back of his neck. "What are you doing here?"

With his gaze downcast, he answered, "Miss Alex, I brought you water." Then he bent to hold the dipper to her lips.

Alex drank, filling her dry mouth with the tepid water. So what if it wasn't purified? She'd die of heat exhaustion without it. She swallowed and asked, "Is Philburn forcing you to work his mine?"

Fariji didn't answer but held the dipper to her lips again. Something fell into her lap. For a moment, his gaze met hers, and then his eyelids lowered and he backed slowly away.

Alex drew her knees up, hiding whatever Fariji had purposely dropped.

"Out!" the guard barked at Fariji.

The gentle, sweet man turned and hurried out of the office.

The guard glared back in at Alex and then slammed the door shut.

Footsteps sounded, fading away.

When Alex was certain the guard was gone and

wouldn't suddenly reopen the door, she looked down at the article Fariji had left in her lap.

It was a small steel file, probably from a toolbox of one of the workers at the mine.

Alex rolled over, letting it drop to the floor, then scooted around to grab it with her hands behind her back.

Once she had it between her fingers, she sawed at the zip tie. A couple minutes later, the tie snapped and her wrists were free.

A quick rush of joy spread through her, but she refused to bask in it. She had a lot to do before dark, and she prayed Philburn wouldn't return in the meantime. If he caught her without bonds, he'd just have her restrained again and she'd have to start all over.

With her hands free, she made quick work of breaking the zip tie at her ankles. Once she could move around, she searched the drawers, boxes and containers for anything she could use for a weapon. Alas, she had only the metal file.

She tried the door and discovered it was locked from the outside. The window was small, but if she worked at it, she might get through. Not in the daylight, though. Careful not to let anyone see her, she peered through the window and studied what she could see of the compound.

Big trucks carried massive amounts of dirt from the mine, dumping it in piles near something that appeared to be a sifter.

Workers carried buckets of material on their heads or dragged huge sacks behind them.

Guards carried either rifles or whips or both. When a

worker fell or stumbled with his load, a guard was right on top of him, yelling or cracking a whip.

She managed to open the window slightly to let in fresh air, though it did little to reduce the increasing temperature inside the cramped container. If Philburn didn't kill her, the heat might.

With little else to do, Alex sat beneath the window and waited for dusk and a chance to escape. When she was free, she'd make her way back to Niamey and demand the Niger government do something about the illegal mining, and that they free the conscripted workers. She wouldn't leave Fariji or any of the others behind. The lies, the torture and forced labor had to come to an end. Good people like Fariji didn't deserve to be abused in this manner.

The heat drained her, but she held tight to hope and the eventual setting of the brutal sun. When the shadows lengthened and light faded from the small window, the unbearable heat lessened and Alex pushed to her feet. It would soon be time to make good her escape.

THROUGHOUT THE MORNING, the SEALs prepared their plan of action. They coordinated with the Special Forces in a nearby camp for helicopter transportation, weapons and ammunition. The SEALs would secure a vehicle and meet up with the rest of the SEAL team that had arrived from Djibouti early that morning.

Their commander had the drone up in the air all morning long, scouting and taking digital pictures of the area surrounding the coordinates given, expanding its surveillance to include several miles around the location.

As soon as the drone completed its survey, the images were transmitted to Military Intelligence back at Djibouti. Within a couple of hours, several pictures were sent to T-Mac, and he downloaded them onto the laptop.

Jake and the others hovered over the man's shoulders as they studied the images, zooming in on one in particular.

"That's the mine we came across when we were in the hills," Jake said. "Do you think Quinten Philburn might have taken Alex?"

"If he's worried you two might report him, he might have," Harm said. "You're the only two outside his organization who've put eyes on his operation."

Jake's body tensed. Deep down, he felt this was where they'd find Alex. "We can't wait until midnight. We need to go sooner. I'd bet my last dollar she's there."

"How can you be so sure?" Buck asked.

"My gut tells me it's so." His belly knotted as if in agreement.

A bell pinged on T-Mac's computer. He switched from the images to a screen full of data. T-Mac bent to examine the information.

Harm shook his head. "Big Jake, we can't base an entire operation just on your gut."

"There's something else." T-Mac held up a hand, his gaze still on the screen in front of him. "When I was looking into Snyder Mining Enterprises, and I found that they were owned by Transunion Mining Corporation and then sold to Colorado Holding Company based out of the Cayman Islands, I couldn't get much information out of them."

"So," Jake prompted.

"I also dug into Thomas Whitley's background. I verified that he did work for Ambassador Brightbill when they both were employed by a company whose subsidiary was Transunion Mining Corporation."

Jake fidgeted, too anxious about Alex to take in a long explanation. "What's your point?" he snapped.

"I found where Whitley had significant shares in Transunion. When it sold, he invested in another corporation." T-Mac glanced up into Jake's eyes. "Colorado Holding Company."

"Whitley?" Jake struggled to digest what T-Mac was telling him. "You think Whitley has a stake in that mining operation? Why didn't you say anything earlier?"

"I was running a program, searching for data on Whitley while we were waiting for the drone images. It finished, and that's what I found." He moved to the side so the others could see the screen.

"We need to talk with the ambassador," Harm said.

"Forget the ambassador," Jake said. "We need to get to the mine."

"One more thing…" T-Mac switched the screen back to the images and zoomed in on the coordinates Jake had been given for the rendezvous. "I wasn't sure when we looked a minute before, but if you peer closer, those aren't the tops of trees down there. Those are camouflage nets." He pointed to the spot on the map. "And if you look here, that's not a tree trunk but a man standing there." He zoomed closer, the image getting grainier. "And he's wearing black and holding a rifle."

"An ISIS fighter," Jake said. "The coordinates are a setup. They want us to go there, knowing I wouldn't go alone. It's a distraction to keep us from finding Alex."

"And to get us all killed," Diesel concluded.

"What if Alex is being held there?" Pitbull asked.

"She's not," Jake said with certainty.

Harm's lips pressed into a line. "But if you're wrong?"

"We plan our operation for just after sundown," Jake said. "If we come up short of Alex, we move to the coordinates indicated in the text message."

Harm, Buck, Diesel, T-Mac and Pitbull nodded and replied, "Agreed."

T-Mac placed a video call to their commander. Jake filled him in on what was happening, and they received his agreement and commitment to support their altered plan.

"We only have a few hours until sundown." Jake started for the door. "Let's get to the Spec Ops camp and meet up with the rest of the team. We need to brief them and ramp up."

They borrowed one of the battered vehicles they'd turned in earlier to the embassy motor pool. In less than fifteen minutes, they were racing out of Niamey into the countryside, headed for the camp where they'd meet up with the rest of the SEAL team their CO had sent to help.

Jake counted the passing seconds, wishing they could have had the team pick them up at the airport and helicopter them out of Niamey. They could have been at the Spec Ops camp in less than an hour. As it was, they would be on the road for well over an hour and a half. He wanted to be there already, and in the air, on the way to find Alex. The minutes went by as if in slow motion.

When they finally pulled into the camp, the place

was a hive of activity. Jake, Harm, Diesel, Buck, T-Mac and Pitbull met in the ops tent with the rest of their team from Djibouti and the army Special Forces trainers from the camp and laid out the plan.

The Special Forces guys offered to take the Niger counterparts they'd been training, pre-position them near the rendezvous coordinates and then wait until they received word from the SEAL team before moving in. With or without the SEALs, they were prepared to take out the ISIS fighters they suspected were hiding under the camouflage netting.

With a contingent of eighteen SEALs, three Black Hawk helicopters and enough firepower to take down all of the ISIS militants who'd surprised them less than a week before, they were trained and ready for the mission.

They had everything they needed to get in, take care of business and get out. Now all they had to do was wait until just before sundown. The flight would take less than an hour. They'd fast rope down a couple miles from the mine and go in on foot. They would be there a few hours before the midnight deadline given for the other coordinates.

The hours ticked by slowly. Finally the SEALs loaded into the Black Hawks, the Special Forces team filled trucks and Humvees, and they took off.

Jake's pulse hummed a steady beat as he settled into "go" mode. He channeled all of his energy and focus on the task ahead: rescuing Alex.

Dusk cloaked the land as the helicopters skimmed the treetops and buzzed over herds of wild animals grazing on the grass and brush.

Jake checked and double-checked his weapons, from his HK416 assault rifle with the ten-inch barrel and suppressor to his Sig Sauer P226 handgun. He patted the Ka-Bar knife on his hip and the many extra magazines filled with ammo tucked into the straps on his bulletproof vest.

"Here we go," Harm said as the helicopter slowed to hover over an open patch of hillside a couple miles away from the mining compound. He was first out, fast roping to the ground.

Jake followed, then Buck and the rest of the team.

The other two helicopters hovered nearby, the men slipping to the ground like ghosts in the gloom.

Once on the ground, Jake tapped his headset. "Comm check."

One by one the team checked in, until all eighteen of the SEALs were accounted for.

"Let's do this," Jake said, and took point, leading the men up and over the first ridge. From the top, he could see lights glowing in the distance. Based on the direction, he bet they were coming from the mine. Although why they'd be running at night was beyond him. Then he noticed they weren't lights, but flames rising into the sky.

"You see that?" Jake said into his mic.

Harm came to a halt beside him and took in the scene. "Not a good sign. Let's get there." He dropped over the ridge and ran down the hill.

Jake was on his heels and easily overtook him on the way up the next rise. His calm, professional perspective had taken a hit when he'd seen the flames. He had to get to Alex. Fast.

Chapter Seventeen

At dusk, Alex checked out the window. Men seemed to be working feverishly. But something was different about what was happening. Instead of bringing the dirt and minerals out of the mine, bulldozers were pushing them back into the hole. Men were throwing boxes, shovels, picks and anything that wasn't nailed down into the pit, as well. The displaced brush and trees that had been uprooted to make room for the mining pit were pushed in on top of everything else.

What the hell was going on?

As she watched, the guards herded the dusty, dirty, barefoot men up to the edge of the pit. Several of them had jugs in their hands. They spilled the contents into the pit over the trees and brush. One of the guards lifted a tank with a hose on it and lit a match in front of it. Then he aimed the hose at the pit and blasted a red, blue and orange stream of flame at the debris. The flame caught the accelerant and flashed into the darkening sky.

Alex stood, transfixed by the rising flames, her heart racing.

They were destroying the mine.

Then the guards standing behind the conscripted workers took another step backward and raised their weapons.

"No, they wouldn't," Alex whispered, her pulse leaping and a lead weight dropping in her gut. She scrambled up onto the stack of boxes she'd pushed up against the wall beneath the tiny window. She was desperate to get through the window before the horror began. She had to stop them from killing the workers and dumping them into the pit of flames.

She pushed the narrow rectangular window up as far as the little hinge would take it. Then she turned her head sideways and pushed it through the opening.

A guard was just disappearing around the end of the container box, pouring liquid on the side of it from what appeared to be a gasoline jug. The pungent scent of gas burned Alex's nostrils. Then a flame blasted around the corner from the direction the guard had gone and raced toward her.

Alex ducked her head back in, panic threatening to overwhelm her. They were lighting the container box on fire with her in it. What happened to using her as bait? What kind of bait would she be if she was dead?

With renewed determination, Alex poked her head out of the shipping container office again and stared down at the fire licking up the side of the metal box. Surely it wouldn't do anything to the box but burn the paint off the exterior. Whoever had poured the gasoline had forgotten the box was made of metal.

Smoke rose from the grass around the box, filling her lungs and making her eyes sting. The box itself might not burn, but Alex had to get out before the smoke and heat consumed her. She pushed her arms and head through the opening and then shimmied her body halfway through.

Near the edge of the mine, the guards stood with their weapons raised as if waiting for a signal from someone.

Two men strode up to one of the guards.

One was Philburn. Alex could tell by the man's annoying swagger. The other was Whitley, the US ambassador's executive officer. They must have given the guard instructions because he walked back to the other guards watching over the workers. Meanwhile Philburn and Whitley moved in the opposite direction, heading for a leveled patch of ground where a helicopter waited.

Anger burned inside Alex, fueling her determination to free herself from the tomb of a box they intended her to die in.

Once the gasoline had been consumed, the fire around the box died down. The rumble of heavy machinery starting up sounded nearby, followed by the clanking of a tracked vehicle moving. The shipping container office lurched, jolting as if it had been hit hard from behind. The force jerked her body and made her flap against the side of the container like a rag doll. Someone was pushing the container toward the pit.

Alex had two choices: get out or die. She wiggled and shoved her way through, the window's edge catching on her hips as she hung halfway out.

With all attention focused on the guards holding the guns on the workers, no one seemed to be watching the container. The office building moved ever closer to the pit, picking up speed as it slid across the uneven ground.

Alex grunted and cursed as she pushed and pulled herself as far as she could, until she could move no more. She needed help.

A shadowy figure ran in front of her.

Alex swallowed a yelp. Fariji grabbed her shoulders, braced his feet against the side of the box and pulled as hard as he could. Alex barely moved.

"I'm stuck," she said. "You have to go, Fariji," she begged. "Save yourself."

"I won't go without you, Miss Alex." Walking backward as the container moved closer and closer to the pit, Fariji planted his feet on the side of the box and pulled again.

This time, her hips slipped past the window frame and she fell to the ground on top of Fariji. They rolled sideways, away from the oncoming structure. They couldn't seem to move fast enough to get to the other end. Fariji grabbed Alex's arm and leaped out of the way, pulling her with him as the container was pushed over the edge and crashed into the mining pit.

"You just can't leave well enough alone, can you, Miss Parker?" Quinten Philburn stepped out of the darkness, a handgun pointed at Alex's chest.

Fariji still held on to her arm.

"We don't have time to deal with them," Whitley said, and turned away. "Shoot them." And he left his partner and walked toward the waiting helicopter.

When Philburn shifted the barrel of the pistol toward Fariji, Alex reacted.

She swung her leg out, hitting Philburn's hand.

The gun went off, but the bullet went wide instead of hitting Fariji in the chest.

Without giving the man the chance to aim again, Alex grabbed his wrist with both hands. "Run, Fariji!"

Her friend didn't move. "I won't leave without you, Miss Alex."

Philburn wrestled Alex for control of the handgun, his greater strength moving it to between the two of them and pressing it to her belly. When Fariji lunged forward, Philburn yelled, "Back off, or I'll kill her."

Fariji raised his hands and stepped back. "Don't kill Miss Alex. She's a good person."

Philburn snorted. "I've had more than enough of you, Alexandria Parker. Your interference has cost me too much."

"You're a cold, heartless bastard. You deserve all the bad juju you get." Alex stared into the man's face and spit in his eye. She closed her own and braced herself for when the gun went off.

JAKE REACHED THE edge of the camp first, running full on to get to Alex before something awful happened. The flames leaped high into the air, lighting the area in and around the mining pit. Dark silhouettes stood out against the bright blaze—men standing by the pit, other men carrying weapons, a commercial helicopter nearby.

"There!" Harm pointed toward a woman with long hair struggling with a man who had something in his hand. A gun?

Jake raced toward them, anger, fear and adrenaline pushing him faster. He came up behind the man and attempted to jerk him free of Alex. As he did so, the loud crack of a gun made him flinch and his heart come to

"Alex?" he cried, staring at her in the glow of the fire.

"I'm okay," she said, her voice strained as she held on to the man's wrists with both hands to keep him from shooting her.

Running on instinct, Jake knocked the weapon out of the man's hand and flung him to the ground.

The man beneath him was Quinten Philburn.

Alex grabbed the gun and took off.

"Where are you going?" Jake asked.

"To stop them from shooting the workers." She waved toward the helicopter. "Don't let that chopper get off the ground!" she yelled, heading toward the group of men near the lip of the pit.

"Harm, take over here." Jake leaped to his feet and raced after Alex. Was she insane? One woman with a handgun against a dozen men equipped with semiautomatic rifles didn't bode well. "I could use some help near the pit," he said into his mic.

"We see the problem," Diesel responded, "and we're right behind you."

"Good." Jake caught Alex around the waist and yanked her back from tearing after the guards.

The SEAL team overtook Alex and Jake and raced toward the guards who had raised their weapons to their shoulders like executioners.

Diesel, Pitbull, Buck and T-Mac pointed their rifles into the air, fired and whooped like wild men.

The guards jerked around, saw the SEALs running straight for them and freaked out. Half of them threw down their weapons and ran. The other half turned on the SEALs, pointing their weapons at the charging fighters.

Before the guards could fire, the team dropped to their knees and unloaded their magazines on Quinten's men fighting back, careful not to hit the unarmed men who'd been held captive to work the mines.

Alex struggled in Jake's arms. "We have to stop that helicopter," she said, then wiggled free of Jake's hold and took off in the opposite direction toward the chopper as the rotors began to turn.

Jake caught up to her. "Is Whitley on board?"

"Yes," she said, racing across the uneven terrain.

"Stay back and let me handle it." Jake sprinted ahead, leaving her behind as he ran toward the chopper. The wind whipped up by the helicopter blades fanned the flames in the pit, making them leap and spit giant flakes of hot ash and soot.

As Jake reached the aircraft, it lifted off the ground. He dived for the open door.

Whitley slammed it shut.

Jake fell over the skid, hooked his arm around the metal runner and held on as the helicopter rose higher into the air. He pulled himself up until he was standing on the skid. Then he yanked open the door, grabbed Whitley around the throat in a headlock the man couldn't break and pressed his P226 handgun against Whitley's temple.

"Put this aircraft on the ground!" he shouted to the pilot.

When the pilot hesitated, Jake redirected his aim and fired a shot through the door next to the pilot. "Now!"

The pilot adjusted the helicopter flight controls suddenly, tilting the craft toward Jake in an attempt to throw him off the skid.

Jake held on to Whitley's neck. The safety harness securing Whitley in the aircraft held both men.

Whitley clawed at the arm around his neck, but couldn't break Jake's stronghold.

"I'm not going anywhere, and the next bullet will be in you!" Jake shouted above the roar of the spinning rotors. "And to hell with landing this bird. Crash it, and I crash with you." He pointed the pistol at the pilot. "Go ahead. Try me."

"For the love of God," Whitley wheezed into his headset. "Put it down."

The pilot looked from Whitley to Jake and back, and then maneuvered the helicopter back over the trees toward the mining pit now spewing flames high into the sky.

As they neared the clear pad from which they'd taken off, the wind shifted suddenly and the smoke and flames blew toward the helicopter, engulfing them in a thick, acrid cloud.

Jake's eyes stung and his throat tightened as he inhaled a big gulp of smoke. He blinked and glanced down through a sudden break in the smoke and noted the ground only ten feet from the bottom of the skid on which he stood.

Not willing to take a chance on the pilot's ability to fly or land the chopper in blackout conditions, Jake made a split-second decision and took a chance. He released Whitley's neck and dropped out of the helicopter.

ALEX STOOD TRANSFIXED, her heart squeezing hard in her chest as she watched the drama unfold.

She nearly had a heart attack when Jake leaped onto

the helicopter. And how he held on to the side of the aircraft was nothing short of phenomenal. How he would get down without falling back to the earth would need another miracle.

She held her breath, praying out loud, "Please, let him be okay. Please, let him come down in one piece. Oh, God, let Jake be all right."

Harm raced over to her.

"What happened to Philburn?" she asked.

"Zip-tied and gagged. I have one of the guys standing watch over him." He looked around. "Where's Jake?"

Alex swallowed hard and pointed up at the helicopter.

Harm squinted up into the night. The blaze gave just enough light that they could see the silhouette of a man hanging on to the outside of the chopper.

"Tell me that's not Jake," Harm muttered.

"I wish I could." She stared up at the sky, her body trembling, tears stinging her eyes. "What was he thinking?"

"That's Jake for you. He doesn't like leaving loose ends." Harm shook his head. "Damned fool. What am I supposed to tell the CO if I have to bring him back in a body bag?"

Alex gasped and tears spilled from her eyes.

Harm glanced down. "Sorry. If I know Jake, he'll find a way out of this. That man's always coming up smelling like roses. See? The chopper is coming back this way and looks like it's going to land."

Hope swelled in Alex's chest. The helicopter was returning and hovering close to the ground. But just when she thought it might land, the wind shifted, blowing smoke across the sky, blanketing the helicopter, hiding it and Jake from sight.

"Where'd they go?" Alex ran forward, her heart lodged in her throat.

A hand snagged her shoulder and pulled her back. "You can't run into that smoke."

"But I can't see Jake. Oh, sweet heaven, where'd he go?" she sobbed.

And then a break in the cloud of smoke and ash showed the helicopter hovering just above the ground, a black cloud whipping around it. Then the chopper shot back into the air and disappeared into the thick smoke.

The wind current shifted again, clearing the sky over Alex's head and carrying the smoke back over the pit.

The helicopter was nowhere to be seen in the night sky.

Suddenly, a loud crash sounded in the pit. Rotor blades broke off and flew out of the smoke, and a ball of flame lit up the sky.

Alex and Harm ran toward the edge of the pit and looked over into the flames rising up from the crashed helicopter.

"Jake!" Alex screamed. She would have leaped over the edge and slid down into the pit if Harm hadn't wrapped an arm around her waist and held on tight. "Let go! I have to find him."

"If he's down there, you don't want to find him. Aviation fuel burns hot. There won't be anything left to find."

"He can't be gone." Alex turned and buried her face against Harm's shirt. "I think I might love him," she sobbed.

"Alex!" a voice called out.

The sound cut through Alex's sobs. She looked up and blinked the tears from her eyes.

A tall man, covered in soot, walked out of the smoke toward her. "Alex?" He held open his arms.

Alex ran toward Jake, stumbling in her hurry, her tears falling again, blinding her with her joy. She slammed into him, knocking them both off their feet. Jake landed hard, but cushioned her fall.

He chuckled and coughed. "Hey, why the tears?" He pushed to a sitting position and gathered her in his arms. "Did you think I wasn't coming back?"

"Yes!" She grabbed his face between her palms and kissed him hard, then leaned back. "I died a thousand deaths when you jumped on that skid. What were you thinking?"

He shrugged, a crooked smile making his teeth shine white against his blackened face. "I wasn't really thinking. I just acted."

"Don't do that again," she said.

"Yes, ma'am." He cupped the back of her head and kissed her thoroughly before letting her up for air. "I nearly died a thousand deaths when you went missing. Why did you leave T-Mac? He would have kept you safe. What were *you* thinking?"

She gave him a sheepish smile. "I wasn't really thinking. I just acted."

Jake shook his head. "We're a pair, the two of us."

She nodded. "Yeah, Big Jake. So, what are we going to do about it?"

"I guess we'll have to make a go of it." He hugged

her tight. "I kind of got used to having you around on our little trek in the hills."

"Same here." She leaned her forehead against his. "Thank you for coming after me."

"Are you kidding?" Harm said as he walked over to them. "He was coming, with or without us." He held out a hand and helped Alex to her feet. "Sorry to break up this little reunion, but we have more work to do."

Jake rose to his feet, nodding. "Philburn or Whitley sent us a different set of coordinates to find you. We think it was a setup, sending us into a hotbed of ISIS. Our Special Forces counterparts are pre-positioned to launch an attack. We want to be there to help out."

Alex frowned. "And what about the people here?"

"Our guys have secured Philburn's guards and their weapons," Harm said. "We put out a call to our command to coordinate the transport of the conscripted workers. They will be returned to their villages."

With a sigh, Alex nodded. "Okay. I guess I'll let you go."

Harm laughed. "Mighty generous of you. T-Mac and some of the others are staying behind while the rest move out."

Though Alex wanted to ask why Jake couldn't stay, she bit down on her tongue. The SEALs had a mission and a method. She'd have to be patient.

"If all goes well, I'll see you back at the embassy in the morning." Jake pulled her into his arms and kissed her again. Then he set her away from him and followed Harm and a dozen SEALs to the clearing where three helicopters swooped in one by one. The men loaded

ey lifted off, the sound of the
the night.

breath and tried not to think
ey'd be facing at their next ren-

was that Harm was right and
elling like roses. In the mean-
d her eyes stung, on the verge
't have time for tears. She had
elp ensure the repatriation of
opriate villages.

ore at the night sky where the
ared, and then went to work.

Chapter Eighteen

Jake hurried through the gate at the embassy, anxious to see Alex. He was dirty, covered in smoke and grime from a hard night's fight.

The coordinates Philburn and Whitley had given them had been as they suspected. The site was an ISIS militant camp. Thankfully, the Special Forces unit had done a good job of reconnaissance and hadn't been spotted by the rebels.

The mission had gone off with textbook accuracy. The ISIS fighters had been stockpiling munitions and explosives, and had been building improvised explosive devices in preparation for an attack on Niamey.

Not only had they stopped them from succeeding in a devastating blow to the capital city, but they'd also captured Abu Nuru al-Waseka, the leader of the Islamic State faction in Niger. The leader was more than willing to bring down those infidels who'd enlisted his assistance in stirring up trouble and finding free, able-bodied men to work the mine. He quickly named Quinten Philburn and Thomas Whitley as the Americans who'd paid him in weapons.

The debrief with Ambassador Brightbill and President Rafini had gone on for hours, but had finally ended.

Now all Jake wanted was to find Alex, get a shower and eat something. In that order.

He stopped in front of her door and knocked loudly.

When she didn't answer right away, he knocked again. Perhaps she'd gone out to eat, since it was well past noon and the sun had been up for hours. Or had she gone with the displaced workers to help them find their way back to their respective villages? In which case, he might miss her altogether.

That last thought had him frowning heavily. Now that their mission was complete—the ISIS rebels contained and the missionaries saved—they had no reason to stay in Niger. By the next morning, they would be redeployed to Djibouti and another mission in some other part of Africa.

Jake wanted to see Alex before he had to leave. He didn't want to leave without talking to her. Hell, he didn't want to leave her at all. He had known her for such a short time, but it felt like a lifetime. He knew what he needed to know about her to realize she was special. The kind of woman he wanted in his life. No… She was the only woman he wanted in his life.

He couldn't leave without telling her that he wanted to see her again. Not just once, but a lot. How they would make that happen, he wasn't sure. But somehow he would, even if he had to spend all of his leave time flying back and forth to Niger to see her.

Once more he knocked on her door, but no one answered. Disappointed, he went to the room next door, let himself in and closed the door behind him.

"About time you realized I wasn't in my room," a soft voice said from the shadows.

Jake's heart lit up and he swung toward Alex.

She lay on her side on the bed, wearing a sexy night-gown and nothing else. Her shiny black hair hung down over her shoulders and her eyes sparkled.

He sighed. "Alex."

She slid her long legs over the side of the bed and padded barefoot to where he stood at the door. "Need some help getting out of that gear?"

He shook his head. "No. I'm filthy and you're not. Don't touch me until I've had a chance to shower."

"I don't care if I get dirty," she said. "You've seen me covered in dust and grime and in nothing at all. Let me help you." She reached out, unbuckled the clasps on his protective vest and slid it over his shoulders. When it dropped to the ground, a puff of dust and soot rose around it.

Jake gripped her shoulders and set her away from him. "There's nothing I want more than to hold you and let you touch me, but I need a shower first." He held up a finger. "Hold that thought and don't change a thing. I'll be right back." Then he ducked into the bathroom, stripped out of his clothes and jumped into the shower. He didn't care that the water coming out of the fau-cet started out icy cold; all he cared about was getting clean so he could hold Alex's perfect body against his.

As he soaped and lathered, a muddy, sooty stream of water swished off his body and down the drain. He squirted an entire trial-size bottle of shampoo into his hand and ran it through his hair and down over his arms and shoulders.

Then he ducked beneath the showerhead and rinsed.

"You missed a spot," Alex said behind him. Her hands reached around him for the bar of soap in the dish.

He turned to find her standing in the shower, naked and beautiful, her hands filled with soapy lather.

"Let me," she said, and ran her hands over every inch of his shoulders, back, chest and torso. As the water rinsed the soap away, she pressed kisses where her hands had been, working her way downward, her body and hair getting wetter as she went.

Her hands smoothed over his thighs, down past his knees to his ankles until she'd touched every part of his body but one.

Jake's shaft rose to the occasion, jutting straight and stiff. He wanted her so badly he could barely breathe.

She took him in her hands and stroked him until he felt like he'd explode.

Past his ability to contain himself, he bent, clasped her thighs in both hands, lifted her up and wrapped her legs around his waist. Then he marched out of the shower and bathroom and straight to the bed.

She laughed. "Aren't we going to dry off?" She kissed his cheek and nibbled on his earlobe.

"Can't," he said.

"We'll get the sheets all wet," she said, clinging to him as he tried to lay her on the bed.

"Don't care," he replied. Since she wouldn't let go of his neck so he could lay her down, he turned his back to the bed and lay down with her still in his arms.

Alex slid her legs down his, wet, warm and delicious. "You're a man who knows what he wants."

"I am. And I want you." He kissed her and then flipped her over onto her back. "When we're apart, all I can think about is being back with you." He stared down into her gaze. Though he was desperate to plunge into her, he wanted her to see the sincerity in his eyes. "I'm not into one-night stands."

"Neither am I." She reached up and cupped his cheek. "So, what are we doing here?"

"Starting something that I hope will last a lifetime," he said.

Her eyes glistened with unshed tears. "You don't think it's too soon to feel this way?"

He shook his head. "I knew the moment I found you in the village coming back to help the missionaries."

Her lips trembled as a smile pulled at the corners. A single tear slid from the edge of one eye. "I didn't know until you held me in your arms in that cave."

"It's not a contest, woman. I want you in my life."

She gave him a watery smile. "And I want to be in your life."

"I have a dangerous job."

"I won't always like it, but I know it means a lot to you." She brushed her thumb across his lips. "I'll be there when you come home."

"You'd give up Africa?"

She smiled. "I'd give up breathing if I could be with you even some of the time."

"Please," he said, and bent to kiss her lips. "Don't give up breathing. I need you too much. Can we make this work?"

She nodded. "Look how far we've come in just a few short days. The rest of our lives will be a piece of cake." She wrapped her arms around him and pulled his mouth to hers.

"Is this what love feels like?" he asked against her mouth.

"I'm pretty sure it is." She reached a hand over to the nightstand and grabbed a foil packet. "Now, if we're done talking, I'd like a little more action."

Jake laughed out loud. "A woman after my own heart." He made quick work of the protection and slid into her, feeling as if he'd finally come home. Whatever the next day brought, he and Alex would find a way to be together. No matter how hard the task. As always, for any SEAL, the only easy day was yesterday.

* * * * *

COMING SOON!

We really hope you enjoyed reading this book. If you're looking for more romance, be sure to head to the shops when new books are available on

Thursday 13th December

To see which titles are coming soon, please visit **millsandboon.co.uk**

LET'S TALK
Romance

For exclusive extracts, competitions
and special offers, find us online:

f facebook.com/millsandboon

🐦 @MillsandBoon

📷 @MillsandBoonUK

Get in touch on 01413 063232

For all the latest titles coming soon, visit
millsandboon.co.uk/nextmonth